LANDSCAPES AND LIVES

The Scottish Forest Through the Ages

LANDSCAPES AND LIVES

The Scottish Forest Through the Ages

JOHN FOWLER

CANONGATE

First published in Great Britain in 2002
Canongate Books Ltd, 14 High Street, Edinburgh EH1 1TE

10 9 8 7 6 5 4 3 2 1

The publishers acknowledge the following sources for permission to reproduce illustrations in this book. Copyright in the images on the pages listed here is held by the party named alongside. Extensive efforts to ensure that the source of each image has been acknowledged; if any images have been incorrectly attributed or overlooked, please contact the publisher with details.

Anna Ashmole 253
Dick Balharry 237
Blair Castle Archive 46, 86, 88, 90, 91, 97, 138
Jock Carlisle 214
Laurie Campbell 20, 209, 226, 259, 261, 268
Christies of Fochabers 145, 147
Basil Dunlop 61, 63, 67, 73, 74, 75, 76
Forest Life 47, 113, 163, 179, 181, 191, 193, 194, 200, 202, 203, 212, 228, 236, 240, 242
John Fowler xii, 5, 11, 24, 32, 52, 69, 80, 93, 98, 120, 171, 199, 206, 207, 217, 224, 231, 243, 247, 250, 252, 255
Glasgow Museums 36, 164, 166, 167
Glasgow University 40, 100
Historic Scotland 60
Eric Hosking Trust 258
Jeanie MacAlpine's Inn Restoration Group 28, 31
Jim Kirby 59
Millennium Forest Trust for Scotland 264
National Galleries of Scotland 43 (left), 43 (right: in the collection of the Earl of Haddington), 103, 114
National Library of Scotland 26, 114, 216
National Trust for Scotland 135
Oxford University Museum of Natural History, MacCulloch collection 96
Perth Museum 108
Peter Quelch 265
Royal Botanic Garden, Edinburgh 111, 130, 134
Royal Commission for Ancient and Historical Monuments from Tom and Sybil Gray Collection 16
Royal Scottish Forestry Society 117, 127, 133, 137, 139, 148, 152, 153, 146, 160, 173
RSPB 234
Iain Ruxton, Lighting Architects Group 30
Scottish Crannog Centre, Loch Tay, Perthshire 9
Scottish Life 72, 81, 141, 150, 189
Trinity House, Leith 33

British Library Cataloguing-in-Publication Data
A catalogue record for this book is available on request from the British Library

ISBN 1 84195 326 1

Design and typesetting by Lucy Richards, Edinburgh

Printed and bound by Cromwell Press

www.canongate.net

CONTENTS

Prologue

for Catherine
who has walked with me among the trees

Here again shall ye see a dry knowe, or a thin forest,
there a thick wood, all marvellous to the eye

John Leslie

I in Scotland as Pindar in Greece
Have stood and marvelled at the trees
And been seized with honey-sweet yearning for them

Hugh MacDiarmid

PROLOGUE

LONG AGO, before Scotland took its present shape and name and dry land linked it to Europe, trees in the Scottish landscape formed part of a great northern forest that stretched from the Hebrides to the Bering Sea. Ghosts of that ancient forest still linger in some semblance of the natural state – notably in small pockets of relic pinewood surviving in Highland glens.

Wander among these rugged old pine trees and, as you brush through clumps of heather and blaeberry within earshot of a rushing burn, you cannot fail to feel their magic. Part of the enchantment is a feeling of timelessness: 'To stand in them is to feel the past', as a friend of the pinewoods wrote. Ancient relic pinewoods have many faces. In places you will find the trees ranked tall and straight and handsome in impressive stands, but often they are ragged and sparse, the few individuals all bent and twisted and crook-boughed, growing at random in the open forest, dotting the brown moorland as solitary survivors, or clinging precariously to rocky cliffs or the sheer walls of a gorge.

Nostalgia enhances the appeal of these resinous old Caledonian pines. But equally evocative of the past are the oakwoods of the western seaboard. In the moist Atlantic air is biodiversity par excellence – temperate rainforest, a naturalist's dream. Most of the trees are modest in height, even stunted, and hazel, birch, alder, rowan and other natives share the ground with the oak. This is a far cry from the noble oakwoods of southern England. Everything is damp and dank, heavily mossed and dripping with lichens, the undergrowth a sponge.

Ten millennia stretch between the arrival after the Ice Age of the native green-leaf trees and Scots pine – icon of old Caledonia – and the modern influx of 'foreign' conifers (so invasive that today Sitka spruce outnumbers any other forest tree in Scotland). Even such familiar species as beech or sycamore, now completely naturalised and quite at home, are relative newcomers on the scene.

This book tells the story of the changing forests of Scotland within that time span, how they have altered with climate and the influence of people – and how people have been touched by the trees. Landscapes and lives are my subject.

In this book I have used the word Caledonian somewhat randomly as a picturesque, resonant and not too specific label for the trees and woods of Scotland. Most authorities, whether environmental writers, historians or ecologists, might fault me for that. They cringe at the C word, arguing that it is at best imprecise and at worst fallacious, and smacks too much of some mythological never-never. It's true that they may condescend to describe, somewhat loosely, those rugged specimen trees in relic ancient pinewood as Caledonian, but that's as far as it goes. But for me the word has great charm – indeed I once hoped to call this book – and I think not whimsically – *The Groves of Caledon*. (I was dissuaded.) Which leads to the matter of a Caledonian Forest, or its variant Great Wood of Caledon, an expression that has great historic and emotional appeal. Did that forest exist, and if so where? I debate the question in Chapter 2.

The book also has a personal perspective. A friend who read the manuscript described it as 'a long love letter to the forest'. I like that. In the ten years or so since I began to study woodlands as an enamoured novice, I have spent as much time as I could tramping through Scotland's many and diverse woodlands – in all weathers, sometimes alone, or in company with naturalists, botanists, ecologists and foresters, all of them enthusiasts in their own way. It has been a journey of discovery. And so in these pages I intersperse the narrative with passages describing my impressions of woods and forests. You see through my eyes.

A note on the notes:

Since this is not a learned work I have not disfigured the pages with references – always an irritant to the general reader. My main sources of information and quotation can be found in the notes at the end of the book. Finally, I have occasionally elided quotations without altering the sense, and I have silently modernised the spelling of some quotations written in the old Scots tongue – but not where it would diminish the force and flavour of the original to do so.

A cone collector dwarfed in the crown of an old pine tree at Barisdale on the Knoydart peninsula. The beleaguered Barisdale trees belong to a distinct genetic group whose origins stretch back into prehistory. Harvesting seed is important to ensure their survival and regeneration.

I

IN THE BEGINNING WAS THE WOOD

WHEN the last glaciers melted at the end of the Ice Age a strange and harsh landscape emerged in what would be Scotland. As the ice withdrew between thirteen and ten thousand years ago there came into view mountains of naked rock, deep valleys bare of all vegetation, vast stretches of floodwater inundating the coastal shelf. Debris carried down from the hills by volleying torrents choked the plains. There were no trees.

The first signs of life came creeping over the ground in a flush of lowly vegetation, blots of lichens and mosses on bare stone. As the permafrost loosened its grip windblown seeds and spores lodged in crannies. Roots probed the primal soil and pale shoots sought the light. Then a fuzz of scrub woodland appeared, dwarf tree species and other hardy, shrubby things suited to arctic climates. And as the sun grew stronger, tall trees advanced, coming up from the south unhindered by sea barriers. The Channel had still to form and great rivers like the Rhine dissipated in low marshlands where the North Sea is now.

What trees came first? Juniper, a spiky evergreen and hardly a tree at all (but how do you draw the line between tree and shrub?) rushed in at the start, swarming all over the countryside, with birch close behind − clouds of birch seed on papery wings blown far and wide by the winds. Aspen, called the shaking tree because of its shimmering foliage, arrived early. Hazel came in fast, fanning out swiftly all along the west. Birds gave the hazel nuts airborne passage in the gut; mice, squirrels and other small animals helped disperse it. Elm arrived early and then suffered a shock. A sudden, catastrophic decline some five thousand years ago implies a killer epidemic like the Dutch elm disease that hit Europe in the late 1960s. Oak, normally a slowcoach, reached the far north and west with surprising speed some six thousand years ago. Lingering ash took longer.

Other settlers crowded in – willow, rowan (also known as mountain ash), gean or wild cherry, and holly. Alder, a poor competitor which could only survive in damp places, established itself late.

Where was pine in all this? Scots pine, the archetypal tree of the old Caledonian forest, *Pinus sylvestris* in botanical terms. There's a puzzle about pine. Eight or nine thousand years ago a great pine forest grew around Loch Maree and the sea lochs of the far northwest. Where did it spring from? Did the first seeds blow across the sea from Ireland in the distant past? Or did scraps of an ancient pinewood survive the age-long winter in nooks and crannies at the edge of the ice – perhaps on some outpost of dry land beyond the present western seaboard – from where it could expand inland when the climate improved?

Meanwhile far to the south Scots pine (long before it had the name) raised its shaggy head over the Thames and bent to the wind on the sandy dunes of the Dogger Bank, from where it spread northwards by fits and starts, always giving way to more aggressive rivals like oak and elm before it found security in the glens of the Grampian hills. A spell of drier weather around five thousand years ago allowed pinewoods to reach out almost to Cape Wrath in the north and Loch Lomond in the south, but not for long. When the rains returned the population crashed.

Scots pine, oak, ash, holly, hazel, yew, birch, rowan, willow, alder, aspen, gean, wych elm, crab apple, hawthorn, juniper – these are our native trees, species that gained a foothold before island Britain was cut off from the continent and all immigration ceased. Now, at the start of the twenty-first century, such trees get a special seal of approval from conservationists. Some of our familiar trees never made it on their own. Sycamore for one. Beech failed to cross the Cheviots. And spruce, best known of our plantation trees? Spruce was still progressing northwards through Europe when the Channel flooded, severing the overland route to the British Isles. Spruce missed the bus.

There was a time, possibly six thousand years ago, when the early forests reached almost to the highest summits. Below the bare tops a patchwork of dense forest alternated with open woodland, meadows, scrub and savannah grassland. There were swamps and barren shorelands where no trees grew. The weather was kind and soils receptive. How mild it was then! Summers were warmer than they are now, less rain fell and the winds were gentler (a tourist board would have been in clover). It didn't last – it never does. Balmy spells when the forest could spread alternated with periods of cold and wet when it shrank. Nowadays there are few reminders of the character and scale of that long lost forest.

> *A rag of woodland, a tangle of small woody growth hugging dip and scarp on the island of Islay. Here within the sound of Atlantic breakers are birch and willow and hazel in profusion, a stem or two of aspen, and the occasional oak. It's a wildwood in microcosm.*
>
> *We have come to this spot by way of the dunes and across a marshy field. It's awkward to walk in, forcing a way through the short whippy birch, hopefully seeking a track (non-existent) or at least a gap in the undergrowth. There's honeysuckle in flower, and bog asphodel and orchid spikelets on patches of wetter ground. A buzzard floats overhead.*
>
> *The oak trees, when we find them, are small and stunted, though they may be, I guess, hundreds of years old. Their mossy trunks are just a few spans around, and at shoulder height they sprout branches that intertwine with neighbours to form a vault of hazel, birch, willow and oak. The whole wood is a crypt, and we walk under a tracery of branches through which specks of daylight filter. I wedge myself in the low crown of an oak, garlanded by bronze-edged leaves, and imagine a distant past and a greater, unseen woodland stretching for miles around.*
>
> *This is a far cry from any true forest. Yet here, ensconced in the leafy heart of a tiny Hebridean wood, I find it easy to picture great forests of former times – thousands of years ago – spreading in their virgin state across the face of the land.*

Maps have been made to illustrate the ebb and flow of native woodland in the first millennia after the Ice Age. The evidence is supplied by tiny grains of pollen trapped in bogs or the muddy bed of lochs, where they resist decay. These tiny bits of evidence can reveal what plants grew in the neighbourhood many thousands of years ago, and different tree species can be identified under the microscope and accurately radiocarbon dated. So a grain of pollen in the bog serves both to identify the plant which produced it and the date when the plant grew.

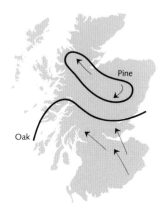

As the ice retreated trees spread over the land like an incoming tide. This map shows the known extent of two common species around 7000 years ago. Oak has advanced northwards, pine is reaching out from its Highland strongholds. Among species present but not shown, birch is widespread, hazel pervasive in the west, but ash has still to appear. (Map by Roy Petrie, based on research by HJB Birks.)

Other clues are visible to the naked eye. Tracts of the Scottish uplands and moorlands are blanketed by peat bog which everywhere yields up remains of the ancient forest. Tractors often turn up tree stumps in Highland bogs. You see them sticking through the surface where Landrover tracks have been driven or ditches dug. But not all are the great originals. Some stumps are quite recent while others have been authenticated as thousands of years old.

> At the edge of a hollow in the peat I peer down at a lost forest. Rannoch Moor, a waste of heather, moss and dark peaty pools glimpsed from the road north to Glen Coe and Fort William, is almost treeless now. The moor is scored with peat hags, trench systems gouged out of the black bog by wind and weather. This is what we see today. Shanks of shattered trees bleached white by long exposure litter the damp floor and emerge from the peaty banks. These pine trees lived and died thousands of years ago, long before there was a Scotland, an England or a Britain.
>
> Jim Dickson, a palaeobotanist familiar with the plants of the past, digs his fingers into the oozy peat where a weathered trunk pokes from the bank, picks at something in the depths and hands me a scaly wedge of woody material. 'Four thousand year old bark', he says.
>
> It's the oldest thing I have. It looks much like the bark of a living pine tree, dark and rough, but it flakes easily and I have to handle it with care. Just a handful of bark – but my relic of the Caledonian Forest.

Here grew the ancient forest. Pine stumps and branches at least 4000 years old, preserved in a Highland peat bog where trees would struggle to grow now.

Peat built up in the cold wet weather. It grew thickest in the west where rain clouds blowing in from the ocean broke on the high hills. (Then as now, eastern Scotland enjoyed better weather than the west, being drier and warmer, and there the forest had a better chance of survival.) It blanketed the valley floors and crept up over all but the steepest slopes.

Peat swamps the roots of all living trees in its black, waterlogged, acid and airless embrace, giving nothing back – a lethal combination of drowning and starvation. The advance of the mire was inexorable, and under this tide of partially decaying moss and vegetable matter, nine metres deep and more in places, the forest sank. The resultant landscape of the Highlands emerged much as we know it – brown hills, bog and tracts of moorland where long ago the greenwood flourished. Plod through the bog and you walk on the first Caledonian forest.

Stumps in the bog are a sign that the weather fluctuated over long cycles in previous ages – as it still does. In wetter, cooler spells the trees were swamped and the forest gradually retreated, only to regain lost territory as the bogs dried out and trees could grow on the peaty surface again. They would be invading again today if we let them.

'We can picture that dim, long forgotten time. . . ' So saying, Geikie proceeds to do it for us – Sir Archibald Geikie, geologist, writing in 1901 when scientists were free to indulge in a spot of purple prose:

We see the skirts of the dark Caledonian forest sweeping away to the north, among the mists and shadows of the distant hills. The lower grounds are brown with peat-bogs and long, dreary flats of stunted bent, on which there grows here and there a hazel or an alder bush, or, perchance, a solitary fir, beneath whose branches a herd of wild cattle browse. Yonder, far to the right, a few red deer are pacing slowly up the valley, as the heron, with hoarse outcry, and lumbering flight, takes wing, and a canoe, manned by a swarthy savage, with bow across his shoulders, pushes out from the shore.

Geikie asks us to bear in mind the magnitude of the forest

. . . which, when man first set foot in Scotland, swept in long withdrawing glades across its surface – the wide black mosses and moors, the innumerable lakes and fens, dense and stagnant indeed on the lower grounds, but which, in the uplands, were the sources when streamlets and rivers descended through glen, valley, and woodland, into the encircling sea. Beasts of the chase, and among them some that have been for centuries extinct here, abounded in these ancient forests; birds of many kinds haunted the woods and waters; fish swarmed in lake, river, and bay. Among such primeval landscapes did our aboriginal forefathers excavate their rude earthen dwellings and build their weems of stone; from the fallen oaks they hollowed out canoes, which they launched upon the rivers and lakes; and through the thick glades of the forest they chased the wild boar, the urus, the bear, the wolf, and the red deer.

Many birds and beasts – some of them strange to us now – inhabited the forests of Old Caledonia. What birds? Much as now, probably. The chaffinch and the wren were everywhere, the summer visiting willow warbler (fond of birchwoods), the crossbill, uniquely able to snap pine cones open with its scissor-beak, the siskin, the woodcock, the crested tit – now found only in the northeast but possibly more widespread when the climate was warmer. There were rooks, wood pigeons, woodpeckers and cuckoos. Woodcock inhabited damp dripping places, and in the heather in open woodland were red and black grouse. The great capercaillie – large as a capon, cock-o'-the-woods, a rooster on old pine boughs and a gobbler of tender pine shoots – were there, along with birds of prey, resident or visiting – owl, kite, kestrel, sparrowhawk and buzzard, osprey and golden eagle.

The forest was a Serengeti. If we could be beamed back in time we might spy brown bear scooping salmon from the Spey, or glimpse the shadow of a lynx, a spotted cat with greyish fur, three feet long in the sinuous back, stalking its prey through the undergrowth. Or its smaller cousin the wildcat (still in the Highlands but hard to find). Beavers worked the riverbanks. Boars ran in the underwood.

Herds of red deer, today exiled to the inhospitable open hill, found shelter in woodland where they fed on mosses and green shoots. Fine beasts they were too, compared to their punier descendants. The zoologist James Ritchie described the discovery some two centuries ago of a great stag's remains in the Meadows of Edinburgh – once covered by the waters of a loch. It was, he wrote, probably no exceptional creature in its day, 'yet today it stands out as a giant.' Shy roe deer slipped through the deeper glades. Others of the deer tribe ventured into the more open parts of the wood. There was reindeer, and elk (the moose of north America), a tall, lanky-legged, ungainly looking creature six feet high at the breast, carrying wide, plate-like antlers.

All these creatures exist today somewhere in the world, if not in Scotland. But one former resident of Caledonia is extinct. This is the auroch or urus, a powerful, thick-coated wild ox of massive proportions whose broad forehead bore long, curved horns. The auroch fed on the grassy vegetation of the forest floor where plenty of light percolated through a thin canopy. But the auroch was doomed. Now its bones provide the only evidence that it lived here (though in the broad woodlands of central Europe it survived into the seventeenth century). But what bones! The auroch stood six feet high at the shoulder, and its horned head was at least a third larger than the skull of our domestic cattle. James Ritchie refers to an old picture by a German artist which he thinks represents the auroch or urus, 'a bull without a mane, but rather rugged, with a large head, thick neck, small dewlap entirely sooty black, the chin alone white, and the horns turning forward and then upwards, pale in colour with black tips. Probably the urus was of a dark reddish-brown colour verging on black, with long, black-tipped horns, and with hair short and comparatively smooth, except on the forehead where it was long and curly'.

The last aurochs may have fallen prey to a scavenger still with us, though not in this country. During long ages the howling of the

The great auroch or urus,
the wild ox – now extinct –
which once roamed the
open woodlands of
prehistoric Scotland.
(From Cuvier's *Mammalia*,
1827 edition.)

THE WILD OX

wolf was heard throughout the land until finally silenced several centuries ago. Many other creatures inhabited or visited the ancient forest, among them the fox, the badger, the pine marten, stoat and weasel, the polecat or foumart (foul marten, because it stank), the squirrel (red, not grey). One creature, seldom seen but soon to have a dramatic effect on the woodland and everything that lived there, lurked on the forest fringe. That dangerous biped, man.

Chop! A sound not heard before. Chop again. Men with axes are at work. This is the beginning of the end of the forest. For five thousand years and more, since the first farmers began to make inroads on the forest, the natural woodlands have been subject to human attack.

Many trees, few people; but wherever the earliest inhabitants halted they created space for themselves. They lopped, felled, and lit bush fires – real forest fires, perhaps, in the resinous pinewoods. On the newly opened ground they grew their crops or herded their part-domesticated beasts – short-horned, skinny, thin-legged Celtic cattle, pigs and goats and the frisky ancestor of our sheep. These sheep were small, possibly a foxy-red or fawn in colour, and chiefly valuable for their milk and their skins which could be used as clothing. The rams carried long curved horns on their heads. They were agile creatures, leaping from rock to rock, scampering over scree; not easily checked by the first herdsmen and their domesticated dogs. Browsing or grazing by these puny beasts around lowland settlements and high summer pastures checked the growth of young trees.

A crannog or loch dwelling on the margin of Loch Tay – a modern reconstruction based on archaeological evidence from 2600 years ago. The building materials have been replicated – oak and alder for the main structure, hazel for walls and roof, but reeds have been substituted for the straw or bracken thatch of the original. Crannogs were in use over a long timespan, from 5000 years ago until the seventeenth century.

From the surrounding woods the early settlers got timber to build their homes, whether on land or loch, and for their tools and implements – the ploughs with which they broke the ground. They collected firewood for cooking or for warmth. They erected stockades against wild animals and human enemies. In places they probably planted thorn hedges to contain their herds. It's very likely that they developed woodland skills such as coppicing or pollarding so that the trees could renew themselves.

And they had technology. Stone axe heads look primitive in a museum case but they worked pretty well. Herbert Edlin, a writer about the forests, picked up one by chance on a Surrey down where, he says, it had lain for perhaps four thousand years. Clutching it in his hand he attacked a tree with it and found that it 'was still sharp enough to bite effectively into a beech trunk when held in the hand alone without the customary wooden haft'. Other people have made more systematic trials of Mesolithic implements. Sixty years ago two Danish scientists borrowed flint axe heads from their national museum and fitted them with wooden shafts modelled on prehistoric axes. A photograph shows one of them wielding his old-new implement in a forest in Jutland; jacket off, his sleeves rolled up, baggy cap tipped on the back of his head, legs braced and axe poised on the upswing. These two amateur woodmen were surprised that it took them only fifteen minutes to fell a fifteen-inch-thick alder. If two smooth-handed academics could cut down a sizeable tree in quarter of an hour what might a sturdy axeman of the New Stone Age, skilled and practised in the craft, achieve?

How fast the settlers made inroads in the forest and how permanent these were is a matter of conjecture. While settlements were few and the land thinly populated their influence may have been slight. We might take this view:

> If one could have flown over northern Europe it is doubtful whether more than an occasional wisp of smoke from some camp fire, or maybe a small cluster of huts or shelters by a river bank or old lake bed, would have advertised the presence of man: in all essentials the forest would have stretched unbroken, save only by mountain, swamp and water, to the margins of the sea.

But opinions differ. The aerial viewer might have witnessed altogether thicker billows from around the margins of the forest, evidence of deliberate efforts to clear the ground by igniting bush fires, maybe on a quite a large scale.

The little we know about early mankind and its influence on the surrounding wildwood is gleaned from what scientists have been able to piece together from scraps of evidence found at archaeological sites throughout Scotland. Slowly the shadowy picture builds up . . .

> *Over Rig on a March morning with a thin frost on the ground is peaceful. I stand here today but in my mind's eye see the landscape change through six thousand years. The White Esk river below makes an elbow bend under the steep bank, where dark water ripples over shingle banks. Plantation trees above the narrow road have recently been felled, leaving a stubble of stumps on the hillside. On my side of the road the ground falls away in the shape of a bowl, the slope dotted with gnarled hawthorn trees crusted with lichens. There are a few other trees, mainly willow and rowan, on one of which a wren briefly alights and chirrups.*
>
> *The site is bounded by tall conifers beyond which – unseen from my position – is a spinney of beech trees (in which rest the red-rusty remains of an abandoned car slowly being reclaimed by nature), but mainly the impression is of open country. The slope is grassy and mossy, with bracken here and there and whippy willow wands and briars sprouting near the water.*
>
> *Patches of reed fringe the river. By a pool of standing water thinly iced over, a scoop of raw grey soil is exposed in a ditch, under a fringe of hanging turf, with a shrubby alder much damaged by grazing animals, a clump or two of heather and a few saplings of self-seeded Sitka spruce close by. This, I guess, is where the archaeologists*

The bend in the river at Over Rig where clues to the prehistoric woodland of the Borders were found.

and palaeobotanists have been digging, uncovering the past. All's quiet and deserted now.

Into this ditch at Over Rig the debris of millennia fell and accumulated. And from the pollen grains and other debris trapped there and at other sites in the region a picture can be built up of the changing vegetation, including woodland, that has mantled southern Scotland over thousands of years.

Six thousand years ago, then – what do the lowest layers at Over Rig tell? That all around was dense woodland of oak, hazel and elm. Succeeding layers indicate that over time the forest retreated, until by the late Iron Age, a few centuries before the Romans came, the woodland was under heavy attack and serious deforestation had already taken place.

Shortages of timber may have been severe. Far from being surrounded by limitless forest, the Iron Age inhabitants may have had to nurse what was left. Clues in the Over Rig ditch suggest they were already conserving woodland by coppicing – cutting trees at the base to encourage new shoots to spring from the stumps. Sustainable forestry, it seems, has a long history.

The Romans came and went, but civilisation did not collapse with their departure. In the green haughs, down in the valleys, crops were grown and cattle fed on lush grass enriched by sediments left by the floodwaters. Cattle grazed on the cleared ground. And throughout the Dark Ages scrub woodland advanced and retreated according to the needs of the shifting local population, until by the early Middle Ages, in the thirteenth and fourteenth centuries, it seems that willow woodland had invaded much of the ground at Over Rig. But that, too, was only a phase.

2

THE MEDIEVAL GREENWOOD

FROM prehistoric time to the dawn of the Middle Ages lies a huge span of time in which dim figures emerge from the shadows of the shifting forest – 'our hatchet wielding forefathers', in Archibald Geikie's descriptive phrase – but all are nameless. Who will be the first man of the woods to make his mark in Scotland's story?

Could Wallace be that man? William Wallace, Scotland's hero, freedom fighter, liberator (died 1307, cruelly). But also by the way, a great haunter of woodlands, as recorded by the poet Blind Harry, writer of the first *Braveheart* script.

Wallace is almost literally the first recognisable figure to step from the embracing forest. He was, according to tradition, forever darting in and out of the woods. He had to – his life and those of his men depended on it. In the account of Blind Harry, Wallace would head straight for the forest to elude or ambush his pursuers, to seek shelter, regroup his forces and lie doggo with his men, bide his time to sally out and take the English by surprise.

His frequent resort to the forest was good guerrilla tactics. To Wallace, the greenwood of lowland Scotland was the *maquis* of the French resistance fighters, the impenetrable jungle of the Viet Cong, Fidel Castro's mountains of the Sierra Madre.

'The rone [woodland] was thick that Wallace slept in' (I quote Blind Harry). Long before Shakespeare heard of Birnam Wood Wallace sheltered there. Often he and his forces holed up in the woods for lengthy spells. 'In Clyde's wood they sojourned twenty days.' 'Bide me seven days in this forest strang,' he tells his men before setting off to

William Wallace, Scotland's hero. Like any good guerrilla leader, he knew the defensive value of the forest. (From Taylor's *Pictorial History of Scotland*.)

reconnoitre the English garrison at Perth. On occasion his freedom fighters improved on natural cover by building a stockade – 'a manner dyke' – with felled oak trees, or a barrier of 'thwarter' trees among the groves of holly that grew 'baith thick and green' on the banks of the Tay.

> Syne Wallace and all his men withdraws
> And lodges safely in the Short-Wood Shaws

In Harry's account the forest was always a place of safety in a countryside occupied by hostile forces.

Thieves, outlaws, desperados and broken men were notorious frequenters of woodland, as they have been until relatively modern times. After Culloden the fierce old Jacobite Alexander Robertson of Struan could flout the Hanoverians from the safety of his thickly wooded domain in remoter Perthshire. Blind Harry tells how Wallace recruited the outlaw Chrystal Seaton and Kirk Patrick, a refugee from English oppressors 'who cruel was and keen' – both habitual lurkers in the darker thickets of the forest.

Hiding in a single tree is something else. The number of so-called Wallace trees in which our hero is alleged to have taken refuge is legion. One significant enough to be marked on the map as the Wallace Oak can be found in Methven Wood in Perthshire, where it grows on the fringe of old woodland among plantation conifers. One glance demolishes its claim. It isn't hollow (so no place for a man to hide in), the foliage is scanty and above all it isn't old enough, not by centuries. Maybe a true Wallace oak grew there long ago, but this tree isn't it.

Wallace hid here? The shattered Wallace oak at Torwood as it was when drawn by Alexander Nasmyth in 1771.

'In Dunipace parish is the famous Torwood, in the middle of which there are the remains of Wallace's Tree, an oak which, according to a measurment, when entire, was said to be about twelve feet diameter. To this wood Wallace is said to have fled, and secreted himself in the body of that tree, then hollow, after his defeat' − this from the second Statistical Account, published in the 1840s. Wallace is alleged to have wedged himself inside the tree after the disastrous battle of Falkirk nearby. The tree is no more, having fallen prey to generations of souvenir hunters.[*]

Legends accrete around Wallace; indeed there is little factual evidence to back up Blind Harry's narrative. But Wallace lived; he was a historical figure, a man. Elsewhere, in the poetic world of the old Border ballads (whose origins may stretch back to the Middle Ages), legendary characters like Lord Randal, Brown Adam, May Margaret or Clerk Saunders inhabit an embroidered tapestry of romance.

The greenwood setting of balladry is decorative and usually benign, though desperate deeds may be done within it, and death the outcome. Star-crossed lovers meet in their leafy bower, caress, and die when surprised by vengeful husband or brothers. In such case one or both may be buried 'amang the hollins green' or in 'a new-made grave beneath a green aik tree'. In death there's life: from the grave spring birch sapling and wand of brier, twining in a posthumous vegetable

[*] Sir Walter Scott presented a snuffbox made from the Torwood tree to George IV on his visit to Scotland in 1822.

Hunting scenes are often portrayed on Celtic stones.
This ninth- or tenth-century stone found on Rossie Island in the
South River Esk, Angus, shows rider and hound chasing a hind.
In medieval times the term 'forest' indicated a hunting ground,
not necessarily wooded. Celtic stones are rich in symbolism –
the lone tree in the corner may signify the tree of life.

embrace. 'I hae been to the wild wood,' the dying Lord Randal, back
from hunting and an assignation with his true love, tells his mother –
'O I fear ye are poisoned,' says she. Brown Adam 'bigged a bower in the
gude green wood' for his lady but returns from the chase to find her in
the embrace of a false knight. He draws his sword and cuts off a few of
his rival's fingers (it could have been worse). May Margaret follows
the ghost of her slain lover Clerk Saunders 'until she came to the green
forest and there she lost the sight o' him'.

Lord Randal, being of noble blood, hunted in the forest with impunity;
his bad luck was to drink from the fatal cup. But forest, in medieval
terms, came to have a specific meaning as a royal hunting ground
where the chase was reserved for the king and his nobles and woe
betide any commoner who poached. And in spite of the name, which
today is associated almost exclusively with thick woodland, such
medieval 'forest' may have been only lightly wooded and even – so the
argument goes – open ground. The word, according to sticklers for
etymological accuracy, is a bit of a banana skin.

So when is a forest not a forest? Sir Walter Scott in his *Tales of a
Grandfather* described a great hunt in the glens of upper Deeside,
where, 'upon a signal given, the hunters begin to move inwards,
closing the circle, and driving the terrified deer before them, with
whatever else the forest contains of wild animals who cannot elude the
surrounding sportsmen'. Scott's forest in that description implies trees,
the great pinewoods of Braemar.

A forest is a place full of woods, but not every wood is a forest, declared Mark Anderson, historian of Scottish forestry.[*] A paradox. A forest, according to Chambers Dictionary, is 'a large uncultivated tract of land covered with trees and underwood. Woody ground and rude pasture. A preserve for big game. A royal preserve for hunting'. Ignoring the historical and semantic niceties today's Forestry Commission blithely named its huge new plantations Kielder Forest, Glentrool Forest, Queen Elizabeth Forest and so on, though most of them were man-made creations on open heathland where no tree had grown before for thousands of years.

A few years ago I met a Dutch artist and botanist who came to Edinburgh to make an exhibition celebrating Scottish forests at the Royal Botanic Garden. I see his impish face yet, fringed with a fuzz of white whiskers, as he flitted among the arboretum glades. Called herman de vries – he doesn't use capital letters – he saw the word forest written large over a map of the Scottish Highlands and was shocked to find the landscapes bare. herman soon learned that a Highland deer forest has nothing to do with trees; more with knickerbockered Victorian gents stalking stags on barren moors, but this didn't stop him. His exhibition contained a wall on which he chalked in a round hand the names of all the Highland 'forests' he could squeeze in – Aberchalder Forest, Braeroy Forest, Cluanie Forest and so forth. herman's list added up to more than two hundred. It was, he said, a tribute to and lamentation for the ancient forest we have lost.

These days, the global warming debate gives the word a political slant. Since growing trees trap carbon any woodland, new or old, high forest or scrub, can be represented as a carbon sink, a negotiable asset to trade against greenhouse gas emissions. Hence recalcitrant industrial nations may cite the 'forest' to get them off the hook.

*

---

[*] Mark Loudon Anderson, who will be frequently referred to in this book. As both practical forester and theoretician his influence has been great. His two-volume *History of Scottish Forestry*, which he wrote while Professor of Forestry at Edinburgh University, was assembled from manuscript after his death in 1961. He joined the new Forestry Commission after World War One, in which he won the Military Cross, and in a distinguished but never smooth career – being too outspoken – he served forestry in Scotland, Australia and Ireland. He was a linguist, proud of his Scottishness; and finally, he edited a book of Scottish proverbs.

In the prologue I asked if there was there ever a Caledonian Forest or Great Wood of Caledon? *Caledonia Silva*, *Coit Caledon*, the Wood of Celyddon, the Great Wod – there are many variants, few facts. Did it exist? Where? What was it like?

This fabled Caledonian Forest was named, and therefore validated by the Romans, but what they meant by it is another matter. A forest, or vast forests, certainly existed before the name, and a great part of the landscape was covered in trees long before the legions looked out from their northern fortifications.

Roman writers fostered the impression that in their time north Britain was shaded by deep and extensive forests from which the native population launched guerrilla raids and into which they melted afterwards. It suited the invaders' book to imply that this forest was a great barrier to their progress. These Roman invaders have been blamed for the supposed 'destruction' of the forest. They came, saw and cut it down – or so it was argued.

But views have changed. The forest was already much less widespread than Roman authors implied. Homesteaders had already been clearing the land over much of Scotland for thousands of years, and long before the Christian era wide stretches of the land had been deforested.

On a medieval map based on Ptolemy, astronomer and geographer of the Roman world, a vague *Caledonia Silva*, dotted with tree symbols, stretches roughly from Loch Lomond to the Beauly Firth. How closely this reflects reality is anyone's guess. It's not encouraging that Scotland on this projection veers drunkenly to the east.

More often than not we now identify the legendary Caledonian forest with the few relics of ancient pinewood that survive in Highland glens. Stray gleanings from the so-called Dark Ages imply a forest of another kind situated vaguely in the south, anywhere from the Border country to the Forth valley. There, according to a sixth century document, in the Wood of Caledon – *Coit Celidon* in Brythonic – Arthur won a great victory. Merlin the Arthurian magus – himself reputed to be as old as Caledon's ancient oaks – found refuge in the Caledonian forest, a dense 'nut rich' wilderness whose extent he could survey from a mountain top screened by foliage.

From medieval times onwards the site of the Wood of Caledon was located variously over many parts of the country, and increasingly in the north. Thus it was said to have reached from Stirling into Atholl and Lochaber, according to the chronicler Hector Boece, Bishop of Aberdeen, writing in the 1520s. His contemporary John Major or Mair inclined to think that the great woodlands clustered round the foot of the Scottish mountains – where 'an incredible number' of stags and hinds could be found – were Ptolemy's Caledonian forest.

Much later it was confidently stated that 'the forests of Strathspey are a portion of what was once the great Caledonian fir forest, said to extend from Glenlyon and Rannoch to Strathspey and Strathglas, and from Glencoe east to the Braes of Mar'. The English historian, traveller and antiquary William Camden, writing at roughly the same time as Boece and Major, gave a graphic word image of 'that Wood of Caledonia' which he placed in the highlands of Atholl; he described it as a wilderness 'dreadful to see and for the sundry turnings and windings in and out therein, for the hideous horrors of dark shades, for the burrows and dens of wild bulls with thick manes'. The idea lingered on. As late as 1708, in a map published in Paris, the pinewoods of Glen Orchy appeared under the rubric Caledonian Forest.

The idea of a particular forest of Caledon was sustained by the fertile imagination of poets, historians and geographers. Current scholarly opinion tends to dismiss the forest as a production of overheated nineteenth century Romanticism, owing more to Teutonic tradition (wildwood as angst) than to fact.

The environmental historian Christopher Smout suggests that we could just as well, and probably more accurately, refer to a great bog of Caledon. Elsewhere the notional grand forest has been debunked as the Great Myth of Caledon: 'The sceptic might even doubt whether it existed, and that all we are dealing with is a myth repeated by many writers.' Hugh Boyd Watt argued persuasively as long ago as 1898 that the name of a specific (though vaguely defined) woodland had been hijacked to embrace all forests in the land: 'Caledonia has long been used to designate the whole of Scotland, and in a similar manner and with something of the poetic glamour that surrounds the name, the Caledonian Forest of old has broken its bounds, and rolled over the whole country'. I'd not quarrel with that.

*

The wolf in medieval times had a price on its head. By the end of the eighteenth century it had been harried to extinction.

Wild beasts as well as outlaws, robbers and the occasional freedom fighter haunted the medieval forest and of these the wolf was dreaded most. Packs of wolves hunted in prehistoric Scotland and their descendants survived persecution until the last of them perished less than three centuries ago. The sound of their howling, a blood-curdling arc of sound in the night, or the mere thought of their curled lip and bared teeth, was sufficient cause to demonise them.

In Scotland it was said that the great pinewoods of Rannoch and Lochaber were almost impassable because of the ferocity of the wolves that roamed there, and refuges were set up along the tracks through the forest to give shelter to unwary travellers caught out at nightfall. Did they really attack grown men and women or was their howl worse than their bite? 'Many an old story' (according to Mark Anderson) tells how Malcolm II was forced to flee for his life pursued by a wolf through the forest on the outskirts of Aberdeen. The weak and the young were particularly vulnerable. Two children were reported torn to death in Moray as late as 1743. 'Many and maist cruel' wolves roamed the north country, declared a chronicler towards the end of the sixteenth century, where they killed sheep, oxen and even men, and 'especially women with bairn'.

That sheep might safely graze and pregnant women go unmolested, wolf must die. Woodland fires are said to have been started in medieval times to force them into the open. Wolves were fair game at a time when beasts of the chase were strictly protected. The monks of Melrose, barred from trapping in Eskdale in the fourteenth century, were allowed carte blanche in the case of wolves. These they could kill on sight. Posses of local people might be called out when required. James I decreed in 1428 that every baron 'shall chase and seek the whelps of wolves and have them slain'. Tenants were expected to join in, and the man who killed a wolf and brought its head to the baron was to be paid two shillings. (The price escalated. Two hundred years later Thomas Gordon was paid six pounds thirteen and fourpence for killing a wolf in Sutherland.) In 1615 tenants in Breadalbane were ordered to make spears for killing wolves. Inhabitants of Strathnaver were instructed to follow the sheriffs in wolf hunts three times in the year. Grand wolf hunts were organised, such as those in the forests of Atholl presided over respectively by James V and Mary Queen of Scots.

The last exit of the wolf was recorded variously and gleefully. Some time in the reign of Charles I a band of armed men cornered and killed two running wolves in the woods near Crieff 'and these were said to be the last wolves heard of in Scotland'. They were not. In 1644, a last wolf (at least in the northeast) was killed near Kirkmichael in Banffshire. When Sir Ewen Cameron of Locheil, a great sportsman and destroyer of wildlife, despatched a wolf with his own hands at Killiecrankie in 1680, it was said to be the last seen in the Highlands; after that Sir Ewen had to content himself with the fox as quarry. But in Sutherland a man called Polson was credited with killing the last wolf and her cubs a decade later. Three other wolf kills were reported around that time in other parts of the country. Indeed last wolves lingered into the following century. In 1743 the child-killer of Moray was pursued and slain on the banks of the Findhorn by a hunter known only as Macqueen.

Good riddance. Who needs wolves? Yet contrary to the black propaganda, naturalists insist that wolves fear humankind and avoid us when they can. Folk wisdom tells another story and old views die hard. All over Europe the wolf has been chased, trapped, poisoned, clubbed, speared and shot. In Spain the hunt for a lamb-killer takes on the air of a ritual celebration. Once in a seedy *auberge* in alpine Provence I saw a photo on the wall of local hunters grinning over the corpse of a wolf they'd killed – with a sheepskin stuffed between its fangs. A hungry wolf is a sheep killer and pursuit of the culprit is an old country pastime. No wonder we shift uneasily when radicals propose returning a pack or two to some unspecified Highland wilderness.

Wolves might lurk in the deeper recesses of the forest, but on more open ground trees provided food and shelter for domestic animals. Wherever open woodland adjoined their holdings, herdsmen grazed their stock among trees throughout the first two Christian millennia until well into the eighteenth century. Sheep, goats, cattle, and the bristly little pigs which snuffled in the undergrowth for oak mast shared pickings in medieval times with wild creatures of the forest.

Even herds of horses, wild and semi-wild, the property of the rich, the royal and the ecclesiastical, roamed through the woodland and were rounded up when required. David I had brood mares running in his forests of Fife and Forfar and in the 1430s royal horses were kept in the forest of Mar on Deeside. Broken and unbroken horses wandered through the forest of Glenshee. Nine hundred horses were at large in woodlands belonging to the monks of Melrose.

Monks – or more likely their labourers – were great levellers of woodland. The Cistercians and their lay brothers the white friars, being agriculturists dedicated to hard manual labour, felled trees, grubbed out the stumps and ploughed the land. Mark Anderson argued that the siting of religious houses gave 'some indication of those districts where primeval forests still survived on fertile soils worth reclaiming for farming'. By his reckoning large areas of oak forest must have still existed from Beauly in Inverness-shire down Sweetheart and Glenluce in Galloway; forests which have since vanished. But the woodlands were too valuable, both for sheltered grazing and as a source of timber and fuel, to be wantonly destroyed by the brothers. Woods played their part in the monastic economy and the monks protected them behind hedges and dykes.

Commerce and Christian orders went hand in hand. Members of the great religious foundations, besides being tillers of the soil, were the sheep ranchers of the day; as the wool trade between Leith and Flanders flourished sheep rearing became increasingly profitable. An estimated two million sheep cropped the Scottish Border hills in late medieval times, not the fat breeds of today but small dun-coloured animals thinly fleeced. Teams of pack horses brought the wool – each fleece weighing no more than a meagre two pounds – to the coast for shipment. But so long as grazing in the open 'wood pastures' was light and seasonal some young trees came through and the woodland survived. 'It takes a lot of browsing to stop regeneration altogether,'

Gothic architecture as petrified forest. Trunk-like pillars uphold a canopy of foliage-encrusted vaulting in the fifteenth-century Rosslyn Chapel, near Edinburgh. One pillar is said to represent the sacred ash tree linking heaven and earth. (From Taylor's *Pictorial History of Scotland*.)

says the woodland writer Oliver Rackham. The caveat, of course, is that the delicate balance can be all too easily and fatally disturbed. Rackham again: 'The more animals graze the pasture, the more difficult it becomes to replace the trees'.

Goats posed a potentially greater threat than sheep; greedy and omnivorous, they can devastate a countryside; witness the bare white hills of the Mediterranean, a legacy of centuries of over-grazing. Goats were important to the Scottish economy, particularly in the Highlands, long after medieval times.

Those grand umbrageous pine trees of the Highlands may have developed their outreaching crowns in an ancient pasture-wood system. And not just pines. The historian Christopher Smout argues that the oaks at Firbush Point beside Loch Tay, whose crowns spread ninety feet in diameter, or the great ash trees at Rassal in Wester Ross, may have been enabled to expand in the freedom of open grazing woods. If they had been cramped together like plantation trees, shooting upwards for light, they would have grown tall, straight and narrow.

The last degenerate relics of what was once thriving wood pasture survives today as scrub woodland on many a grassy lowland slope or Highland valley; patches of scattered trees, jaded old stagers, twisted and stunted and often showing signs of having been lopped in the past, some already lifeless. No sign of any young trees growing up to succeed them – this is deadwood in the making. It's surprisingly common. Most of the time you pass by without a second look.

The scattered veteran trees at Glen Finglas – such as this specimen clinging doggedly to life – indicate that sheep and cattle were pastured on this former royal hunting ground. Grazing animals prevented the renewal of the woodland.

The water is low in Glen Finglas reservoir, a man-made loch near the village of Brig o' Turk in the Trossachs. Roaring burns fed by a recent deluge have filled it with silt, making the water unfit for Glaswegians to drink, and it has been been drained to allow the sediment to settle. Drystane dykes and ruined walls with gaunt chimney stacks, relics of former habitation, stick out from the mud.

In the upper glen the slopes and gullies are dotted with a random growth of small trees. 'Knackered woodland on its last legs' was the comment of a forester on seeing it for the first time, and it seems an apt description. It's geriatric. We wander among rickety specimens of birch, hazel, alder, much damaged by nibbling sheep. Some seem to be perching on stilt roots where the base has rotted away. One hazel has split to reveal a sturdy aerial root plunging down the hollow stem. For a naturalist, such wrecks are a treasure trove. One of our number gently prizes a flake of bark from a rotting log to reveal a host of small scuttling things in the dark red interior, feeding on decay, breaking it down even further.

Peter Quelch, forester and lover of old trees, has found real veterans higher up the hill in sheltered gullies. Some are nearly five metres in girth, and aged, he reckons, at least three hundred and perhaps five hundred years old. They are encrusted with lichens whose presence implies a continuity of woodland since ancient times.

We pick our way among boulders in a gully where a gnarled ash tree has found a niche, benefiting from soil enriched by minerals brought down from the limestone crags. A wand of rowan sprouts from a fork of the ash, where its seed germinated in the moist debris lodged there.

The trees spreading over the open hill are mostly hazel and alder, stubby things, often with a topknot of branches springing from the stem two or three feet above ground which may be evidence both of past cropping by animals and cutting for small timber by the local peasantry.

In former times Glen Finglas was hunting ground for the Stewart kings. In spite of the efforts of royal foresters to keep them out, and the threat of dire penalties, the locals snatched any chance to graze their animals among the trees and to lop branches for fuel, for fencing (hazel being particularly suitable for this) and innumerable domestic uses. According to Christopher Smout, tenants didn't win free access generally until about 1700, but long before that they took what they could.

In many parts country people had the right to cut firewood and pasture animals in woodland and often, no doubt, they overstepped the limits. From time immemorial people had plundered the forest as if by right. Mother Nature had supplied it for their good. They took fuel for the fire and carted away small timber for all their building and a hundred and one other needs. Apart from stray windfall boughs or whole tree trunks laid low on the ground – theirs for the taking, it must have appeared – they lopped branches or felled standing trees as the need arose. Often, even when barred by law, they took what they could surreptitiously and without permission. An early law aimed against 'peelers of greenwood, greenwood stealers, closure breakers and stealers of tree or fruit' was one of many. Both local superiors and the crown laid down stiff penalties, though how rigorously applied and how effective they were is another matter.

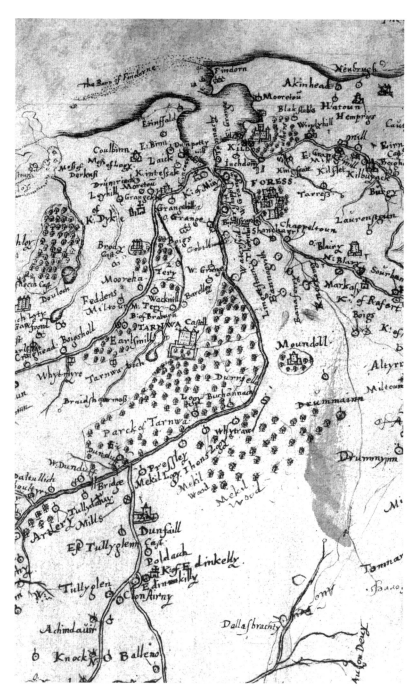

Darnaway forest as it appears in Timothy Pont's late sixteenth-century map.
Darnaway was heavily exploited for timber in the Middle Ages.
Today only a line of huge oak trees remains alongside the Findhorn river.

3

WHEN THE TREE FALLS

MEDIEVAL SCOTS, highlanders and lowlanders, lived in a wooden world. Wooden artefacts were everywhere. Their homes, their agricultural implements, their tools and their household equipment were wooden: trees, timber, wood, the foundation of all domestic life and the economy from prehistory almost to the present.

Birch, most common and adaptable of all native trees, served a multitude of needs and was universal in the Highlands. Ploughs were fashioned from birch and birch poles were used as a framework for sleds before wheeled carts were common. Chairs, tables and beds were made from its lightly grained, easily worked wood, as were dishes and spoons. Whippy birch branches were woven into hurdle fences and the sprays thatched cottages – as well as providing besom and broom heads. Fish casks were commonly birch. Ropes and horse harness could be twisted from heated birch sprays. The bark became an early staple of the tanning industry and birch coppice stems were cut for making charcoal. Logs burned well in the hearth and imparted a fine flavour to hams and herring (as did sprays of juniper).

Oak, strong-grained, hard and durable, whose boughs often grew with a natural crook, provided prime heavyweight shipbuilding and house construction material, and it could be fashioned into countless articles. Houses were constructed on a skeleton of oak crucks; oak beams roofed palace banqueting halls and the naves of cathedrals. It served as keel, ribs and planking for seagoing ships. Whisky matured in oak casks. Oak served best of all for the charcoal and tanning industries.

A 'hangin lum' – the stage between hole in the roof and built-in chimney – reconstructed at Jeanie MacAlpine's Inn, near Aberfoyle. The framework of wattled hazel will be plastered with mud.

Pine, softer and lighter than oak, was also widely used for building and joinery work. Pinewood made deal floorboards. Small trees (with their foliage) were cut to erect movable fencing and the timber could be used for palings. Pine casks and crates were suitable as dry goods containers. Splinters were often gouged from the living tree to make so-called pine 'candles' which burned brightly. The scars may still be seen. As coal mining grew in importance in succeeding centuries the colliers secured their galleries with pinewood pit props.

Ash, strong and shock-absorbent, was the ideal material for coaches and carts, both for frames and wheels; and equally good for ploughs and other farm implements down to the handles of rakes, forks and spades. Millwrights prized it. Coopers made hoops of ash, boatmen pulled on ash oars.

Hazel's thicket-like growth made a natural for many uses. Its wands were twisted into wattles for walls and fences and its rods could be easily turned into crooks, poles, staves and broom handles. In dwellings chimneys were lined with hazel wattle plastered with mud (such early chimneys – better than a hole in the roof – were called 'hangin lums'). Hazel charcoal was said to be the best for making gunpowder.

Like hazel, willow wands made hurdles, hoops, rods and poles, and the soft, light timber was valued for rake and scythe handles. Willow planks, not prone to splinter, made a good shock-proof lining for carts and barrows. The branches, when cut at the dead time of the year and woven into a river bank would sprout into a living web which stabilised the embankment.

Alder, being rot-resistant, was the preferred timber for bridge piles, sluice gates and any foundation work in watery places. Clog makers liked it; so (in the form of charcoal) did the gunpowder millers. Shoots cut in spring were widely used in the Highlands to dye cloth a cinnamon colour; its catkins dyed green.

Large or cumbersome doors and gates could be usefully made from aspen, a timber which like willow is soft, white and above all light. Also kitchen furniture – plus platters for the kitchen table. Thorn, on the other hand, being hard, made good mallets and teeth for rakes. Tool handles were often made of rowan. Posts of yew defied decay longer than any other timber.

Beech, once it had been lured north of the Cheviots, was found to make a fine blazing fire – nothing better – and served well for underwater piling. And sycamore, that other early and welcome incomer – pale, close-grained, hard and strong – proved to have a multitude of uses, from heavy duty timber to fiddle backs; it was also said (more than a century ago) to be 'good for household vessels such as bowls, cups and other articles of turnery in general use during a bygone age but now superseded by earthenware'. A woodworker's delight.

Terraces of stone cottages fronting village streets today give a false impression of how the common people lived. Timber was the main structural element in domestic houses until roads were built in the eighteenth century to transport quarried stone. Walls were made of wattle, a woven basketwork plastered with turfs, and windows were were also wattled. In the Highlands roofs were thatched with straw, bracken or heather. These were known as creel houses, creel being the Scots word for basket.

It's thought that the knotwork patterns on Celtic stones may indicate interlaced osiers, as used in simple buildings. The technique is age-old and stretches forward almost to modern times. Archibald Menzies, general inspector for the commission administering forfeited Jacobite estates after the 1745 rising, reported that 'in all Highland estates they have nothing excepting creel houses which are formed of basket work covered with fale [turf]. They make use of the most pliant plants for that purpose, which are generally young trees'. He said these frail buildings lasted only a few years which implies a constant demand

The lofty hammer beam roof over the Great Hall at Stirling Castle was rebuilt in 1999, from fifteenth-century drawings and using, as far as possible, the techniques of medieval craftsmanship.
This photograph was taken by the Lighting Architects Group, the Edinburgh-based company which tackled the complex task of illuminating the roof to show off its impressive construction.

for young trees.[*] Grander buildings required more solid construction for which the forest supplied the raw material. Celtic castles were wooden, as were the castles of the Gaelic chieftains. Picture postcard gaunt stone ruins belong to later days.

Towns were timber-built. Timber couples formed the gable ends. The remains of timber frame houses, the earliest dating from the eleventh century and the latest from the sixteenth, were uncovered in Perth when the foundations for a Marks & Spencer store were dug in the 1960s. Other examples have been found in Dundee and Elgin. Old pictures show what appear to be timber-fronted buildings in the High Street of Edinburgh. Roofs were either thatched or shingled with wooden tiles. The roof of Edinburgh's Tolbooth was slated only in the middle of the nineteenth century; before that it had been shingled. A timber town is a tinder town and disastrous fires were frequent. Lanark burned down in 1244 and Kelso in 1674, eight years after the Great Fire of London, and in the intervening centuries others suffered the same fate.

Logging flourished in the periodic construction booms encouraged by David I in the twelfth century and James IV in the late fifteenth. Woods, and especially oakwoods, resounded to the thud of the axe, the crash of great trees falling and the clangour of heavy teams of horses and oxen engaged in the extraction of the timber.

[*] Pressure on the woods must have been great. 'It may be supposed that a small house erected in that manner will destroy two thousand of the straightest and best of the young wood as the old does not answer to the purpose' – from a report of 1767 referring to Lochaber.

A volunteer craftsman uses a side axe to square or 'box heart' a timber beam for the restoration of Jeanie MacAlpine's Inn.

Oak was preferred for the more important construction work. Oak from the west side of Loch Lomond was in demand in the mid 1200s for the construction of the newly founded religious houses. In 1291 forty trees from the great oakwood at Darnaway in Moray were ordered for the roof of Dornoch Cathedral. At the same time the Bishop of St Andrews reserved sixty oak trees in a forest near Selkirk, no doubt for a similar purpose. Forty oaks were cut down for Arbroath Abbey.

Two centuries later an estimated two hundred oak trees were required to build a hammer beam roof in the Great Hall of Stirling Castle. The hall was built between 1480 and 1503. None of the original timbers remain, but a core taken from a beam in the nearby Church of the Holy Rude shows that the tree from which it came was felled in the 1470s, which makes church and hall almost exact contemporaries. After the 1719 Jacobite rising the castle was occupied by the Hanoverian army as a garrison. Partitions and floors were put into the great hall, holes were knocked in its walls and the old rafters were replaced by a messy utilitarian network of trusses and ties.

Now restored to its former glory, the great hall roof is like a huge upturned boat. Keel and ribs. High overhead it extends from the the dais where James sat enthroned to the gallery at the far end of the hall where minstrels played; fourteen great trusses, 43 secondary trusses, a total length of 125 feet and 37 feet wide. Few oak trees in Scottish woods today are big enough to make single rafters of the required dimensions, more than thirty feet long by at least six inches

Woodman Peter Matyjasek inspects a twin-stemmed oak stump in Bailefuil Wood near Strathyre, where trees were felled to re-roof the Great Hall at Stirling.

square, and some had to be jointed. Modern joiners used saws where their predecessors cleft the trees along the grain with an axe, or squared them with a side axe – 'box-hearting' is the term. No nails were used in the roof, both the ancient original and the modern reconstruction. Iron and oak do not agree, neither in buildings nor in ships, for the tannin in oak is corrosive and nails rust. Wooden pegs pin the joints together.

More than two hundred oak trees from woods in Perthshire, on Loch Lomondside and at Darnaway were felled to re-roof the great hall.

April: Bailefuil Wood, near the village of Strathyre. A quiet place. Little hillocks and knolls above the Balvag river. On the ground, outcropping rocks, bracken, grass. Bluebells poking through, still to flower. Creeks of standing water where otters visit. Birch trees grow down there, but the core of the wood is oak, surviving within conifer plantations. Freshly cut stumps show where some of the oaks have been felled – gone to make roof beams for Stirling. Some trunks cut into logs for transport lie on the ground along with piles of lopped branches, most of them patterned with lichens. Not all the good trees (in forestry parlance) are destined to fall. 'This one's here for the rest of its days,' forester Mike Steward says fondly, patting the bark of a giant.

There are constraints on what and how many trees to cut down at Bailefuil. A reserve of good timber must be kept, seed trees need to be conserved, the view from the road on the opposite side of the river has to be protected – the oakwood is an essential part of a bonny scene – and finally (most important, some would say) the woodland ecology, a delicate balance easily disturbed by the loss of too many trees, must be preserved.

Like most representations of the *Great Michael*, James IV's ill-fated flagship, this highly speculative sketch fails to capture the scale of the 'monstrous great ship'. Few details apart from the bare measurements survive to give any clue to what she looked like. Perhaps a thousand oak trees were felled to build her.

Steward points at a tree – it seems to me a likely candidate for the chain saw – that will not be touched. A buzzard nests in it. Nor will trees that the woodpeckers visit. As we talk we hear the mocking call of a green woodpecker, a rarity in Scotland. A dead oak nearby is sacrosanct because of the colonies of insects that inhabit it.

May: Bailefuil Wood. Peter Matyjasek is completing his felling contract. 'Come on, big man,' he says, slapping Danny the Clydesdale on the flank, and Danny lunges forward, down the woodland slope at a lick with a grand tossing of mane, tail and leg feathers, a snorting, a thumping of iron-shod hooves and a chinking of chains as he hauls a felled tree trunk behind him.

It's like old times. Horsepower was the height of forest technology five centuries ago and long after. But nostalgia has no part of this deal. Danny's labour has a practical advantage. Care is called for where the ground is rough and damage to surrounding trees has to be avoided. Danny, unlike heavy vehicles, can weave in and out among woodland trees, and compared to churning wheels and pounding caterpillar tracks the light trails left by Danny's tread are forest friendly, scraping and scarifying the ground, loosening the tangle of moss and turf, encouraging fresh growth and enriching the soil with fresh deposits of dung.

Peter Matyjasek looks up at the spruce plantation above Strathyre where a normal harvesting operation is going ahead. Large swathes of conifers on the steep hillside are being cleared by the latest machinery. When Peter was learning his trade in the 1960s he helped to plant those very trees at a time when horses were still a force in forestry work. Danny is a link in a thousand-year chain.

*

For the first three months of 1512 James IV, most tragic king of Scots, rode regularly to Newhaven on the south bank of the Forth to watch the fitting out of his mighty man-o'-war. At the dockside with his admiral Sir Andrew Wood he viewed the huge vessel, newly launched and now nearing completion. This was to be the flagship of his growing fleet and the envy of all maritime nations including his arrogant English neighbour. The first mission of the *Saint Michael*, named after the avenging angel but popularly known as the *Great Michael*, was to be a voyage to the Holy Land on a crusade against the Turk.

The *Great Michael* was truly 'ane very monstrous great ship' in contemporary eyes. If we can believe one report (there is little other evidence to go on) she measured 240 feet – twice as long as the Great Hall roof at Stirling – and 36 feet in breadth at her waist, a staggering size for a ship of the time. No plans exist, no contemporary drawings and no precise description. Perhaps some idea may be got from the *Vasa*, an ill-fated Swedish warship built more than a century after the *Great Michael* and raised recently from the bottom (she sank in shallows on her maiden voyage). She measures 226 feet from stern to tip of the bowsprit (155 feet of hull length) with a beam of 38 feet, and from ground level in the Stockholm museum where she has been restored she towers as tall as a Glasgow tenement. Both ships are likely to have been unwieldy, top heavy and slow to answer the helm.

The *Great Michael*, the most splendid ship in James' fleet, was the last in a line of royal vessels. There was the famous *Yellow Carvel*, built before James came to the throne. In 1489 he had a royal galley under construction at Dumbarton, and the *Christopher* warship was built five years later. Ambitious to make Scotland a maritime nation, James initiated a shipbuilding programme, decreeing that all coastal towns must build ships of at least twenty tons, burthen for the merchant and fishing fleets.

Since there was a shortage of tradesmen skilled in the craft experts were hired on the continent, beginning in 1502 when the shipwright John Lorens was head-hunted in France. Soon afterwards he was dispatched with a team of loggers to select suitable timber in Cambusnethan wood. Lorens was followed by other compatriots including one Jennen Diew (or possibly Dieu) and two others identified only as John and Robinat. One of the French master shipwrights was sent north on horseback to scour the woods of Badenoch for likely shipbuilding material. Other French shipwrights sailed from Dieppe in 1506. Guest shipwrights also came from Spain and Portugal. A mixed team of Scots, Spanish and French craftsmen was at work in the Torwood in 1512, possibly preparing timber for the *Great Michael*. Timber was routinely fashioned on the spot in the woods where it was felled. In 1503 a Highland landowner was reimbursed for payment made to 'the wrights that squared the timber' in the Forest of Mamlorn. Much of the timber was sent to the shipyards by sea, by far the easiest method of transportation at a time when a road system barely existed and haulage was primitive. Though timber could be worked in forests as far afield as Inverness-shire and Ross-shire, proximity to water transport was a necessary condition, and inland forests could not be exploited.

Forests far and near supplied the timber needed for the *Great Michael* to such an extent that an observer reported that the ship 'took sae meikle timber that she waistit all the woods of Fife, except Falkland, besides the timber that cam out of Norroway'. Whether the Fife forests – what was left of them – or any other woodland in the realm were laid waste by James IV's shipbuilding zeal is a matter of conjecture. To what extent were the woods destroyed? No doubt there was a desolate look about the newly cut woodlands, but only a proportion of the growing oak trees would be suitable for ship timbers, and though the stoutest and tallest might fall to the axe, slender young trees and elderly rejects would be left standing to provide seed and new hope for the future.

The *Great Michael* had a bad end. In 1513, a year after her launch into the Forth, James rashly marched an army into battle with the English and was cut down on Flodden field along with many followers, nobles and commoners – like the flowers o' the forest, as the song goes. No dirge laments the *Great Michael*. Sold abroad (what need of a navy had Scotland after Flodden?) she was laid up in the French port of Brest where her timbers rotted, seawater flooded in and she settled in a grave of foreign mud.

Warlike figures in a barren Highland landscape – just three trees on the skyline.
After Culloden, tree planting and widespread woodland improvement helped to soften the aspect
of estates forfeited by defeated Jacobite lairds.
(From *Military Antiquities Respecting a History of the English* (sic) *Army*, 1812.)

4

POOR LAND, WITH PROSPECTS

WHEN did the landscapes we know today emerge from the retreating forest? Possibly, if we could skip back in time to the Middle Ages, we might be able to recognise the broad character – not the precise features – of the countryside, at least in the lowlands, with its alternating pattern of woods, tilled land and open ground. Many clearings for agriculture would be visible.

Looking on the pleasantly variegated scene around him in the mid sixteenth century John Leslie – bishop, historian, confidant of Mary Queen of Scots and adversary of John Knox – could remark (in the words quoted at the head of this book) that 'here again shall ye see a dry knowe, or a thin forest, there a thick wood, all marvellous to the eye'. His description seems not dissimilar to what we might see today in, say, Ayrshire or Fife. Though nowadays, of course, the 'thick wood' is likely to be a plantation of spruce, a tree unknown to the bishop.

Others pictured a bleaker landscape than Bishop Leslie. There was the Mr Sletcher who arrived at Glamis Castle uninvited and presented himself to the Earl of Strathmore. He must have made an impression on his host. 'To this man I gave liberal money,' the earl noted in his day book (misspelling the name).

Sletcher – properly, Captain John Slezer – was often out on Scotland's bad roads, calling at this stately home or that. German by birth, by choice a Scot, by profession a military surveyor, he had become Chief Engineer for Scotland, Surveyor of His Majesty's Stores and Magazines and Captain to the Scots Train of Artillery: all important posts. Professional duties which took him round garrisons and barracks subsidised travel for his obsession, which was to make a compendious record of the castles, palaces, towns and private houses of his adopted homeland, illustrated by his own engravings. Noble patrons like Strathmore were persuaded to support the scheme in return for having their homes engraved on copper for posterity.

The first and only completed volume of this masterwork, *Theatrum Scotiae*, published in 1693,[*] gives some impression (if we may assume its accuracy) of what the lowland country looked like three hundred years ago. Treeless, it would seem, or if not quite treeless, bare, bleak, exposed. It's assumed that Slezer used a camera obscura, a tent-like structure raised over a table on which an image of the chosen view was reflected. Thus from his awning beside the ruined abbey of Cambuskenneth he was able to present his prospect of Stirling, showing castle, church and rooftops emerging from clusters of foliage. Straggling lines of trees criss-cross the open ground below, perhaps lining roads or marking field boundaries. From Birnam Hill he viewed Dunkeld and its then roofless cathedral, with trees in the foreground – remnants of Birnam Wood – and more on the slope below the town, but the woodland is altogether skimpier than it is today. In the background looms Craigvinean, a hogback hill now heavily forested but apparently bare in Slezer's day.

Slezer's large engraving of the town of Edinburgh 'in two great sheets', taken from Calton Hill, shows long gardens stretching down from the back of the High Street and the Canongate, some laid out with trees in rectangles or orderly rows. They may be orchards. In other engravings of Edinburgh, the surrounding land is naked. The castle sits on its rock, tall tenements huddle on the ridge of the Royal Mile, and the rolling slope of farmland in the foreground bears not a wisp of a tree upon it. From another aspect the city is glimpsed over the rooftops of Dean Village, sunken in its gorge, across intervening agricultural land bare of trees.

Most of Slezer's rural settings are curiously (to modern eyes) untimbered, and in general his townscapes (how small and countrified

---

[*] Slezer lost heavily on it. He had a great talent for losing money. By the time of his death in 1717 he had debts of more than £2000 and latterly was forced to shelter in the precincts of Holyrood Abbey, then a sanctuary for debtors. It was not a strict confinement. He was free to go about his artillery duties and had leave to visit his family on Sundays.

are his cities) look more wooded than his landscapes. Perth, dominated by the stubby spire of the kirk of St John, sits on a spit of land jutting into the Tay, pleasantly fringed by foliage. In his 'prospect of Perth' small patches of woodland are visible on higher ground beyond the town, but in the main his landscapes are treeless. Unsheltered country scored by run-rig furrows is the rule, traversed here and there by muddy, rutted roads without benefit of hedge, shelter trees or even a dyke to please the traveller's eye. We glimpse Inverness, Elgin, Musselburgh from a desert.

The English traveller Fynes Morison, rounding off a tour of Europe and the Middle East with a foray into Scotland in 1598, found a few signs of grace in a countryside otherwise bare of trees. In Fife, for example, the houses of the gentry were often 'shadowed with some little groves pleasant to the view'. Such sheltered oases in a bleak landscape – usually to be found in the eastern lowlands counties – were remarked on by others. Thirty years after Morison and sixty before Slezer, another Englishman Sir William Brereton passed Seaton House, near Dunbar, 'a dainty seat placed upon the sea' around which apple, walnut, sycamore and other trees flourished in spite of the salty air.

How trustworthy is Slezer's eye? He showed what he wanted to be seen. Concerned with the delineation of towns, castles and mansion houses rather than landscape, he focused on buildings. Allowing for occasional adjustments (he sometimes Picassoed together different aspects of a building) his drawings are architecturally correct, but perhaps he was less meticulous with the landscape around them. A number of contemporary accounts, usually by Englishmen venturing north, corroborate his point of view. It should be noted, however, that they tended to travel lowland routes in the arable east, and that the high roads took them well clear of the remoter glens where the great pinewoods still flourished.

The arch traducer of supposedly treeless Scotland was (in a later century) Samuel Johnson, the great lexicographer: 'The whole country,' he declared after his celebrated journey to the Western Isles, 'is extended in uniform nakedness'. 'I wonder how they managed to take him about without letting him see a tree,' was the acid comment of William Cobbett (of the *Rural Rides*) who had a better eye for these things.

'The country is rough and barren. There are no trees, except in the orchard.' So declared Dr Samuel Johnson after his visit to Dunvegan Castle, Skye. It confirmed, in the doctor's mind, the treeless state of Scotland. The castle and its surroundings were depicted in Thomas Pennant's *Tour in Scotland and Voyage to the Hebrides* of 1772, the year before Johnson's visit.

To the historian GM Trevelyan, 'the Englishman who rode from Berwick to Edinburgh, despised the lowland scenery as divided between melancholy wastes and ill-managed fields of oats. It was unenclosed; almost treeless; devoid, except in the immediate neighbourhood of Edinburgh, of the fine mansions and parks, well-built farms and stately parish churches which the traveller had left behind him in his own country'. Conditions north of the Forth were no better and possibly worse.

> Far as the eye could reach no tree was seen;
> Earth, clad in russet, scorn'd the lively green

– so Scotland was presented in *The Prospect of Famine*, a satire on all things Scottish by Charles Churchill.

Before the agricultural 'improvers' of the eighteenth century took things in hand the condition of the countryside was certainly neglected (in agricultural terms) and lamentably short of tree cover. Roads, where they existed, were execrable. Wheeled vehicles were rare and primitive, the wheels being fixed to an axle which turned with them – 'tumbling wheels' as they were called. When young Archibald, later Sir Archibald Grant of Monymusk was given permission by his father to undertake land improvements he found that there 'was not one wheel carriage on the estate, nor indeed any one road that would allow it'. As late as 1766 it was observed in Cromarty that 'they use a kind of cart with solid wheels not above two and a half feet diameter which does not carry as much as a common wheelbarrow'. David Murray, chronicler of the York Buildings Company (of whom more later) observed that agricultural implements were 'of Oriental rudeness'. Iron was little used and the cumbersome ploughs, drawn by a ponderous procession of horses or oxen, were mostly wooden. Not surprisingly, furrows were seldom straight and weeds, reeds, briars, brambles and thistles flourished between the ploughed strips of arable ground.

Compared to the cared-for countryside of today the land was desolate, the soil wet and heavy, undrained and sour, the fields unenclosed. This was still the harsh environment that faced Robert Burns, ploughman poet as he may be called with some licence, on the farm of Mossgiel (situated 'mostly on a cold wet bottom' as his brother Gilbert wrote). Mossgiel in Ayrshire was not untypical. Throughout Scotland much of the lower ground was swampy, covered in reeds, subject to inundation in wet weather when the unembanked and many-channelled rivers spread freely. Much of it was permanetly waterlogged under standing pools. Cattle were scrawny and ill fed; over winter they starved and 'those that survived came forth in the spring blear-eyed, dizzy with weakness, and staggered drunkenly to the pasture grounds' where they were often tempted by lush swamp greenery and, enfeebled, wallowed helplessly in the bog. Cowquake was an expressive local term for this springtime infirmity. The plight of the country people was little better. They lived on the edge of survival under constant threat of famine. A series of crop failures between 1692 and 1702 brought widespread suffering; seven 'ill' or 'hungry' winters were known to Jacobites as King William's years, and throughout the following century spells of bad weather were followed inevitably by wholesale misery and hunger.

As a means of improving the productivity of their estates, improving landlords planted trees to shelter their stock and crops. Some lairds encouraged their tenants to plant trees round farms and cottages, often with a threat of punishment if they did not. Sir James Pringle, who grew sycamore, pine and something unidentifiable he called 'sith' on his 'a very pretty park' in Selkirkshire, instructed each of his tenants to plant six forest trees and a dozen other kinds, presumably fruit trees, on pain of a fourpenny fine for each unplanted tree.

Cottagers who did not share their landlords' enthusiasm for tree planting grumbled at the loss of good land to trees and the haven trees gave to crop-eating birds and animals. They perceived no benefit from the laird's zeal for such improvements, and sometimes took direct action. 'Occasionally they carried their objections to extremes by destroying plantations overnight,' according to James Handley, historian of Scottish farming. Did these night raiders gang together, creep out when the moon was down, hack down young growth and pull up tender shoots by the roots?

But tree planting was in the air, and not just on the modest scale of clumps around farm steadings and the mansions of the gentry. As early as the seventeenth century the notion was abroad that trees might be turned into profit, pounds and pence, as in the case of a woodland at Keir in Perthshire, which – it was claimed in the 1630s – 'within short space will be worth the sum of ten thousand pounds money'. That's a lot of money for the time.

Black Duncan of Breadalbane was the first of the great tree planters – Black Duncan, *Donacha dhu na curich*, otherwise Sir Duncan Campbell of Glenorchy. For nearly half a century until his death in 1631 at the age of eighty-six, this gaunt, fierce-visaged man held the wide lands of Breadalbane in his grip. His seat at Taymouth lay in a crook of the River Tay close to where it issues from the loch, below Drummond Hill (now covered by Forestry Commission plantations). He ruled over a large chunk of the the southern Highlands from Loch Lomond to the southern edge of Rannoch Moor, including the fertile valleys of Glen Lyon, Glen Dochart and Glen Orchy.

Black Duncan's portrait, dated 1607 when he was in his sixties, shows him in dark doublet, eyes glowering sidelong from under black brows; his high forehead and prominent cheekbones giving the face a cadaverous look. His hair is black, likewise the thick curly beard. There are rings on his long fingers and his left hand clasps the pommel of a sword. His crest bears the motto 'Follow me'.

This is the picture of a martial man. Yet Black Duncan evidently had a passion for trees. 'He knew the profit as well as the beauty that might accrue from clothing the hill-side with timber and securing shelter around his mansion.' Besides compelling his tenant farmers and

Thomas Hamilton, sixth earl of Haddington, and his countess, Helen. She converted him from manly pursuits to the milder pleasures of planting trees. (Portraits by John Medina)

cottars to grow trees round their dwellings he created several parklands where he 'caused sow acorns and seed of fir' and planted out young fir and birch saplings. He had a plentiful seed source at hand on his domain in the remnants of the old natural forest which grew and still survive there – in the Old Wood of Meggernie in Glen Lyon, only ten miles from Taymourth Castle, and in Glen Orchy and the Black Mount.

Word of his activities spread, and friends, neighbours and relatives eagerly sought pine cones from the Breadalbane woods. In 1636 Lady Lauderdale wrote to Black Duncan's son and heir Sir Colin Campbell asking for 'a good quantity of fir seed' to be sent to the Lauderdale estate at Thirlestane in the Borders. The seed having been dispatched and received, Lady Lauderdale requested a second batch, followed by Lauderdale himself asking for more. The formidable Anna, Marchioness of Hamilton, also received a consignment of pine cones from Sir Colin. 'Honoured cousing' [*sic*], she addressed him in thanks, remarking that she thought more of pine trees 'nor you can imagine, for I love them more than all the fruit trees in the world'.

Thomas Hamilton, sixth Earl of Haddington, loved his pine trees too, and planted them in such abundance that he has been called the father (in Scotland) of tree planting for profit. Abetted by a green-fingered wife, he converted his estate at Tyninghame on the sea coast south of Edinburgh from a windswept sandy spit into a demesne of temperate groves and bosky shade.

Haddington was not a planter born but, in youth, a hot-blooded harum-scarum who 'took pleasure in sport, dogs and horses'.[*] Later he involved himself in politics – he was one of the parcel of rogues who voted the Scottish parliament (now happily restored) out of existence. An opponent described him as 'hot, proud, vain and ambitious' whose 'talent lay in a buffoon sort of wit and raillery'.

In 1696, at the age of sixteen, Thomas married his cousin Helen Hope, two years his senior. Four years later they settled at the Haddington seat of Tyninghame, which had been sadly neglected. Hedges had been pulled up and ploughed over and the ditches were choked. 'As I was not then of age,' Thomas wrote later, 'I had no manner of inclination to plant, enclose, or improve my grounds.' Helen thought otherwise and won the permission of her sporting husband to try her hand at tree planting.

Her first big project was the conversion of Tyninghame Muir, a stretch of 300 barren Scots acres (a Scots acre was greater than an English acre by one fifth) into woodland. Thomas was sceptical but indulged her whim, his mind being on manlier things. Work began in the fateful year 1707 when Haddington, by then in his late twenties, was busy selling Scotland down the river. Helen, who was rumoured to have sold her jewels to pay for it, christened her creation Binning Wood.

For all his previous scorn Haddington was impressed and belatedly took a hand. It was the convention that all policy woods required walks and rides terminating in a point of interest (where a piece of classical sculpture might become the focal point). Surveying the nascent wood he imagined the trees in maturity with gentle alleys set out in the approved pattern. Having identified the most suitable 'centre' or spot to which all ways would tend he hastened to tell Helen, who 'went and looked at it, liked it very well; but walking about, lighted on a spot of ground that she thought more proper. I preferred mine, she hers'.

Two house guests, Sir John Bruce and Lord Marchmont, were invited to arbitrate in this domestic argument, whereupon the whole

---

[*] He had a horse shot under him when he galloped to the field at Sheriffmuir as a gentleman volunteer loyal to the House of Hanover. He himself received a wound in the shoulder.

party took to the site, followed, I assume, by a tail of servants carrying the necessary surveying instruments. First Helen's preferred situation was visited and surveyed, then Thomas', and finally a third proposed by Sir John, who had wandered off to prospect his own. On returning to the house papers were laid out on the table and while the others looked on Marchmont marked out a plan of the wood with the various centres and radiating walks and alleys included. In the end a harmonious expedient was adopted: 'It was agreed unanimously that all the three should be laid out on the ground'. This was done, with the addition later of some serpentine walks and other refinements suggested by Haddington's ten-year-old son. Binning Wood stands today, altered by time and wartime felling, but still a place of peace much visited by common folk like you and me.

Helen, her appetite whetted by the work on Binning Wood, now observed a stretch of scrubby, sandy dunes stretching along the shore. A gentleman 'who had lived some time at Hamburg' (no more is known of him), walking one day along the dunes with her, remarked that he had seen fine trees flourishing on the sandy coastline of northern Germany. Helen's fancy instantly took flight: 'She took the hint', as Thomas put it. Trees were planted, though 'all who saw it thought that the time, labour and trees were thrown away; but, to their great amazement, they saw them prosper as well as in the best grounds'. It was a great success and Thomas himself was encouraged to take up the work of afforestation: 'Many millions of trees hath he planted on sandy downs or links between his house and the sea, and they thrive mightily.' Rugged old pines still grow on the edge of the shore where the gentleman from Hamburg suggested they might, a spaced-out, wobbly line of bent and crusty old-stagers clinging to life above the tideline.

It was not Thomas, of course, who put the trees in the ground. Few of the planting landowners, then or after, got their hands seriously dirty. That was the job of the unsung heroes of forestry, the squads of labouring men out on the hillsides in all weathers with spades in their hands and satchels fulf of saplings on their backs.

A wilderness was the latest thing, and one of Haddington's earliest schemes was to lay out such a wilderness *à la mode* in the Dutch style.

Tulloch Park in the policies of Blair Castle as it appeared in 1744, laid out in formal avenues of trees to suit contemporary taste. (From Charles Esplin's plan of Blair in Atholl.)

Varying degrees of formality in gardens and policies came to be designated Dutch or French, the continental way of taming nature being favoured by the enlightened Scotchmen of the age. In their gardens, neat rows and parterres were laid out in a gridiron pattern. On a larger scale, vistas through avenues of trees were essential. Soon any gentleman (or his lady) wishing to enhance his property desired a wilderness.

The word is misleading. Far from being a dark tangled desolation, the wilderness of the improving Scottish landowners was designed as a silvan annexe close to the house where the laird, his family, friends and visiting gentlefolk might stroll amiably, in safety and comfort, through the glades of a charmingly artificial imitation (at a safe remove) of wild nature. A shaggy geometry was aimed at. In all ornamental planting schemes trees were regimented in rows leading to pretty clearings. Quincunces were much favoured, setting trees in repeated patterns of five so that from within a grove one had the pleasant impression of trees radiating all around, 'look which way a man will'. The architect and landscaper William Adam, brother of the more famous Robert, laid out the gardens, wilderness and great avenue at Arniston and the grounds around Hamilton Palace. By the time of his death in 1748 he had surrounded his own house at Blair with a geometrical patchwork of straight lines of trees with thicker masses at the front through which ran diagonal walks and a wide, tree-lined drive leading from the door. This went out of fashion. 'The strips of planted ground were very narrow, and in straight lines,' his grandson

Diana the huntress, restored to health and beauty in her 'wilderness' at Blair Castle.

wrote disapprovingly, 'and the trees which he planted round the house were disposed in regular form of squares, circles and triangles, without any regard for the shape and diversity of the ground'.

The focus of interest might be a temple, statue, obelisk or as simple as a sundial. James, Duke of Atholl, created a pleasing arcadia in his Wilderness of Diana in the centre of which he placed a statue of the goddess wrought in lead by the sculptor John Cheere. (Gale damaged, showing her age a bit, she has now been reconstituted in stone.) Sir Archibald Grant, who succeeded to Monymusk in 1713 when 'there was not one acre upon the whole estate enclosed, nor any timber upon it but a few elm, sycamore and ash about a small kitchen garden and some straggling trees at some of the farm yards', set about making several plantations, among which was a Wood of Paradise. A visitor to this paradise garden towards the end of the century described how the trees – ash, beech, chestnut, elm, sycamore, larch and other species – marched up the hillside, 'some of them in rows, others in a kind of regular confusion'.

One of the attractions of a long view through an avenue of trees was that it could focus the eye, like a telescope, on a distant feature. Through the woodlands created by John Erskine, Earl of Mar, in Clackmannanshire there were said to be (by 1729) thirty-two vistas 'each ending on some remarkable seat or mountain, at some miles distance', best of which was the castle at Stirling on its rock. At Arniston, in grounds laid out by William Adam the elder, the great avenue was trained on Arthur's Seat twelve miles away. Nearby, at

Hopetoun, were several vistas, 'some ending in a Parish Church, some in an old Tower', but the pièce de résistance was the view down the avenue coming triumphantly to rest on 'North Berwick Law, near the Bass, at Thirty Miles Distance, appearing like a Sugar-Loaf'.

There's no vista leading to the lofty peak of Lochnagar, though on a fine day they tell me it's visible from this estate. We (mainly foresters and woodland owners) are visiting Invercauld on Deeside. There's tea and biscuits laid out for us in the hall – also a display of old maps.

Tastes change, I reflect, cup in hand. The earliest plans indicate parkland devised in the formal French style with fan-shaped woodlands, serpentine walks, long rides, grand vistas – a rococo splendour (if it was ever achieved) later adjusted to suit the cultivated naturalism preferred by landscapists of the romantic era.

Simon Blackett the Invercauld factor – tall, lanky, of military bearing – marches us out of doors to discuss in the field current plans for restoring this somewhat neglected and languishing designed landscape. For instance, what to do with the curious roundels, clumps of old trees, mainly larch, perched on hillocks in the flatlands of the River Dee, which catch the eye from the road running by? These were a curious whim of the nineteenth-century incumbents (neighbours of Victoria and Albert down the road at Balmoral), and the mood of the moment is for keeping them as they are, with some suitable restoration.

By and large, such estates as Invercauld present the vision of well mannered countryside still preferred today. Rolling grassland, serpentine waters, fine trees given space suit our modern mindset. The ordered formality of Haddington's day is as uncongenial to our style as his powdered wig.

It's clear from his his writings that Haddington developed a love and understanding of silviculture. How much of the inspiration for his work at Tyninghame was due to his energetic countess is a matter of conjecture. As a practising politician and a representative Scottish peer, much of his time was spent in London;[*] this suited his temperament. Bath, too, was a diversion. He cultivated a taste for poetry (he tried his hand at versifying) and opera. Helen kept the keys and outlived him by more than thirty years. She died in 1786 at the age of ninety-one.

---

[*] He once complained about the dullness of his 'accursed' native land, 'which affords nothing that can be a diversion to anybody above ane advocate or a Presbyterian minister', though 'drinking indeed succeeds pretty well'. And 'We have neither singing, dancing, nor playing, but for prayers, God ha' mercy on Scotland.'

Having embraced the art of planting, Haddington resolved to pass on the knowledge he had gained by writing his posthumously published *Treatise on the Manner of Raising Forest Trees*. It was neither the first nor the last of such instructive works, which proliferated. Haddington had little regard for his rivals in the field, not excluding the most august and influential of his near contemporaries, the scholar and diarist John Evelyn, whose *Sylva* had been published in 1664: 'his style was too cramp, he was too credulous and regarded the age of the moon too much and other niceties too trifling for so grave a man'. Others he scorned: 'Some have writ like philosophers. These entertain rather than instruct their readers, while some like quacks and chemists, promise a great deal, but perform nothing.' He was particularly scathing of their bad advice on the cultivation of the pine, of which they were 'so entirely ignorant that I am surprised they were not ashamed to set their names to a book'. Not he: 'I shall advance nothing but what I can show'.

Like his fellow educators, Haddington listed the trees available to the early planter, providing a brief compendium of the native and the introduced species at hand by the early eighteenth century, and enlivening descriptions of their character with amiable revelations of his own preferences and prejudices. The horse chestnut (he wrote 'chesnut') 'is the most beautiful tree I ever saw'. Rarity may have helped to add to the appeal of this candle and conker tree, which had been introduced to Britain barely a hundred years before.

If big horse chestnuts were uncommon in Scotland at the time, the sycamore (or plane as he called it) was everywhere. 'There is no old seat, no gentleman's house, nor any place where old trees are, but the planes are most numerous,' he wrote approvingly. He liked beech, which, with its clean grey stem and great shady canopy turning from fresh green in spring to russet in autumn, he considered the proper tree for avenues, walks and groves. It pleased him that since coal was now a common fuel this elegant tree could be spared from cutting for firewood. 'Oak is a tree I like very much, I have planted it everywhere', and everywhere it did well; 'on rich, poor, middling, heathy, gravelly, spouty, clayey and mossy land, nay, upon dead sand'. There was good news and bad about ash, 'a tree that is so long of putting out its leaf that it gives a winter look to the whole field, though when it puts out its leaves they are of a cheerful green, and it carries them when most others have shed theirs'.

The aesthetics of bark and blossom pleased his eye, as with the black cherry, 'called here the Gin', i.e. the gean, which 'have a very fine shining bark' and 'are in great beauty in the end of April and beginning of May, when all covered with white blossoms'. Likewise the rowan or rodden tree 'carries a fine cluster of white blossoms in May that make an agreeable show, after them the red fruit which hangs long on it, give it a very rich look, and is a great relief to the thrushes and the blackbirds'. There was gratification for all the senses. He took pleasure in the the smell of birch trees after rain.

While affected by the beauty and grace of trees, he remained a practical man. Oak and pine were the basis of his forestry, and he recognised the importance of birch – 'no tree is more sought after by the country people both for their houses, ploughs, and other utensils of husbandry'. But he had little time for hazel and less, at first, for alder, 'for which tree I have laid out more money than for all the rest about this place'. He had bought over-priced alder trees in Holland – though he could have taken seed in plenty from the trees growing wild by any burn – and 'had the misfortune to employ unskilful people to plant most of them'. Aspen, another native, was dismissed as a weed and rooted out wherever seen. 'I know of no use they are for.' (Matchwood was still to come.)

Haddington's advice on planting and cultivation was particularly detailed in the case of Scots pine. Finding good seed was a problem. 'I had heard there were fine fir woods in the Highlands and for some time bought my seed from Highlanders, who bring great quantities to sell in the low country.' The casual exchange operated by Black Duncan among friends and relatives had now grown into a regular trade between the Caledonian pinewoods and the Lowlands. Dissatisfied with his Highland suppliers ('lazy fellows'), he turned to 'an honest old gardener', who supplied him with good seed and good advice into the bargain.

Honest old gardeners, and no doubt young ones too, were setting up flourishing nursery businesses to meet an increasing demand from the landed gentry. Seedlings or 'imps' were grown in 'seminaries' and serious planters like Haddington created nurseries on their own estates.

In due course Haddington was able to raise seedlings from cones collected from his own maturing trees, laying the cones in the sun to encourage them to open.

A domestic drama taught him to avoid haste. On delivery of thirteen horse loads of cones and fearing that he had too little time to get the seed by natural means, he had the cones brought indoors and heaped before an open fire. A maid was detailed to keep an eye on them and shift them about when required, keeping them neither too near nor too far from the heat. This tedious task 'she observed for some days, and we got out some very good seed that way; but one day she laid down too great a heap, and wearying, went out to divert herself' – bad housekeeping! In her absence a live coal fell from the fire and ignited the tinder-dry cones. The girl returned to find the whole lot ablaze, and in her panic dashed out again, locking the door behind her. Disaster threatened, though Haddington confined himself (at least in print) to the cool observation that 'by this means I not only lost the rest of my fir cones, but burned the furniture of one room, and with great difficulty got the house saved'. The fate of the servant lassie is unrecorded.

Planting trees became one of the chief activities of the improvers. A sign of the times was the inauguration in 1723 of the Honourable Society of Improvers in the Knowledge of Agriculture in Scotland, among whose leading lights were the dukes of Atholl and Perth and the Earl of Breadalbane, tree planters all.

The Duke of Perth had the temerity to take up arms for the Young Pretender – Charles Edward Stuart, 'Bonnie Prince Charlie' – and in consequence was deprived of the enjoyment of his woods. Some Jacobite lairds who came out in the Fifteen and Forty-five risings were executed for their pains. The luckier ones escaped with their lives but lost their lands. After both uprisings the estates of attainted rebels were annexed to the crown and agents were appointed to manage them in King George's name. Commissions for the annexed estates were set up in both cases and the second of these commissions, formed some years after Culloden, was particularly effective. This group of capable and influential men, several judges among them, was motivated by the

The scattered pinewood in Barisdale could become a valuable timber asset 'if enclosed with dykes, the wood filled up with oak and goats banished', according to the factor appointed by the Commission for the Annexed Estates after the Jacobite rising of 1745. It didn't happen.

progressive ideals of the enlightenment and enthusiastically promoted ambitious schemes for improving the estates under their care. They supported industries old and new, financed road building (and the construction of some eighty bridges) and harbour works, experimented with land settlement, encouraged improved farming practice and, not least, saw to the preservation of woodland and its extension by widespread tree planting on waste land.

Many of the commissioners were improving landowners and foresters in their own right. One such was Henry Home, Lord Kames. Before the debacle of the Fifteen he had corresponded enthusiastically on woodland topics with the Earl of Mar, an exchange that terminated when his tree planter friend raised the Old Pretender's standard on the Braes of Mar and subsequently, when the cause collapsed, fled across the water.

Soon after its appointment in 1755 the Commission for the Annexed Estates sent its General Riding Officer and Inspector Francis Grant on a two-month-long fact-finding mission round the annexed estates, which extended from Perth on the southern edge of the Highlands to Loch Broom on the northwest coast. But it was the factors appointed to the individual estates who bore the brunt of implementing the commissioners' desires, often in the face of hostility from a disaffected population. Some may have been uneasily aware of the fate Colin Campbell of Glenure, the Red Fox, recently shot dead by an unknown assailant as he went about his business on forfeited estates in Appin. Among their tasks they saw to the draining of boggy moorland and the planting of thousands of acres of new woodland.

When Grant had set out on his preliminary inspection of the annexed estates as riding officer he was instructed to survey 'and take the best accounts you can what of the old woods are fit for cutting and how the young woods may be best preserved', and 'to enquire what kind of fuel is used and to report how it may be improved, particularly by the inclosing and preserving copse for firing' (i.e. firewood). His work was continued by his successor Archibald Menzies of Culdares whose reports, like those of the local factors, frequently refer to the preservation and improvement of old neglected woodland and the planting of new woods according to the best silvicultural notions of the day. Menzies, for example, judged that the scattered woods on the hillsides above Loch Hourn and Loch Nevis in Barisdale could be turned to account if 'enclosed with sufficient stone dykes, the hazels cut down, the vacancies in the wood filled up with oak etc., no cattle to be allowed to enter them and goats to be banished'. He was pessimistic about the native fir woods there – the trees now prized as a relic of truly ancient pinewood – and recommended sowing birch among them 'as I have seen them thrive well in ground dirtied by fir woods. After the birch cleans the ground firs will thrive'. On the Lovat estate north of Inverness Menzies was pleased to find fir plantations 'thriving wonderfully well', and he instructed the factor to enclose 'such places as have the appearance of oak rising in them, in order that they may be preserved and afterwards filled up with young plants'.

Menzies tried to stop the habit people had of helping themselves to any small timber they fancied. Woods on the Cromarty and Lovat estates had been badly damaged in this way and he realised it was useless to threaten the culprits with fines because they were too poor to pay. 'It is difficult to make them comprehend there is any harm in cutting a small tree. They don't consider that by that means they can never have great trees'. (Not of much concern to poor tenants since it was the landlord – in this case the crown – and not they who would profit by the growing of great trees.) On the same estates he found that the 'slovenly biggings' [buildings] of the peasants consumed a great deal of wood and ruined the pastures. The devastation he saw during 'a narrow inspection' of the woodlands on the Perth estate 'whilst the leaves were off the trees' was the result of a more entrepreneurial activity. A 'prodigious quantity of timber' had been destroyed at

Drummond; 'many fir plantations cut quite down and other fir plantations thinned so injudiciously that there is a great chance of their being blown down'. After diligent inquiries 'two fellows employed as sawers at Drummond' were arrested and charged with 'being in the practice of selling His Majesty's timber all over the country and even as far as Alloa'. But they were not alone. It was proposed to offer the two sawyers a pardon whereby it was hoped their tongues might be loosened and other culprits brought to justice.

Under Grant and Menzies were factors charged with running the individual estates, where they devoted much time and effort to the cultivation and care of trees. There were remarkable men among these Hanoverian functionaries. John Campbell of Barcaldine, a man of substance and a Justice of the Peace, 'a West Highland gentleman of the finest type' in the words of Virginia Wills, editor of the commission's reports, factored the largest of the forfeited territories from his arrival in Crieff in 1752 until his resignation thirteen years later. From Crieff Campbell supervised the extensive estate formerly owned by James Drummond, third Duke of Perth, who had commanded the left wing of the Jacobite army at Culloden. A place was also found for Campbell's bastard son Mungo, who became factor on Barisdale in the remote Knoydart peninsula. Possibly the greatest challenge was faced by James Small at Struan, a wild hilly stretch of roadless territory with the Black Wood of Rannoch at the heart of it, a notorious haunt of malcontents, a den of thieves and haven for cattle rustlers; the inhabitants were said to be mostly Camerons ('by far the worst') and McGregors – outlawed and forced to assume other names – and a few MacDonalds, all alleged to be on the run and 'come to Rannoch not for building of kirks'. The laird of Struan, old Alexander Robertson, was a staunch Jacobite who had come out in 1689 and fought with Claverhouse at Killiecrankie, and had ridden again in the Fifteen and the Forty-five. For this activity he had been stripped of his lands. But Robertson sat tight and from his Highland fiefdom cocked a snook at King George and his redcoats. No roads led in or out and even on horseback access was difficult and dangerous; any of his majesty's agents who attempted to gain entry was sure of a hot reception. Robertson boasted that friends would find him and he did not care to see his enemies.[*] Three years after Culloden crusty old Struan died in his bed, on his own ground.

Heavy horses in line ahead – a commonplace sight in the woods almost until our own time.
But before the age of improvement in the eighteenth century means of timber extraction overland were
primitive – unwieldy wagons or sleds on poor or non-existent roads.

Small, a former ensign in the Hanoverian forces, determined to civilise this 'common rendezvous of all thieves and stolen cattle' and succeeded very well. Before taking over as factor at Struan Small had been woodman (we'd say forest manager) there, and he did not like what he found. Two sawmills which had been operating for decades past were so antiquated that there were 'perhaps the most Gothic thing of their kind in the world'. Not only had 'the late Struan' – old Alexander Robertson – taken 'a very fatherless care' of his woods, indiscriminately felling trees young and old and allowing his tenants to do the same, but Small's predecessor as the government factor had leased – presumably for felling – four times the quantity of timber than could safely be spared. All the finest and most accessible pine trees had been felled and brushwood clogged the ditches. Small immediately reduced the felling rate, which in 1749 had amounted to two thousand trees. Observing that birch and alder trees were encroaching on the lochside where the more valuable pine had previously flourished, he recommended either the planting of a belt of pine trees or the scattering of 'fir apples' [cones] 'to encourage the firs to occupy their first station'.

In due course he conveyed good news from Struan to his superiors: 'the factor has now the pleasure to acquaint your Lordships that for two years past there has not a single beast been stolen into or carried through Rannoch'. He recognised, however, that it was fear of the gibbet and not love of King George that had tamed the neighbourhood.

---

* He was mean as well as fightable. Piles of his unpaid bills can be inspected at the National Archive in Edinburgh.

He recommended the establishment of a village at Kinloch Rannoch (with resident minister of the gospel), which was done, and the building of a prison, which was not. One of his most useful schemes was the building of a road from Tummel Bridge along the south shore of Loch Rannoch, a project that was intended to form a cross-country link between the king's roads to Inverness in the east and Fort William in the west. The link was never made and Small's road remains a dead end.

By 1767 Archibald Menzies was reporting enthusiastically that the areas enclosed for planting in the Black Wood of Rannoch were 'green as a field of corn in June'. And Lord Kames could justifiably claim that he and his fellow commissioners, having 'bestowed liberally to raise plantations everywhere in the king's estates', had thereby influenced other landowners to do likewise. 'The spirit of planting', he declared, 'is aroused.'

5

HOW GREEN WAS MY BLOOMERY

*On Barr Mor, a thickly wooded little hill on the Knapdale peninsula of
Argyll, I clamber through the bracken among wizened oaks, old
stumps, broken-off boughs and rocks fallen from the crags, all covered
in moss. Near a small willow entwined with honeysuckle I discover a
crescent of level ground cut into the slope. I scrape at the mounds of
exposed soil – moles have been around – and pick out two small lumps
of black crumbly stuff: charcoal. Here's proof that charcoal burners
were busy on Barr Mor long ago. On such patches of levelled ground,
now overgrown by woodland vegetation, they tended their hearths,
gently incinerating logs cut from the surrounding trees to make fuel
for the furnaces of the early iron industry. At this spot four slender
trees, oak and birch, now grow through the carpet of dead leaves –
their chance to spring up came once the charcoal burners had raked out
the embers of their fire for the last time.*

Deep in the forest the charcoal burners plied their smoky trade. These
grimy woodlanders were seldom glimpsed in the open. I picture them
as solitary men, shadowy figures in smoke-filtered glades, their
presence marked only by a blue haze above the treetops. The only sign
of life seen by an eighteenth century traveller on an isolated twelve-
mile stretch of road near Inveraray in Argyll were the few makeshift
cabins inhabited by charcoal burners.

Who these men were and how they lived is unknown to me. The
record is slim. Presumably wives and families shared their lives. Were

Charcoal burners' cabins were the only habitations seen by the eighteenth-century traveller St Fond on his way to Inveraray. They were probably not unlike these primitive charcoal burners' huts photographed in the New Forest in the early 1900s.

there ever communities of charcoal burners, like the mining villages of later times? It doesn't seem so.[*]

Their labour served the early iron industry, charcoal being the necessary agent for smelting ore. In the earliest days timber was converted into charcoal in simple pits dug in the ground; later a more sophisticated system of carefully constructed kilns built on platforms in the open ground evolved. During the brief heyday of the industry in the eighteenth century gangs of men hired by the larger furnaces were involved in the business.

Charcoal burning was a peripatetic trade. Once the stock of suitable timber had been used up in one area the men moved on, leaving the ground scorched by their abandoned hearths to green over. Hearth sites – 'all covered in the most beautiful verdure' – can still be discovered throughout the deciduous woodlands of the west coast.

Charcoal burners started by cutting the small timber they needed for their kilns; logs of young oak, birch or alder which they stacked end-up in concentric circles to form a beehive shape twenty feet or more in diameter. On top they pressed turfs to make a fire- and weather-proof cover, leaving only a flue down which they shovelled the kindling. The vent was closed and the fire crept through the pile, consuming the timber evenly and unseen while pleasantly scenting the

[*] But in France the war correspondant William Russell, covering the Franco-Prussian war, found a village near Rheims inhabited by charcoal burners – 'a very rough looking set, blouses and faces begrimed with black'.

Volunteer archaeologists uncovered this and other platforms in the Sunart oakwoods, where charcoal burners built their kilns.

air around. Too slow a fire might die, too fast a fire produce useless ash. When the thin spiralling smoke changed to a blue haze, a week or more later, depending on the species or the dryness of the timber, they knew the work was done. The fire was left to cool, then they peeled off the turf and lifted out the charcoal rods – now black, lightweight and friable but perfect replicas of the logs in their original state, growth rings and knot marks still clearly visible.

Charcoal had to be handled with care, particularly on the journey from kiln to forge, otherwise it might crumble to dust and be useless. A quarter or more of a consignment might be lost jolting in sacks carried pony-back along Highland trails, and as much could go to waste on shipboard when the weather was rough. Because of charcoal's friability and its bulk, it made sense to bring the iron ore to the woods and smelt it there where the charcoal was produced, rather than the other way round, which is why iron making remained a rural pursuit until coke superseded charcoal.

At sites such as Barr Mor, faint tracks radiating from the hearth platforms through the woods, no more than ruts filled with dead leaves, show where pack animals travelled to and fro with their loads. As the demand for fuel increased, networks of such tracks extended over increasing distances. In the eighteenth-century strings of thirty or forty ponies laden with cradle-panniers of charcoal jogged ten rough miles over the hill from the forests around Loch Awe to the ironworks at Furnace on Loch Fyne. Charcoal for the furnace at Bonawe on Loch Etive was brought from as far as forty miles away – 'as the crow flies',

An eighteenth-century blast furnace similar to that in operation at Bonawe – from Diderot's *Encyclopédie*.

according to the official history – the actual route being necessarily longer than the crow's, though much of it conveniently across water.

Like the charcoal burners' platforms, the sites of primitive iron smelters are dotted all over the Highlands, particularly in the west, in the midst of the greenleaf forests. The rough ingots they produced were called 'blooms' and hence those simple iron furnaces came to be known as bloomeries. Some of the early and smallest furnaces were built on exposed open hillsides where the wind helped to fan the fires.

With diligence and a little luck, traces of the bloomeries can still be found. Rough chunks of black iron, pitted and marked with the bubbles and blisters of their semi-liquid origin, can be picked out of the ground where they fell. Debris of many smelting sites dating from the seventeenth and eighteenth centuries has been discovered in old woodland on the eastern side of Loch Lomond. Sometimes chance brings a new site to light, as path makers discovered a short time ago when digging in a grassy mound on the open hill at Cashel, north of Balmaha. When there I retrieved two or three nuggets from the soil; solid evidence of the past, now paperweights on my desk.

Around the turn of the seventeenth century primitive bloomeries were superseded by the more sophisticated blast furnaces, but still the living forest was required nearby, together with running water to power the mechanical bellows and create a forced draught. On the fringe of the forests, long winter nights were made lurid by the glare of the furnace flames.

Pig iron from the Abernethy smelter.

Such incandescent nights may have been visible on the shores of Loch Maree where by 1612 the equally fiery Sir George Hay[*] established one of the earliest recorded blast furnaces, on the eastern side of the loch. Scattered oakwoods still grow on the lochside and relic foundations in brick and the local sandstone remain near the few houses of Letterewe at a spot known as Furnace, where a burn called the Furneis runs into the loch. Hay employed local men as labourers but imported his skilled workforce from the south, principally from England where the iron trade had been long established, but possibly also from the lowlands of Scotland. It was not a cosy berth. Wester Ross at that time must have seemed savage and hostile territory to lowlanders. Hay's workers were granted permission to carry arms to protect themselves from their Highland neighbours. This intrusive colony of foreigners was no doubt regarded in turn with suspicion, jealousy and possibly enmity by the volatile local Gaelic-speakers.

Not all the blast furnaces were to be found in the west Highlands. In Abernethy forest in Strathspey a forge was built on the River Nethy at Culnakyle. And in south Scotland, near Muirkirk in Ayrshire, a blast furnace operated after 1732 using haematite, an ore streaked blood red (hence the name) mined in the gully of a local burn.

The Muirkirk works was a local enterprise; others depended on inward investment. A Captain Arthur Galbraith of Dublin and his partner Roger Murphey from Enniskillen, having signed an agreement

* 'That old cankered goatish man, at whose hands there is nothing to be gained but sour words', according to Charles I. He became Lord High Chancellor of Scotland.

with Sir Duncan Campbell of Lochnell for timber from his estate in Argyll, set up the Kinglass furnace on Loch Etive in partnership with two other Irish entrepreneurs. Murphey was described as a tanner and so presumably had an interest in the gathering of tree bark for the tanning industry, an activity which went hand in hand with charcoal making. The site was well chosen; iron ore from the north of England could be shipped into the jetty at Ardmaddy on Loch Etive and iron pigs exported by the same route, while a plentiful source of charcoal was available in the neighbouring woods. But for all that, this Irish venture had a short and ignoble history. The fire first flamed in 1722 and by 1738 it was 'out of blast' (the evocative term for an inactive furnace) for good. There was a falling out and a reshuffling among the partners, and as for tanner Murphey, he had the misfortune to be hanged for murder.

The most successful, productive and longest-lived of the ironworks, known as the Lorn, was established at Bonawe, near Taynuilt. The Lorn began operations in 1754 and remained functional for more than 120 years, charcoal-fed to the last. Like others of its kind it was started by ironmasters based in the Furness district of northwest England, and once again the charcoal supply was ensured by a timber agreement with Sir Duncan Campbell. Since the contract extended to 110 years the partners were clearly optimistic about their prospects in the Highlands, now pacified after Culloden. Pig iron stamped with the name Lorn was dispatched by sea to Furness, the Severn estuary and south Wales, and cannon balls were transported to the Thames for Woolwich arsenal.

The four-square furnace and some outbuildings survive at Bonawe as relics of the industrial past. It's easy to picture the glare and smoke issuing from the stumpy chimney as the furnace roared without cease throughout the winter months, fed constantly during the blasting 'campaign' which might continue unabated from September to April. Charcoal, ore and limestone had to be fed in at the top of the chimney, which sounds like an unpleasant job, hot and dirty.

At one time 600 people were employed by the Bonawe company in the busy season, either at the works or in allied woodland operations such as bark peeling. Many of them were incomers and the impact of such an influx of rootless labourers and their families can be imagined – a 'mixed blessing', as Mark Anderson has it. The presence of both

Charcoal hearth near Loch Awe,
a present-day reconstruction
(somewhat overgrown!).

sexes together in the woods led to scandal. Anderson again: 'The employment of many people for a great part of the year at the smelting furnace and of many of both sexes in the wood was unfavourable to the purity of morals'. There were other transgressions. 'Put a stop, if possible, to that confounded drinking', George Knott wrote from Lancashire to his resident agent, 'for I believe there is not such a drunken hole in the kingdom'. (He also complained that the Lorn pier was being used by smugglers.) But perhaps Knott was being disingenuous, since the company had the habit of paying the workers part of their wages in kind, in oatmeal, whisky and ale.

Many trees must char to make small quantities of iron. How many trees? It's been calculated that one acre of well-managed coppice woodland might provide enough charcoal to make a ton of pig iron. Thus charcoal from about seventy-four acres of woodland was required to maintain annual production at the Bonawe blast furnace on Loch Etive during its heyday in the last quarter of the eighteenth century. 'At its height Bonawe would have swallowed the equivalent of 3500 tons of wood each year', according to an information board at Glen Nant. To sustain such a rate of consumption over the years without utterly destroying the forest, the Bonawe ironmakers must have been able to draw selectively on a woodland resource comprising at least ten thousand acres of deciduous trees in varying stages of growth. It has been estimated from a French example that all the small timber within a radius of half a mile would have to be cleared and charred to supply one furnace for forty days. Hence the need to secure long-term binding contracts with woodland owners before smelting could begin.

For a long time, the iron industry was blamed for the destruction of huge areas of ancient woodland. As early as 1609 an Act of the Scottish Parliament condemned the wholesale smelting of 'iron with wood' for 'wasting and consuming the woods'. The belief that woodcutting for charcoal necessarily led to the destruction of the forest persisted to modern time. Mark Anderson claimed that iron smelting with charcoal was 'one of the most potent forces for the destruction of the natural forests still remaining in Scotland at the end of the seventeenth century' and that finally 'the forest could no longer be taken to the furnace because it was no longer there'. Another writer has asserted that 'no other work of man played such havoc with the woodland as the ancient iron industry in Scotland' and 'the effect upon Scottish forests of the continuous manufacture of charcoal on a large scale, through some three thousand years, can better be imagined that described'. And since some of the larger iron companies operating in Scotland came from England, a chauvinist slant could be put upon the argument. The orthodox view was that the English ironmasters, having devastated their own woodlands in the Weald and the Forest of Dean, and having been proscribed from creating further havoc there, turned their destructive energies northwards. The naturalist Frank Fraser Darling gave heavyweight support to the libel when he described English entrepreneurs as 'the greatest agents of destruction in Scottish forests'.

But this extreme view is no longer accepted. The native oak-woods on the east side of Loch Lomond survived in spite of the presence of many bloomeries active during the seventeenth and eighteenth centuries. And even at its heyday the total output of the woodland iron industry was was relatively modest. During that period only nine blast furnaces are known to have been active in the Highlands, some of them in production only briefly or intermittently. The woodland historian Oliver Rackham has pointed out that furnaces were not fly-by-night affairs and the ironmasters were unlikely to have rushed to commit economic suicide by reducing all the woods around to ashes. On the contrary, great efforts were made to protect the woodlands from over-exploitation and to shield them from damage by stock. Hedges, ditches and dykes were made to keep beasts out of the woods, and within the woods coppicing was practised to ensure that new growth might be ready to take the place of extracted timber. Research suggests that 'the presence of the Lorn furnace, the longest-lived of the Highland works, caused no appreciable damage to the woods under the direct control of the furnace management, and may indeed have brought about an increase in the area'. In this scenario the ironmasters are seen not as wasters of the woods but judicious harvesters; conservationists even; tile-hatted friends of the earth in capitalist clothing who managed the forest for their own profit, and thereby protected it.

Nothing went to waste in the eighteenth century wood. From bark came tannin, used in tanning leather. If Napoleon's army marched on its stomach Wellington's men walked on cattle hide. The footsoldiers who tramped across the hot Spanish plains into France wore out their boots on the way to Waterloo and had to be reshod. At home the price of leather trebled during the French wars and Scottish woodlands came under heavy pressure from the tanners. Even after the slump which came with peace (when veterans returned in their broken boots to beg for bread) tanbark remained an essential raw material into late Victorian times when man-made chemicals rendered it redundant. Tanning may have been more significant than iron making in the exploitation of Scottish oakwoods.[*]

The fact that the woods survived without irreparable damage was due to the system of woodland management known as coppicing. The cutting of most trees encourages them to grow again lustily, at least if they are such species as oak, ash, hazel and willow. You get a second bite, and a third, and many more if you go about it wisely. Sensibly managed, copsewood will continue to yield harvests at regular intervals, and if the demand is not allowed to outstrip the trees' capacity to send up new growth a balance is maintained and the forest survives, fresh and green. This is why native woodlands still flourish on the west coast. They were cut and they came again.

[*] Tanning leather was not the only use for bark extract. Fishermen found it a useful preservative for nets and cordage. Birch bark was by far the best for this purpose, yielding 'a softness and elasticity to nets, which cause fish to enter the meshes more readily than when they are preserved by any other material' – John Grigor, *Arboriculture* (1868).

All along the western seaboard of Scotland and the glens reaching inland, from Wester Ross in the north to Galloway in the south, oak woodlands show unmistakable signs of past coppicing. Some of the evidence is very old. Here and there are stools – clump of trees springing from one set of roots – so broad and splayed out that they might be mistaken for single trees growing close to one another. The wider the ring of stems and the more open the centre of the cluster, the older the original tree is likely to be. Stools can often be found measuring eight or nine feet in diameter. Peter Quelch, conservation officer for the Forestry Commission, found sturdy stems growing from a stool ten or twelve feet across in Bailefuil Wood in Strathyre, where oaks were being felled for the rebuilding of the roof in the Great Hall of Stirling Castle.

It used to be thought that woodland practice in Scotland lagged behind the south of England and the shires, where a flourishing tradition of coppice management can be traced back to at least 1300. Poor Scotland, backward in woodcraft as well as the more refined arts compared to its assertive neighbour! But that view, along with some others equally patronising, has been challenged lately. One relic of former coppicing in Mugdock Woods, just north of Glasgow, is thought to have been growing by the early 1600s; roughly the date when some of the venerable oaks scattered in the neighbourhood of Dalkeith Palace, near Edinburgh, sprouted from a last felling. The parent stumps at Dalkeith from which all this regeneration sprang may have been growing sturdily at the time of Bannockburn, a further three centuries before – 'living evidence that the Scots were managing woods as coppicing in the Middle Ages'. Medieval documents prove that coppicing was widely practised in the Borders, as it was by the 1470s on monastic lands in Perthshire. It seems likely that oakwoods on the Clanranald estates on the west coast were being intensively managed by medieval woodmen.

Many deciduous woodlands throughout central and western Scotland were coppiced regularly from the seventeenth century onwards. In some cases at least, it offered landlocked lairds the opportunity of making money out of their otherwise unproductive woods. In an age when roads were few and bad, bark could be transported more easily to market than logs of timber – indeed, cottars often had the obligation to carry bark for their masters written into their tenancies.

Still visible among plantation trees, the overgrown remains of a fale (turf) dyke used to protect earlier woodland from grazing animals.

The shady greenery in Knapdale or Glen Nant once resounded yearly to the stroke of the axe and flourished strictly according to the forester's business plan. The formula, at least by the mid eighteenth century, when the tanbark and iron industry were hungriest, was well defined, though it varied in detail from place to place. A whole wood was not felled at a stroke. Clear felling was not on the agenda. The wise forester marked out one portion of the wood for coppicing and in the following years moved successively through the remainder, so that the wood was always a patchwork in different stages of growth; some patches just cut, others thickets of fresh young wand-like growth, others maturing and approaching their turn for the axe. A few years after coppicing the shoots were ready for thinning and the cut stems used for a variety of purposes – some were bought by the coopers for barrel hoops. Usually a specified number of choice trees were left uncut to grow tall as maiden trees (or in less picturesque language, standards), to be felled after fifty or sixty years' growth for shipbuilding. Sometimes maidens were specially grown from acorns.

Scottish copsewood was created from existing broadleaf woodland, a haphazard natural mixture of species commonly including – as well as oak – birch, rowan, hazel, ash, alder, willow and thorn.[*] Scottish working woodlands still show diversity – more than a dozen different species have been found in the once heavily coppiced Craig Roystan woods on Loch Lomond – but oak was encouraged at the

---

[*] In England copsewood was often specially planted from single species like hazel or hornbeam, interspersed with a few oaks which were allowed to grow into timber trees.

expense of other species, which were dismissed as 'barren wood' and sometimes weeded out. Acorns, sometimes from English stock, were planted to improve the proportion of oak among the resident trees. So the predominance of oak in many surviving woods is not so much natural as artificially skewed.

The unit destined for a single year's cutting was known as a hag (sometimes spelt hagg), derived from an old word meaning 'to fall'. When the timber was cut down and the stumps pared to prevent water lying and rotting the roots, some of the brushwood could be used to make the fences required to keep out grazing sheep, goats and cattle. Some livestock barriers were simply lines of raised turfs surmounted by brushwood, but stone dykes were often built and the mossy ruins of these old boundary walls within and around the woods can still be traced. Few people live in woodland neighbourhoods now, but the shores of Loch Lomond, for example, were well populated in former times when many people made their living from the land. Country folk had to pasture their flocks, and enclosures were often resented and not always respected. Sometimes the locals breached the fences and dykes to give their beasts free range in the woods.

In the Loch Lomond woodlands at the height of their productivity animals were allowed back to graze among the the cut hags after a period of six years, when it was considered the young growth was sufficiently strong to survive, and this seems to have been a commonly accepted interval. Further to the west in the woodlands around Glen Kinglas it may have been as long as fourteen years.

Bark was at its most tannin rich at around twenty years of age, and so when a strict rota system was established in 1735 in the woodland on the eastern shores of Loch Lomond, it was decreeed each hag once harvested should be left untouched for a period of twenty-four years, later reduced to twenty-one. When blocks of woodland were ready to be cut it was customary to offer the contract for auction, after which the successful bidder would recruit his workforce. Old Nicol Luke, when head forester at Ardkinglas estate in the 1940s, remembered how in his youth a gang would be signed on at Falkirk hiring fair and brought up to Argyll for the summer to fell the trees and dress the timber in and around Glen Kinglas and Hell's Glen.

Sunlight dapples the dank and mossy oakwoods of Dalavich in Argyll, still showing traces of past coppicing for the iron and tanning industries.

Late spring and early summer was the season for stripping bark, for then the trees were sappy and the bark peeled easily. During May, June and early July large numbers of men, women and children would be installed in woodland camps for the annual felling and bark-stripping operation. Men would cut the trees and do the heavy labouring, women and children performed the other tasks. Nicol Luke remembered that his first job on leaving school in the 1880s had been to help in the forest camps around the head of Loch Fyne. His last task of the day before turning in was to collect and carry in bundles of fuel for the camp fires. It was observed that pasty-faced people from the smoky towns in the Vale of Leven 'benefitted in their health from the purifying air and wholesome diet of the country' in the Loch Lomond woodland camps.

When a tree was to be cut the bark at its base was first peeled from the trunk so that the axe wouldn't damage it. Once the tree had been felled and cut into lengths the women and children beat the logs to loosen the bark and make it easier to peel. Such animated scenes must have been common in all the western woodlands. Donald McKichen, who was joiner at Ardtornish in Morvern, recalled a year when all the oak along the coastline was cut down and made into separate piles of timber and bark on the seashore, ready to be shipped south. On Loch Lomondside huts were built to store and dry the bark – a necessary preliminary – while rafts and flat-bottomed craft were constructed from the bigger timber. The bark was then loaded on board the rafts and transported to the tanning works in Glasgow and the

Clydeside towns via the River Leven. From the mid nineteenth century much of it went to a factory at Balmaha at the south end of the loch, where wood acids for the dyeing industry were distilled.

By the time young Nicol Luke was gathering brushwood to feed the camp fires on Loch Fyneside the heyday of coppicing was nearly over. At its most intensive it hadn't lasted long, two hundred years at most, well within the lifetime of a healthy oak tree. By the end of the nineteenth century it was falling out of use as industry found raw materials other than tan bark and charcoal in chemicals and coke. Fences were neglected, livestock broke in and the cycle of regeneration declined in vigour. The sweet-smelling charcoal hearths were pulled apart for the last time and the sites abandoned. The clamorous voices of the summer gangs, young and old, died away and the axe fell silent. The oak stools were abandoned to nature. Slowly the dank and mossy glades of the western woodlands aged, tangled and decayed.

Glen Nant, a little off the main road to Oban, is one such seeming wilderness. Once regularly coppiced for industry, is now at peace, categorised by the Forestry Commission as a 'Caledonian forest reserve' and celebrated for the richness of its natural life. An information board tells visitors that the wood hosts more than 150 different species of bryophites (i.e. mosses), over 200 species of lichens, 127 species ('and still counting') of moths and butterflies, masses of spring flowering plants and grasses including globe flower, sweet woodruff, bluebell and thistle, plus rarer things like the butterfly orchid and wintergreen. Notice the many ant nests; note also that the red and roe deer roam, foxes and wildcat prowl, otters swim (but not often in public), red squirrels survive, birds multiply – four species of tit, the great spotted woodpecker, dippers . . .

And more.

No longer a workplace but a sanctuary.

6

TALL FIRS SHALL FRIGHT THE SEAS

Axe and saw sang to a different tune in the northern pinewoods. Cash-strapped Highland lairds might wish to sell their timber, but exploitation was no simple matter – remoteness and the state of the country determined that. In the 1620s woods in Morar were reported 'altogether unprofitable' because 'they lie in the far and barbarous Highlands, circuite and environed about with evil neighbours, who continually cut, destroy and take away the same in great quantities'. But logging in the pinewoods was about to take off on a commercial scale. A few years later Sir John Grant of Grant, whose estates in Strathspey were more conveniently placed than those of his friends in Morar, pioneered the trend by leasing his woods at Abernethy to a speculator.

This was the remarkable John Mason, a former seafaring man turned entrepreneur. Mason probably expected to sell Abernethy timber to the English naval builders, hithero dependent on imports from Norway and the Baltic. From that point on, shipbuilders were to become a prime target for hopeful Highland landowners. The pine trees that grew so tall and straight in the native pinewoods were virtually ready-made masts and spars for the sailing ships of the day.[*] War increased the need. By 1704, during the War of the Spanish Succession, Queen Anne's Naval commissioners identified Abernethy as a prime source of material 'likeliest to serve her majesty and the government'. In 1713, as the long war came to a close, the carpenter Martin Sandford was summoned from London to work in the

[*] Hence in Glen Affric there is a hill called Beinn na Sparra – lightly Gaelicised, the hill of the spars.

A sawmill in the forest, handy for transporting timber downstream, in this case the Spey. An engraving from the 1780s.

Abernethy woods and instruct the laird's labourers on how to cut, square and bring down to the Spey such trees as would make the best masts, spars and bowsprits. And in the same year the British Parliament offered subsidies to transport masts grown in Scotland and for the making of 'pitch, tar and rosin' – all pinewood derivatives – for the Navy's use.

By the middle years of the eighteenth century means of extraction and transportation had been found, even in areas remoter than the relatively accessible upper reaches of the Dee and the Spey, and timber was being advertised widely for sale to willing speculators. Notable as the Mr Fixit of the day was one Aaron Hill, a man whose artistic pretensions were matched by his thirst for dicey speculation.

Aaron Hill had a way with words. He was a poet; not a good one – he fails to make the anthologies. His friends included greater literary talents – James Thomson (of *The Seasons*) and Alexander Pope, who gave Hill a passing nod in *The Dunciad*. But his skills went far beyond versifying[*] and above all he had a keen eye for business. Seeing a gap in the market, he set up the Beech Oil Company for pressing beech nuts into a substitute for olive oil, and with other hopefuls he launched a scheme, to be financed by a lottery, to settle emigrants in southern California. His most enlightened venture took him into association with the dubious and curiously named York Buildings Company.

---

[*] As manager of the new Haymarket Theatre in London he had staged Handel's opera *Rinaldo*. The elaborate effects he contrived included a nest of live sparrows on stage.

The 'golden groves of Abernethy' in our time, managed according to best forestry practice. The poet and entrepreneur Aaron Hill considered such trees ideal for ships' masts and spars in the days of sail – though in his time there is likely to have been a variation in the age and size of the trees, and some may have been giants.

David Murray, the Edinburgh lawyer whose nineteenth-century history of the York Buildings Company (sub-titled 'A chapter in Scotch history') is a succinct account of the Byzantine financial complexities of the York Buildings enterprise, remarked wryly that 'Scotland was in the poet's eyes possessed of great natural resources which only waited to be developed; her subterranean mines rivalled those of Mexico and Peru; her forests were a fund of national wealth.' Thus Hill, gazing on the mighty trees of Abernethy, perceived that heart of oak might have masts of pine.

> High on the mountains of her northern shore,
> The gummy pine shall shed her pitchy store;
> Tall firs, which, useless, have long ages grown,
> Shall fright the seas, and visit worlds unknown.

Hill, on a visit north, had been mightily impressed by the pine trees he saw in 'the golden groves of Abernethy', as he described them in a letter home. His wife was not the only recipient of good news from the forest, and it was due to Hill's persuasive advocacy that York Buildings decided in 1727 to embark on an ambitious scheme to exploit Scottish timber. In January of the following year York Buildings bought sixty thousand of the best fir trees in Abernethy from the laird, Sir James Grant, for £7000. Felling began at once.

The York Buildings Company had no connection with York and little interest in buildings. It had been set up to supply the residents of Picadilly and St James' Fields with water drawn from the Thames (and

Water pipe made from a pine log, one of many turned out by the boring mill at Nethy Bridge. The trade was killed off when competitors nearer London – the main market – supplied cheaper pipes made from local elm.

delivered through pipes bored from elm logs). But then the company changed hands; mere water supply seemed tame; it was the time of the South Sea Bubble, speculation was rife and the rejuvenated company deemed the Scottish Highlands ripe for exploitation. 'It is a peculiarity of joint-stock enterprise that the fields in which it is to gather golden harvests are, like the Hesperides, generally far from home, and their whereabouts only dimly ascertainable. Scotland in those days bore the same relation to London, that Poverty Bay or the River Plate, Arizona or Wynaad,[*] does to Glasgow now' – so said David Murray in 1883. Snapping up lands forfeited by supporters of the Old Pretender after the rising of 1715, York Buildings eagerly commenced prospecting for minerals and promoting various other schemes, of which the Abernethy woodland enterprise was the most ambitious.

Word reached London that 'the trees are certainly the largest and finest in Scotland'. Forty specimens were felled and shipped to the royal dockyard at Deptford where the master mast maker declared their quality to be excellent. As Aaron Hill had perceived, the trees would make splendid masts for the Navy, straight, strong, well grown, fit to withstand the heaviest gale. But there was a snag. Hill had promised main masts for the biggest ships in the fleet and even Abernethy's best fell short of this specification. Murray comments: 'The information came too late. The agreement had been made and possession had been taken. There was plenty of timber, and it was hoped that enough would be got to make the venture profitable' – which it never was.

[*] Wynaad is a rugged stretch of the Western Ghats in India.

Ore mined at this isolated spot near the Lecht was carried by ponies over the mountains for smelting at Abernethy. This building, built in 1841 for crushing ore, replaced the earlier original.

Work went on apace. Timber huts were knocked up for the workers, sawmills erected (and iron mills later), and soon Abernethy's glades echoed to the clunk of the axe, the thump and whine of the milling machines, the trampling of 120 draught horses, and the voices of many men. Money never seemed to be short. Notes of hand were issued liberally in lieu of cash – 'the Scotch have always had a weakness for paper money' (canny David Murray) – and were exchanged freely in the neighbourhood for some years. The toil was not without its pleasures and at times the night was made lurid by incandescent merrymaking. Years later the Rev. John Grant, a minister of the parish, commented disapprovingly in the first Statistical Account that the company and its agents were 'the most profuse and profligate set that ever was heard of in this corner'. 'They used to display their vanity by bonfires, tar barrels and the opening of hogsheads of brandy to the country people, by which five of them died in one night.' But for all its extravagance and dubious moral influence, the minister agreed that the presence of York Buildings had been beneficial in many respects; it had made 'many useful and lasting improvements' such as woodland roads and sawmills, and had improved passage on the River Spey. New skills had been acquired and trade flourished.

A forge and several iron furnaces, some described as 'stupendous', had been set up in the forest and in spite of an outstanding final instalment of £1000 with little prospect of payment, York Buildings signed a new contract with Sir James for small timber to be converted into charcoal. Ponies with panniers strapped to their backs carried ore

Drop forge hammers from the Abernethy smelter. It's said that the laird of Grant, angry at being owed money by the York Buildings Company, sent men to remove these hammers and other equipment from the forge in lieu of payment.

mined at the head of a remote glen near Tomintoul across the bleak hills to the furnaces, an exposed route before soldiers built the road over the Lecht. The supply of charcoal exceeded demand and the surplus was exported to England, Holland and elsewhere. But the iron making side of the business in its turn proved unprofitable.

At the end of the day, not counting the timber taken for charring, no more than twenty thousand mature trees may have been extracted in the York Buildings adventure. It's likely that only selected trees would be felled, and only where they could be most easily got out, so that the core forest was able to survive the depredations of the company.

Not all the ancient pinewoods escaped so lightly. While the western oakwoods, with careful husbandry, might survive the charcoal ovens, heavy logging became a serious threat to the great pinewoods of the north. Unlike oak and most trees of the leaf kind, a pine tree won't grow again from the root; when it falls it dies. Frank Fraser Darling is the arch pessimist in these matters: 'The great forest was the wealth of the Highlands, and our regret is that the succeeding generations of men could not consider the forest to be conserved rather than exploited.'

But the historian Christopher Smout believes that this traditional view considerably overstates the case. In the western pinewoods, where heavy rainfall and sodden peaty soil inhibits regeneration once the forest has been eroded, the damage has been catastrophic. But in the drier eastern Highlands the effects have been less dramatic. In Strathspey and on Deeside professional foresters supervised the felling and subsequent care of the pinewoods, and a more congenial climate and better ground allowed seed scattered by the surviving trees to germinate and to replace – to some extent – the losses suffered by exploitation. So twenty thousand trees or more in Abernethy fell in accordance with Aaron Hill's prophetic vision? The wood survived the onslaught and Abernethy lives.

The tall firs of Aaron Hill's poetic fancy were 'useless' only because they grew in the deep seclusion of inaccessible Highland glens. The giants of Glen Affric, or Rothiemurchus, or the Black Wood of Rannoch might as well have grown on the moon for all the mercantile reward they offered. Fine timber to delight the commercial eye could be turned into cash profit only if it could be got out of the wood, but how? Roads were few, all bad, none reached into the forest, and even where there were roads wheeled transport was rare.

The solution lay in the nature of the country, for this land of the shaggy wood was also the land of the flood. Lochs and rivers could be made to carry the felled timber downstream to sawmill and shipyard. It was recorded that in Strathspey as early as the seventeenth century timber was commonly brought down on the river 'which runneth out of a great loch [Morlich] through Rothiemurchus into the Spey'. Sixty years ago the remains of sluice gates where the Luineag leaves the loch could still be seen.

Logs gathered from the surrounding forest were launched down river to sawmills at Inverdruie, or to the River Spey itself. In July 1704 'four hundred cuts of fir' were ordered to be tossed into Loch Tulla in the Black Mount and the agent, Hugh Campbell, was instructed to put a boat out to guide them. In 1717 on the same Breadalbane lands Campbell was ordered to 'put all the cuts lying on both sides of the water of Orchy into the said river and lead them and any other cuts in any part of the end or sides of Loch Awe to the sawmill'. Floating was regularly practised during the eighteenth century on all the great Highland rivers and lochs and many of the lesser ones. Large pines were hauled as much as two miles to the River Affric where they were cut into logs ten or twelve feet long, carried by horse to the river bank and floated down thirty or more miles to a sawmill on the Beauly river. Heavy felling took place in Glen Affric and the logs brought to Loch Affric were floated downstream. Sixty years ago the forester Morley Penistan wrote that waterlogged trees could still be seen in river pools in Strathconon where they had been snagged en route to the Cromarty Firth.

Natural waterways could be improved. In the Black Wood of Rannoch the company extracting pine timber in the eighteenth century constructed a system of canals, the vestiges of which are still visible, along which the timber was led into ponds and basins, and from there sent down the slope to the loch by means of a timber trough or chute, with bottom and sides made from planks cut from the forest. A grand chute was made in Rothiemurchus. Logs held in a small basin just below Loch an Eilein were diverted down a timber conduit known as the Spout, which led across the moorland and then down a steep slope into 'a pretty set of miniature lakes' known as the Lochans.

It was said that once a year twelve thousand various pieces of timber – anything from large tree trunks to sawn planks – were sent down the Spey, and sometimes there may have been twice as many logs and spars roaring down on the floodwater at one time. I look at these Highland rivers now, flowing deep and brown and silent under bridges or rippling over stony shelves and wonder how this feat could ever have been managed. Some of the larger floats must have been spectacular. Trees felled in the upper reaches of the Dee (now hardly wooded at all) had to negotiate and were often snagged by shelving rocks, most spectacularly at the Linn of Dee, now a beauty spot, where the river six miles upstream from Braemar gushes through a deep, twisting gorge: 'Vast logs of wood, seen amidst the foam of the cascade, are drove with violence against the rocks, and, precipitated from such a height, sound in their fall like distant peals of thunder.'

River banks and beds were engineered to cope with the traffic and where awkward rocks impeded the turbulent flow of timber they were levered away by brute strength or split apart by gunpowder. According to report, what sounds like a cheap expedient was successfully used on the Spey; it consisted of stacking brushwood on the obstruction, setting it alight and then when the roaring fire had raised the temperature sufficiently, cold water was poured over the heated rock causing it to split apart in a great billowing of steam. But mostly gunpowder was used. In 1782, a rock obstructing free passage down the Tay was blown up to allow timber from the Black Wood to be sent downstream. All over the Highlands such barrier rocks were 'blown'. Near Rothes, in Strathspey, logs trundling down on a rapid current were often trapped between the bank and a sunken rock in midstream. In due course it was blasted away, to the anger of some local families who had gleaned a small profit from it. They had undertaken, for a few pence, to stand by with ropes and free any snarl-up. Elizabeth Grant of Rothiemurchus, daughter of the laird, had scant sympathy with them. It was only a pittance they lost, after all. 'The dole they got was small, yet there was hardly more outcry in Sutherland when the Duke wanted his starving cottars to leave their turf huts on the moors to live in comfortable stone and lime houses by the sea than my father met when he got leave to remove this obstacle by blasting'.[*]

Winter was the best time for floating the logs, when days and weeks of rain had raised all the mountain burns in boiling spate, or in the spring thaw when the lochs brimmed with meltwater from the snows above. But at the beginning of the nineteenth century it was reckoned that good water levels on the Spey might be expected any time from the end of August to mid May.

Preparations for a float began with the opening of sluice gates throughout the water catchment, which might involve long journeys far into remote glens in the darkness of a stormy night. The pent-up flood thus released surged down the glen, gathering force as one tributary after another fed into the main stream, until it reached the spot where piles of logs stood ready on the riverbank.

The pines thin out at the southern edge of Abernethy forest, and in this no-man's-land of heather and blaeberry can be found relics of a bygone system of sluices, canals and ponds constructed to send the trees of the forest down to the sawmills and shipyards on the back of the floodwaters.

> *Blue mountains fringe the horizon. Heather underfoot, dry and dusty; my ankles itch with seeds, burrs and prickles. Here's water now, not one pond as the map shows but two or three, dark as sin. Deer prints in the peaty water margin. A clatter of wings as a blackcock, scarlet flash over its eye, rises twenty yards away.*
>
> *The ground drops sharply and I discover a grassy plain below with a burn flowing through it on its way to join the Nethy river. My descent is awkward through birch and pine scrub and high heather. A narrow ridge like a grass-grown dyke, straight as a die, bisects the*

---

[*] Elizabeth's gloss on the Clearances is indulgent. Her Duke of Sutherland is not remembered for his altruism.

A lochan in the open ground between Glenmore and Abernethy, once part of a system for impounding water in readiness for floating timber down to the Spey.

plain and where the burn cuts through it stones are revealed under the turf. This was once a dam. On this flat pebbly ground, dotted with young pine trees now, the waters were impounded and a loch was formed ready to be released when the time came.

Three miles upstream on the high moorland between Abernethy and Glenmore are dreaming pools, the remains of the water system that fed this pound. A walker's track leads to the curious little shed called Bynack Stable where the Nethy emerges from its glen and on the way there you look across a tawny heather landscape dotted with scattered pine trees. A scrap of pale water comes into view, soon revealed to be one of a chain of interconnecting pools. The surface is flat calm. Bony stumps of trees felled long ago rise from the water or its peaty fringe, once a thicket, cut down in a wartime felling. Not everything is dead. A few large pine trees stand near the water's edge, their massy roots writhing over the dry ground. Here and there beyond the banks, peeping above the heather, are little patches of pine shoots eighteen inches high, and a juniper, and a few small, bushy willow plants.

It's high summer and the shrinking water has revealed a stony strand around the serpentine margins of this lochan, making it easy to walk round. More deer slots, but mine are the only bootprints. At another season the peat would be squelchy. A duck rises from a reedy inlet. At the far end of the lochan a thin stream trickles through an outlet far larger than it needs, a wide, man-made cut some three feet deep, now choked with grass and heather. In former times when the sluice gates were opened the water trapped in these ponds gushed down this channel to swell the Nethy a mile away.

A team of floaters on the fast-flowing River Spey. This is a nineteenth-century squad – floating had reached its brief heyday a century earlier.

In old age Elizabeth Grant described in lively detail the animated scenes she had seen as a little girl on her father's estate of Rothiemurchus. First the selected timber, often growing deep in the forest, had to be felled and dragged down to the banks of the river, where it was stacked in readiness: 'so many rough little horses moving about in every direction, each dragging its tree, attended by an active boy as guide and remover of obstructions. The smack of the whip used to sound quite cheerful on those otherwise solitary spots.'

In the early hours of the day chosen for the float men set out from their cottages for the long walk into the forest. Probably they'd had their first dram of the day, 'it being cold work in a dark wintry dawn, to start over the moor for a walk of some miles to end in standing up to the knees in water'. Another refreshment followed on arrival, a lad with a two-gallon cask on his back going round the squad doling out whisky in a horn tumbler to all. 'They all took their "morning" raw, undiluted and without accompaniment, so they did with the gill when the work was done.' But at noon, when they had twenty minutes' break, a bannock and a bit of cheese was taken out of every pocket, to be eaten after the lunchtime dram.

The sound of rushing water as the bore approaches. The men stand to; one gang levers the logs apart and rolls them into the water, another – 'dashing about often up to the middle into the water' – thrusts them out into the current with long poles where they are taken in charge 'by the most picturesque group of all', young agile men armed with a 'clip', a thin pole cut from a sapling with a sharp iron claw fixed to the whippy end. Racing along the river bank, skipping from rock or sawn stump, jumping over the tributary burns, forcing a way through the entangling undergrowth, they follow the swift progress of the logs, alert to any jar or snag that impedes the flow and ready to hook away any stuck log before it forms a barrier. 'The many light forms springing about among the trees, along banks that were some times high, and always rocky, the shouts, the laughter, the Gaelic exclamations, and above all, the roar of the water, made the whole scene most inspiriting.' From her favourite station by the chute at the Spout little Elizabeth and her chums watched with delight as the 'great hulking logs' descended helter-skelter: 'One would rise up here over a lazy leader, another there; above, two or three mounting up on end and choking the passage, stopping all progress and wasting the water. The clips were very busy here, the men jumping about with them hooking this log and sending it forward, hooking that log and keeping it back, screaming to one another as they skipped over the Spout.'

Not surprisingly, 'many laughable accidents happened during the merry hours of the floating'. There were frequent dousings. Men struggling to hold a slippery log in their cold hands, or, striking at an escaping log with their clips and missing it, would lose their balance and tumble into the stream, 'shouts of laughter always greeting the dripping victims, who good-humouredly joined in the mirth raised by their awkwardness'. Elizabeth likened them to a set of water rats. But 'sometimes the accident was beyond a joke'. She doesn't elaborate but it it's not difficult to imagine torn flesh and broken bones resulting from this aquatic dance of the hurtling pines. Whether there were deaths by crushing or drowning the record doesn't say.

On occasion (according to Mark Anderson) there may have been up to twenty thousand logs tumbling and thrashing down the fast-flowing Spey, with as many as eighty men at a time racing along the banks alongside. This loose float, as it was called, happened once a year. Latterly the big timber was routinely being sent down the Spey and other major rivers in the more manageable form of rafts. In places rafting was a short-term expedient. Once logs had been sent down the chute into Loch Rannoch they were bundled together and floated to the eastern end of the loch where the makeshift rafts were broken up and sent loose down the Tummel to its junction with the Tay. There, says Anderson, they may have been gathered into rafts again for the final stage of the journey on the big river, bound for Dundee. Sometimes they inadvertently went further, swept out to into the North Sea and thrown up on the shores of Holland and Denmark. This may not have been uncommon. A consignment sent down the Spey in the early summer of 1714 shot past the port of Garmouth and drifted out to sea, leaving only eighty logs to be loaded on to coastal vessels for delivery as potential ships' masts in England.

Rafting began in a small way. Early in the eighteenth century rudimentary rafts were being sent down the Spey 'in a very awkward and hazardous manner'. They consisted of no more than a dozen or so timbers lashed together and pushed into the current under the uncertain charge of a boatman who bobbed like a bit of flotsam ahead of them in a currach or coracle. The currach was no more than a ribbed vessel covered in hide 'in the shape and about the size of a brewing-kettle'. A line attached to the raft was loosely looped round the boatman's knee, so that if the raft hit an obstruction he could slip the knot before the rope tautened and jerked him out of his tub. The currach was light, being only skin and lath, and on safely reaching journey's end at the mouth of the Spey the boatman could hoist it on his shoulders for the long walk back.

Eighteen such 'small, trifling rafts' served York Buildings on the Nethy until Aaron Hill interested himself in the river traffic and introduced a better method. Much bigger rafts were built. Large trees were bound together and planked with boards, crewed by a couple of men on benches who guided the craft downstream wielding cumbrous oars. Local private enterprise found a niche as country folk on the route hitched lifts on their way to market their produce. So eggs, butter and cheese found a way downstream, and commercial items too, with the freighting of bark, hides, and even lime.

Later Elizabeth Grant saw such rafts in use on the Spey and described them in her sharp-eyed way. She says that once the Rothiemurchus men had got the logs down the Druie to its confluence with the larger river, a gang of specialists took over their passage to the coast. This group of men, many from the village of Ballindalloch beyond Grantown, came up every winter to assemble the Rothiemurchus timber into rafts. This employment traditionally ran in families. These men manoeuvred the logs side by side, skewered each log top and bottom with an iron spike and eyelet through which they passed ropes of twisted wattle (another forest product) to bind them tight. The rafts were decked with planks from the sawmill and fitted with 'two rude gears for the oars to move in'. The crew were constantly soaked, for the lunging vessels shipped water at every lurch on the long passage. But they were old hands to whom 'the whole river, all its holes and shoals and rocks and shiftings, were as well known as had it been been dry'; the work paid well, says Elizabeth, and they liked the life. And moreover 'they had idle times a great part of the year, could live at home and till their little crofts in their own lazy way, the rent being always made up by the floating'.

Their raft delivered, they tramped back, festooned with ropes and irons, the tackle of their trade. Their bothy at the Druie mouth, home for the season, was roughly constructed, windowless, with a hole in the roof through which at least some of the smoke from fire on a stone hearth in the centre of the floor might escape. At night they lay in a ring round the hearth, feet to the fire, and there, tired and possibly whisky befuddled, drifted off to sleep, the steam rising from their sodden clothes, 'for they had been perhaps hours in the river', to mingle with the smoky wraiths. Not to worry (Elizabeth didn't) – 'they were a healthy race, suffering little in their old age but rheumatism'.

Rafting and floating lingered on beyond its heyday. An act of Parliament in 1813 curtailed the practice in order to safeguard bridges which might suffer from the buffeting of unruly logs and current-borne rafts. But the floats, if diminished, continued for another half century and more. The last raft came down the River Dee in 1881 – as Mark Anderson remarks significantly, twenty years after the railway opened. The arrival of railways in Strathspey – lines were operating along both banks of the river by the 1860s – similarly put paid to the great river floats on that side of the Cairngorms. But early in the following century trees felled in Glen Mallie were being rafted to the end of Loch Arkaig where they were broken up and floated down river to the sawmill. And in 1912 logs were still being floated across Loch an Eilein – near where little Elizabeth Grant had watched her merry scenes at the Spout so long before.

A postscript. The timber is piled ready on the banks and the rivers are running high, and Duncan McIntosh, forester at Rothiemurchus, comes over for dinner at the big house of Doune. McIntosh is always a welcome guest, not a gentleman born but married above his station, which may have secured him his occasional place at the laird's table.

He's a sparky wee man and a great fiddler of Scots tunes (he chiselled at the *f* holes in the laird's Italian violin in order to sweeten its tone). More to the point, in view of the float planned for the morrow, he's a grand organiser of the work.

It's late. Candles are extinguished and all indoors sleep. Men are already making their way into the hills, walking miles over the rough untracked moorland to loch and lochan. It will be their job to open the sluice gates and turn the trickle of escaping water into a flood.

A wild night, with storms of hail turning to snow. Young Allan Grant prepares to set out on the long hike into Glen Einich where his task is to open the flood gates at the loch at the head of the glen. Christy Grant, his widowed mother, has hot food in the pot for him, and a bannock and a flask of whisky for his piece. When he's finished his supper she wraps the plaid round his shoulders and sees him off into the snow. He kens the way among the tracks that wind through the forest at the start of his walk where it's easy to lose all sense of direction in the dark among the Rothiemurchus pines.* Once out of the forest he has a long trek across exposed moorland, a journey of a dozen miles or so through drifting snow and ice-cold burns, with rocky ramparts impending on either hand. A goodish walk, lonely, desolate and dark.

Some time in the night he reaches his destination among the boggy flats at the margin of the loch and duly releases the water. Early next morning the floodwater comes swelling down to the river Druie, where a gang waits to launch the logs into the spate.

The day's work's done; he should be home. But widow Christy waits in vain. A search party is called together and walks to the head of the glen where the boy lies huddled by the open sluice, with a half-eaten bannock and an empty flask by his hand. Tired, hungry, his task accomplished, he sat down by the gate, took his dram and closed his eyes for a minute or two.

Elizabeth Grant recounts that the widow never got over the shock of his death. She lost her reason and never talked of him again. She used to work in the house at Doune and would go home to her cabin cheerfully enough except on stormy nights, when according to the housemaids 'she would shake her head sadly and sometimes let fall tears'.

---

* It still is, even with tourist paths, as I know from coming late off the hill with darkness falling.

John Murray, fourth duke of Atholl, in his finery, painted by John Hoppner.
The Tay, slightly romanticised, wanders through a wooded landscape behind his gesturing arm.

7

PLANTING DUKES AND THE MARCH OF LARCH

LUMBERING his way home across the bad roads of Europe, Sir William Lockhart of Lee in Lanarkshire carried in his luggage several young larch trees, a plant whose properties had impressed him while exiled in Venice (punished for taking the Roundhead side in the English Civil War). It was not the beauty of the tree which attracted him, though it's handsome enough, shedding golden needles in autumn and delicately green in spring. No, practical Lockhart of Lee had been struck by the rot-resistant qualities of larch timber in lagoon and canals, where it was widely used for planking vessels and for making the piles on which the city stood.

Larch was little known in Britain. Though it grew wild high in the Alps its early importers considered it delicate and therefore Lockhart, once he reached Lee, gave his specimens the protection of a greenhouse where most of them died. In frustration he had three of the ailing plants pulled up and dug into a sheltered spot in his garden, where to his surprise they came away famously.

Did he guess that larch was the coming tree? It was. Already by 1700, according to Mark Anderson, Scots gentry on their jaunts to London were finding larch among the stock offered by southern nurserymen, and also in nursery gardens nearer home. There was the recorded case of 'a Highland gentleman Mr Menzies of Glenlyon' who 'in the year 1738 brought a few plants of larch from London in the flap of the servants' portmanteau'. He distributed batches of this rarity to acquaintances at stages on his way north, five being left as presents for James, Duke of Atholl, at Dunkeld, and a dozen more at the duke's seat, Blair Castle.

'The Larch now growing in full vigour on Dunkeld lawn was the first brought to Perthshire in 1738 and then planted in a flower pot in the Green house.' By the time this sketch was made in 1824 the taller of the twin trees had reached ninety-seven feet. It blew down eighty years later.

Once larch had been proved hardy in our climate it was taken up on a large scale.[*] Thomas Boutcher of Comely Bank nursery in Edinburgh published a volume in 1775 in which he extolled the larch and regretted that it was not more commonly prized. 'Is it not amazing that thousands who have it in their power, will not be at a modest expense in planting a parcel of small twigs of this plant, on barren heaths, or cold and rugged hills, which, in a few years, would not only adorn, and, by the warmth they would afford, really improve the adjacent country, but, in less than an age, enrich their families?' Taking a leaf from Lockhart's book he noted that 'the famous architect Scamozie built many of the most superb palaces in Venice of it' and that 'posts of it driven into the ground become almost as hard as iron, and will bear an incredible weight. It bears the smoothest polishing, and is so extremely transparent, that rooms wainscotted with it, will make people at a distance, when candles are lighted, imagine the whole room on fire'.

When the aforesaid James inherited the Atholl dukedom by default (his elder brother being locked up in the Tower of London for his part in the 1715 Jacobite rising), he became a pioneering tree planter. One of the first to guess the potential of the larch, he had already planted – even before Mr Menzies arrived bearing gifts – two larch trees in 1727 which sixty years later were observed in full vigour by Warren Hastings, just home from India and shortly to be impeached.

[*] The noted landscape gardener Thomas White, 'very partial' to larch all his life, was lowered into his grave in a larchwood coffin.

They are gone now.[*]

Not content with a few specimens of the new tree, he picked a site at the base of Craigvinean, a lowering hill on the west bank of the Tay overlooking Dunkeld – a landmark now for motorists travelling north on the A9 – where on rising ground covered in rocky debris he mixed seven hundred larch trees with other species, arranged in the formal manner of the time radiating from a small lochan. He was pleased with the results though the trees had made only five years' growth when he died. It was reported afterwards that the plantation 'throve in the most satisfactory way'.

His son John, the third duke of Atholl, took the business a step further. He added to the larch on Craigvinean, raising the height of the plantation to six hundred feet, which was thought to be a daring venture with a tree whose characteristics were not well known and which had been considered tender. Larch formed a component of the mixed woods he established in the neighbourhood of Dunkeld, including the famous Hermitage, and at Blair Atholl. In the relatively short time at his disposal he planted out more than three million trees, including many thousands of oak, ash, elm, sycamore and beech, but above all larch – when he could get it. Larch was expensive and difficult to obtain. But it was in the time of his son, another John, grandson of James, that larch found its greatest apostle. Under him the Atholl lands in Highland Perthshire became the source of a tidal wave of larch which rolled over the country for a century and a half.

The great Atholl estates, stretching northwards from Perth to the Grampian mountains, were to be the setting for one of the most celebrated afforestations in the land. At first the new Duke John, dubbed 'the Planting Duke' because of his obsession, was content to mingle larch sparingly with other species, chiefly Scots pine, but in time he came to despise that old faithful as slow-growing and less useful for timber. Larch he revered. In his account of the Atholl woodlands – *Woods & Forests as they are, as they were, as in all probability they will be* – written in his own hand on foolscap pages bound in leather, the word larch is always highlighted in red ink and given an

---

* In time the legend arose that James was the first to plant larch in Scotland and, furthermore, 'from these two parent trees have sprung all the larches which abound so much in Scotland' (*Scotsman* newspaper, wrongly, in 1813). One of these 'parent' larches still flourishes in the grounds of Dunkeld Cathedral.

The 'Planting Duke' kept meticulous records of his experiments in the use of home-grown timber. This extract is believed to be in his own hand.

initial capital letter, a rash of rubric in the manuscript.

The planting duke admired the tree for commercial and patriotic reasons as well as for its looks. He believed that 'planting ought to be carried out for Beauty, Effect, or Profit', and the profit he had in mind was not merely his own but the nation's. In 1815, when starting on the greatest of his schemes, he calculated that a modest return from his planting would, by the end of the nineteenth century, 'supply all the demands required by Great Britain for war or commerce', and forecast that if other landowners followed his example Britain would become an exporter rather than an importer of timber.[*] He was wrong on all counts. Iron replaced timber ships, world wars found Britain hard pressed for home-grown timber; and the new commercial forests of today fall far short of demand. Duke John, blind to ironclads just over the horizon, vigorously set about proving larch superior even to oak for building ships.

He started modestly in the 1770s, while the idea was still a germ in his mind, with ferry boats for the Tay and a few flat-bottomed cobles, hitherto built of local pine, for the river fishing. Defence of the realm was a more alluring prospect, and he badgered the Admiralty into experimenting with larch, though the Naval shipwrights, who had previously found fault with inferior larch imported from the Baltic, were sceptical. The renowned *Serapis*, once captured by the privateer

[*] 'If one fourth of the product of 2,600,000 larches arrive to maturity in 72 years, by the time the present century expires, it will supply all the demands required by Great Britain for war or commerce, [and will enable her] possibly within a century, to export wood to an immense amount.'

Heart of larch – the frigate *Athole* under canvas. Though eminently seaworthy, she set sail too late for Naval glory.

John Paul Jones in a celebrated encounter, but by then serving as a humble store ship, was extensively patched up with larch. The hoped for breakthrough came in 1816 when eight hundred larch trees of at least sixty years' growth were felled in the duke's woods at Blair and Dunkeld and sent to the Royal dockyard at Woolwich to build a frigate, which was named the *Athole* in his honour. Included in the consignment was one of the first larches planted at Blair by Duke James in 1738, by then more than a hundred feet tall and a solid twelve feet in girth at the butt end.

The *Athole* proved seaworthy but by then, unfortunately for the duke and his dream of glory, Trafalgar was in the past, Napoleon on St Helena and the boom in Naval shipbuilding over. A survey on the *Athole* in later years found that the larch had hardened with time with little shrinkage, that it held iron bolts as well as oak and with less corrosion, and the bilges were dry as the cabin. The same Admiralty report found that a sister frigate built of 'Baltic fir' at the same time as the *Athole*, was 'so very defective as to be proposed either to be broken up or taken to pieces'.

Meanwhile the duke experimented on his own account with a merchant brig constructed in Perth entirely of larch. She was launched in August 1819 and proudly named – what else? – the *Larch*. 'She sailed almost over the entire globe, and never so much as carried away a spar' until due to the incompetence of a pilot she grounded on an island in the Black Sea. The beached hulk resisted wind and waves for two years until bought by 'some people in Odessa' who relaunched her, still sound as a bell.

The duke planted with patriotic zeal throughout the Napoleonic Wars. His 'Great Plantation of Larch', begun in 1800, was completed in 1816, by which time he had embarked on an even more ambitious plan. Being convinced that larch 'at no very distant period' would substitute for oak, 'I became anxious still to increase the scale (however large) of my plantations of that species of fir. Accordingly, I determined to plant a mountainous tract of very rugged ground, and for that purpose, to fence about 3132 acres of rocky hills, including a lake of about 100 acres'. This was Loch Ordie, a small sheet of water set in a wilderness of broken moorland below a rugged eminence called Deuchary Hill. He did not expect to see the work finished, for he was sixty and reckoned that it would take seventeen years to complete – a considerable miscalculation, for he lived to complete planting the ground just three years from the start. Perhaps it was the spade that did it, an implement designed by the duke himself and said to be more efficient that the common-or-garden spade. (What features made it special? – I don't know.) Or the fact that seedlings of only two or three years' growth were used, considerably younger than was then customary for planting out. So successful was the experiment that when the duke saw the result of six years' growth he enclosed and planted out another large tract of moorland to the north. Its central feature was another lochan, now named by the Ordnance Survey, a stickler for Gaelic accuracy, as Loch Oisinneach but then spelled variously (and phonetically) as Hoishnie or Hoisnie. This time the work, slightly less in extent, took only a year, including the construction of five miles of road and six miles of fence, and the planting of more than four thousand seedling trees, the last of which was tramped in on 20 December 1826. It was said that no plantation gave him so much pleasure as Loch Hoishnie, the pride of his final years. In course of time the trees around Hoishnie flourished and grew tall and dense, as Queen Victoria discovered to her alarm some forty years later when her coachman lost his way among them one stormy night.

On Deuchary Hill's rugged western slope a group of Atholl larch trees cling on, all awry. How ancient they look, but beware of seeming antiquity; these trees are survivors of the great nineteenth century planting. Shaggy and bent with exposure and age (a hundred and fifty years or more); all twisted, small, stunted, many blown over in a

Few trees remain as reminders of the great planting schemes at Loch Ordie and Loch 'Hoishnie'. Tracks and the occasional dilapidated bridge show where a network of forest roads traversed the ducal woods.

past gale but still putting out green shoots. A few are quite dead, in ruins. No doubt the planter conceived them as a picturesque crest for the hill; and so they are still, in their own sad way.

From the hilltop (I reach it by way of a scramble up a rocky gully) I survey two landscapes – spreading forests around the valley of the Tay, and elsewhere open moorland dotted with scattered old larch or spruce, the latter refreshed with bright tips of early summer growth. No real sense now of Duke John's great plantations of the past.

Descending by a narrow path I find twiggy shoots at my feet – recently planted aspen, willow and alder and oak. Odd, for I don"t think of this as broadleaf territory. For a century and a half the ground was dedicated to the Atholl larch.

I explore a yet bleaker stretch – a roadless, unpeopled desolation. Here on the barren ground around lochs Oisinneach and Ordie the planting duke laid out his forests between 1815 and 1826. To the north are the dark lines of an extensive plantation, the Forestry Commission's Kindrogan Wood. (Is its drab uniformity what the duke's forest looked like in its prime? I hope not.) Weathered masonry banks and neat stone culverts show that some of the footpaths and tracks I walk on are the overgrown remains of the carriage roads he built.

The two pearly lochans called Oisinneach (for they are twins) add sparkle to the moorland scene. Oisinneach Mor, the greater, appears beyond a shallow pass where old stumps poke through burnt heather – here, evidently, the forest grew. With the sun low at my back, the water gleams a marvellous blue. Between the greater Oisinneach and the lesser my track leads through heather and grass, with clumps of ragged larch and spruce all around. Here's a distressed thicket with only a few trees still standing; the rest lie fallen on the ground. Little Oisinneach sports a few larch on a promontory above green reeds. Above the track crags are grey against the brown of the heather and the reds and greens of moss, with a flush of small white flowers I can't identify.

Eventually a grassy track curls down through a glade of larch, the nearest I've yet seen to real woodland, a green corridor that feels, in my imagination, as if it could be the very spot where Victoria and her party were lost in the dark and driving rain. This evening a light breeze thrums through them.

Now I follow the Buckny Burn into a narrow valley where it flows merrily over stones reddened by minerals, shaded by conifers that thin out towards the top of a hill called Capel. It makes me think of frontier America.

I pass a ruined cottage – bare walls, collapsed roof – with a big living spruce at the front and four others, mere wrecks, lying on the ground. Once they gave it shelter. I look across wide moorland, open and boggy, and picture its few trees multiplied, till – in my mind's eye – the planting duke's great forest spreads seamlessly across the hills and hollows.

During his custody of Atholl the fourth duke is said to have planted more than twenty-seven million trees. It was he who, in the words of an admirer, 'clothed the previously desert and dreary ranges of the valleys of the Tay and the Tummel'. Another witness, one Sir Bourchier Wrey, approaching Dunkeld from the west in 1817, marvelled at the grand sight stretching before his eyes, 'a whole range of mountains covered with larch fir principally and many other trees of infinite variety'.

8

MACCULLOCH'S RIDE

OUT OF PERTH the great north road follows the course of the rivers Tay and Tummel through Atholl country, a stretch, according to John MacCulloch, unequalled for the beauty and variety of its wooded scenery anywhere in the British Isles, and probably in all Europe. MacCulloch knew it well. As a boy he had wandered around Dunkeld and Dunsinane and later he travelled the whole route, either on horseback or by coach. Enthusiasm illuminates his otherwise dry *Description of the Scenery between Dunkeld and Blair in Atholl*, the work of a romantic age (his contemporaries were Scott, Wordsworth and Coleridge). Now, almost two hundred years after his *Description* was published in 1823, the traveller – these days by car, bus or train – is still enchanted by the wide vistas of mountain, river and plain, chequered by splendid trees and undulating forests.

Much has changed, of course. He saw the Atholl larch plantations in their infancy; they've since grown tall and been cut down, and two centuries later new forests arise. The once erratic Tay and Tummel have been constrained since his day and most of their islands and shallows are gone. The A9 has been superimposed on much of MacCulloch's old road. Dunkeld and Pitlochry, down whose main streets he went, have been bypassed, and in the narrow glen of Killiecrankie traffic speeds by on a high concrete viaduct jutting out from the hillside. A railway runs alongside for most of the way. But it's still a green way, infinitely varied, with picturesque glimpses of dark water, fields, pebble banks, rock cliffs shaggy with pine and spruce, vistas of distant wooded hillsides, borders of oak and birch. 'There is scarcely a blank spot throughout the whole twenty miles' – agreed.

John MacCulloch, connoisseur of woodland scenery. Surgeon, scientist, geologist, mineralogist and no mean musician and artist, he deserves greater fame.

MacCulloch, forgotten man, was a polymath respected in his day. After a military start as surgeon in the artillery he practised medicine privately for a while until the Board of Ordnance approached him in 1811 to survey Scottish mountains for rock suitable to be milled for gunpowder. Geology and mineralogy were his particular interests, and in 1819 he published a notable account, with hand-coloured maps, of the geology of the Western Isles. There followed a four-volume work, *Highlands and Western Islands of Scotland*, written in the form of letters addressed to Sir Walter Scott. He spent six years preparing a geological map of Scotland, travelling the country in summer and assembling his sample stones and arranging his notes and papers over winter. His many scientific publications included papers on the naturalisation of exotic plants and animals, on malaria, and on the properties of Indian ink. He rated a footnote in Darwin's *Voyage of the Beagle.*[*]

MacCulloch made his approach through the pass of Birnam, narrow and wild between abrupt hills with 'huge, bare and broken faces of grey rock'; the pass served as a window giving the traveller a first glimpse of the riverside route. The window frame now is a skewed railway bridge over what has become a back road – the modern A9 cuts a brutal swathe below.

Dunkeld presents 'little else but close and wooded scenery'. He elaborates: 'The larch, the spruce, the silver fir and other pines, intermixed with the oak, ash, elm, beech, chestnut and other forest trees,

---

[*] 'Dr MacCulloch says, "It is asserted that on the arrival of a stranger at St Kilda all the inhabitants, in the common phraseology, catch a cold".'

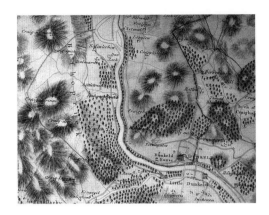

In his 'boyish wanderings' on holiday John MacCulloch explored the woods and hills around Dunkeld and Dunsinane. Stobie's map in this 1815 copy depicts Birnam and Dunkeld as MacCulloch knew them.

serve to produce an endless variety.' He draws attention to the 'romantic village of Inver' whose backwater appeal is now blunted by two caravan parks. Close by is the green-painted wooden Forestry Commission office. Over the brown river Braan he goes and under Craigvinean, 'a lofty and solid mass against the sky', until suddenly emerging from a tunnel of trees, a prospect towards distant blue mountains opens before him, 'the rich variety of the open valley of the Tay displaying itself in perspective series of diminishing woods and trees'. Plantations at Dalguise descend, 'wooded in gay and rich confusion', and in the middle distance a small hill stands 'crowned with dark firs'. 'As the bright meandering line of the river advances towards the eye it becomes lost among numerous wooded islands, till forcing its dark way under an abrupt woody hill it rolls its huge volume of waters beneath the lofty banks' (these crowned by noble beeches). Ben Vrackie slices the skyline above Pitlochry, with Ben y Gloe, a distant warning of the Grampian mountains. He jogs on, remarking on the Duke of Atholl's young oak trees in the flood plain 'raising even now their little heads above the grass'. At the hamlet of Moulinearn he finds the hospitable Mrs Pennicuick in her inn, 'beautiful as an albergo', with hams and sausages hanging from the ceiling and festooned outside with honeysuckle and rose; he eagerly samples her potent Atholl brose, which every traveller should sup 'though his horses were willing to go forward without corn or water'.

Moulinearn now is off the road, reached by bumping over a railway crossing. Two or three houses, a farm track down to the Tummel,

A view of Craigvinean hill and surrounding countryside seen across the River Tay. Much has altered since MacCulloch rode this way, but his impression of 'wood surmounting wood in endless variety of form and colour, descending to the Tay' still applies.

a little bridge over a burn. A plain, well-proportioned two-storey dwelling on a lane going nowhere – MacCulloch's road and Mrs Pennicuick's *albergo*, as I learned from the woman who lives there now and asked what I was up to in her garden (but how was I to know? There's no gate.) No honeysuckle and roses, no hams indoors. No Atholl brose.

At last – 'The road has now entered the celebrated pass of Killiecrankie'. 'The hills seems to close. Rising steep and sudden on both banks, they meet below in a deep chasm, through which the river seems to struggle for a passage, among rocks and under precipices and beneath the overshadowing foliage of the woods that hang feathering over it, giving occasional glimpses of the water as it runs, now silent and dark, and now boiling and foaming.' And so: 'Let the tourist dismount, reckless of time, and heedless of the transient mishaps of bogged shoe or torn galligaskin [breeches], make his way into the woods. Here he will find mossy stones and banks of thyme where he may sit without any companions but the mountain and the mountain bee; where he may look from a dizzy height over a precipice of forest plunging deep down into the invisible abyss beneath him.'

No banks of thyme that I can see – plenty of wood anemones, though – no buzzing bee. MacCulloch's 'green alley wandering through a wild thicket of birch and alder' becomes a tunnel of hazel wands, with logs stacked at intervals on the way. They're cutting down the young beech trees, since beech is out of favour – it's not considered native. Ash trees and birch in profusion, some big trees among them.

They're safe, they'll stay. The railway viaduct arches high above; the line disappears abruptly into a battlemented tunnel in the hillside, heading towards bare moor and mountain where few trees grow.

Poor John. At the age of sixty he takes a bride. As the newlyweds drive along rough Cornish roads the carriage door swings open and MacCulloch – reaching to close it, perhaps – falls out, catches a leg in the spokes of the turning wheel and is dragged along. Torn flesh, broken bones. The crushed leg is amputated but MacCulloch fails and dies, comforted at last by his friend, a Captain Giddy, and I presume his wife. Next year there is a posthumous issue: the publication of his masterpiece, in four sheets, the great *Geological Map of Scotland*.

Page 25

LADY OF THE LAKE.

Ellen, Lady of the Lake, aboard her skiff, meets handsome stranger emerging
'from the hazel shade' on Loch Katrine's shore – an illustration from the first edition of Scott's poem,
a paean (amongst other things) to native woodland.

9

VERY ROBIN HOODISH

EVERY YEAR the ad hoc Blair-Adam Club gathered at the house of
the lawyer and politician William Adam for a weekend of light historical
and archaeological research in the neighbouring countryside, taking
with them 'a basket well supplied with cold meat and some bottles of
good wine'. Chief in this convivial company was the writer Walter
Scott. Scott was frequently at Blair Adam where, as an inveterate
enthusiast for tree planting, he could admire the improvements Adam
was making in the grounds.

Adam had his *Remarks on the Blair Adam Estate* privately printed
for the benefit of other planting lairds. A set of coloured maps tucked
into the back cover unfolds to reveal the progress of the estate from its
original state of nakedness – 'then moor or russet ground' – before 1733
to the landscape of ornamental glades and plantations which it had
become a century later.

Three generations of Adam took a hand in the developments:
the first William Adam, the famous architect, then his son John, and
finally John's son William. The sparse wooded walks and rides projected
by the first William were still young and growing when John set about
enlivening the bare ground beyond the vicinity of the house with little
archipelagos of woodland. 'His general rule', as his son described it,
'was to plant ground that was unfit for any other culture. He planted
rocky hills and eminences, and high long ridges unfit for the plough,
and at that period not of much value as pasture; and he added to the
picturesque rocky glens and dells the beauty of wood. After those woods
were considerably advanced in growth, he united them by planting the

intermediate spaces.' One picturesque eminence, known simply as the Hill, rose directly behind the house, its rocky whinstone slopes originally given over to goats which John Adam banished. By his son's time, when the Hill was 'covered with lofty splendid wood of infinite variety', Scott thought it 'very Robin Hoodish'.

Before the second William embarked on his own programme of planting there were pig-styes and dunghill to attend to. These, set close to the house wall in a less refined age, offended the more fastidious William, who promptly had the styes demolished and the dung barrowed away. Then there was the matter of the view, or lack of it, down to Loch Leven. William had an obstructive hedge uprooted and windows knocked into a wall so that from the drawing room he and his guests could at last enjoy the play of light on water. Displeased by the bare bastion of Benarty Hill which dominates the loch, he bought the hill and planted it out. With these and later acquisitions he was able to exclude 'an unsightly country' from his critical eye.

Thus the map headed 'Blair Adam as arranged by the Right Hon'ble William Adam' shows extensive woodlands threaded by sinuous walks and rides, with large irregular plantations towards the boundaries. The blank colour wash which sufficed in the first map had been overlaid in the last by a rich patchwork in shades of green.

The gate is open – a gap between stone pillars. Dogs in the old courtyard bark at me. The side of house (or is it the front?) is dilapidated and buttressed with timber, and some of the adjoining buildings are mere shells, roofless with empty window frames. The clock on the turret has lost its face. An upstairs window in the good wing opens and Mrs Adam (Adams live here still) asks my business. I guess I shouldn't be here. We talk about Walter Scott, who described Blair Adam in his novel The Abbot.

At the front of the house (or is it the side?) an overgrown terrace overlooks a dipping grassy slope with a few trees scattered over it and, at the far end of what has been a lawn, one shattered giant recumbent. I climb a steep bank through bracken – this must be the Hill. There are sycamores and pines above, and a tangle of small birch, rowan and beech pushes through the undergrowth. I descend into dell with trickle of a stream in it, clutching at branches to help me over mossy ledges. Very Robin Hoodish.

I emerge into the open with a view to blue Loch Leven under Benarty Hill. The sunny plain below is bisected by a motorway. 'Ten

Sir Walter Scott at his desk at Abbotsford. Here on New Year's Day 1819 he penned the first entry in his tree planting journal. (Painted posthumously by Sir John Watson Gordon.)

miles north of the Frith of Forth' – as Adam wrote in his Remarks – *'the great road from Edinburgh to Perth passes through'.*

On his deathbed the Laird of Dumbiedykes called for three tumblers of brandy and between swigs offered sound advice. 'Jock,' he croaked in his son's ear, 'when ye hae naething else to do, you may be aye sticking in a tree. It will be growing, Jock, when ye're sleeping.' Then he 'soughed awa'. Dumbiedykes had gone to meet his Maker.

His true creator Sir Walter Scott put the words into his mouth in *The Heart of Midlothian.* Scott was no mean planter himself. On his lands on the banks of the Tweed he gradually transformed bare glen and hillside into a scene of silvan beauty. In a painting he can be seen sitting pensively on a height above the river with his house of Abbotsford gleaming in a shaft of light, and all that lies around is well wooded. Both as a practical forester and as novelist and poet Scott landed the nature and virtues of a wooded landscape. He is the laureate of tree planters.

In *The Lady of the Lake*, six cantos of high romance in a picturesque setting, he celebrated the rocky hills, rushing streams and wood-fringed waters around Loch Katrine (where tourists now set sail on a steamer called *Sir Walter Scott*), line after line expressing his delight in trees and woodland. Lady Ellen's skiff slides 'from underneath an aged oak' while the water eddies 'the weeping willow twig to lave'. The stranger huntsman advances to her 'from the hazel shade'; she leads him through the tangles to a clearing

Where weeping birch and willow round
With their long fibres swept the ground

and at last to her rustic bower with its 'lodge of ample size', woodcrafted

Of such materials, as around
The workman's hand had readiest found.
Lopped of their boughs, their hoar trunks bared,
And by the hatchet rudely squared,
To give the walls their destined height,
The sturdy oak and ash unite:
While moss and clay and leaves combined
To fence each crevice from the wind.
The lighter pine-trees overhead
Their slender length for rafters spread
And withered heath and rushes dry
Supplied a russet canopy.

In prose, too. In *Rob Roy* he describes a small hill on the approach to the clachan of Aberfoyle, said to be the haunt of fairies, 'clothed with copsewood of hazels, mountain ash and dwarf oak, intermixed with a few magnificent old trees, which, rising above the underwood, exposed their forked and bared branches to the silver moonshine'. Such a fond cataloguer of native trees is Scott. And in *Old Mortality*, where 'a few birches and oaks still feathered the narrow ravines, or occupied in dwarf clusters the hollow places of the moor' – how clearly you may see them today.

Scott bought the farm Cartley Hole and its surrounding fields, soon to be dignified as Abbotsford, in 1812, when he was deputy Sheriff of Selkirk ('the Shirra') and the unfinished manuscript of *Waverley* lay neglected in a drawer. When he came to 'Clarty Hole', as scoffers called it, there were only a few poor trees in the grounds, a row of Scots pine near the farmhouse which the locals called the doctor's redding kame (i.e. comb) planted by the previous owner, a Doctor Douglas, plus some young plantations at a distance from the house. This would not do. No sooner had Scott acquired these bare heathlands and swampy flats than he set about persuading nature to conform to his muse. In place of scoured heath and sour bog there would rise groves, dells and banks of leafy splendour fit to rival Ellen's isle. As he rode between Edinburgh and the Borders on his frequent excursions to oversee building work on the new baronial pile his mind was filled with forestry. Sitting at his desk at the window overlooking the Tweed, he would plan his woodlands in detail; a good vantage point, for when he saw his forester Tom Purdie passing below he could simply lean out to give instructions or discuss a point.

Scott, in the youth and enthusiasm of the early Abbotsford days, was a hands-on planter: 'Planting and pruning trees I could work at from morning till night'. Given half a chance he'd be out there working with his men. For three days in the snows of February 1812 he was out and about dirtying hands and clothes in 'planting, ditching, and fencing', and later that spring when the weather was more clement he persuaded his wife Charlotte to join him sowing acorns. Friends and acquaintances obliged him with parcels of acorns. One was Joanna Baillie, the Scots-born 'poetess of Hampstead', whose now forgotten plays he admired and with whom he corresponded affectionately: the oak seedlings she had sent were now growing 'nearly as tall as your knitting needle'. A coach-load of acorns arrived from Yorkshire, a bagful from Windsor Forest, a consignment from Ireland by ship (most of which, once planted, were nibbled in the ground by fieldmice). The losses didn't deter him; he was soon sowing 'with my own fair hands' more acorns on the ground. Oaks were a particular favourite but many other species, both broadleaf and conifer, were planted in profusion. Beech and elm figured largely; a load of pinasters (an old name for the maritime pine) contributed by Joanna Baillie were put in all over the north side of a hill near the house. Scots pine, however, he planted with some caution.

By the time he sat down on the first day of January 1819 to pen the opening words in a notebook he entitled *Sylva Abbotsfordiensis* – 'Memoranda concerning the woods and plantations at Abbotsford' – he had between three and four hundred acres under young trees 'chiefly (indeed almost entirely) raised by myself'. Not everything succeeded. In what he called the Thicket, a neglected stretch of ground originally planted by Dr Douglas, he had attempted to fill gaps with beech and other broadleaf plants with 'injudicious prodigality'. Seven years later the new growth was so thick that many young trees had to be cut out again. Low-lying ground near the Tweed known as the Haugh (haugh – a river meadow) was constantly flooded despite several attempts to

Instant woodland might be created with the help of such a tree planting machine devised in the early 1800s. It looks a rough ride for the helpers.

buttress the river banks with trees, including an attempt one Christmas to transplant a number of large trees 'removed with balls of earth around the roots and very carefully planted by the water-side'. Natural catastrophe was not confined to flooding. An entry for April 1822 records that the Saintswell plantation had 'suffered terribly from the long continued drought of 1821 which was the driest season I ever knew. The hardwood is almost all dead.' There was hope, however, in the survival of larches which were 'doing well enough to stock the whole ground'. The following year a less than enthusiastic report was made on the state of a wooded bank facing Abbotsford where planting 'has succeeded as ill or worse than any plantation on the property' – due, he surmised, to the ground having been exhausted previously by heedless turf cutting.

Whatever the setbacks Scott doggedly planted on, always aiming to create a natural effect. Scott hated regularity and stiff discipline. The lines must ebb and flow like a green tide, pleasing to a beholder observing from the corbelled windows of the big house or from the roads and pathways of the estate. His views 'On Planting Waste Lands' – the title of a lengthy review published in 1827 – condemned those who ignored nature's way. 'Here you shall see a solitary mountain with a great black patch stuck on its side, like a plaster of Burgundy pitch, and there another, where the plantation, instead of gracefully sweeping down to its feet, is broken short off in mid-air.' (And do we not see them still?) The curious habit of crowning a hill with an isolated clump of trees riled him: 'We have seen a brotherhood of beautiful hills, the summits of which, while they remained unplanted, must have formed a fine undulating line, now presenting themselves with each a round circle of black fir, like a skimming dish on its head.' Imagine the triple peaks of his beloved Eildon Hills disfigured in such a way!

Scott's guiding principle that planted woodlands should conform to the landscape is one that all environmentalists and most foresters would accept today. He would bring his woods 'down the glens on one side, sweep them round the foot of the hills on another, conduct them up the ravines on a third, giving them, as much as possible, the character of a natural wood'. Future woods should 'advance and recede from the eye, according to and along with the sweep of the hills and banks which support them, thus occupying precisely the place in the landscape where nature's own hand would have placed them'.

A reader absorbed in his book while the young tree grows.
Magnus Jackson labelled his 1860s photograph 'Pine Tree' (in fact Chile pine or monkey puzzle)
but didn't identify the setting – probably in Perthshire.

10

A YEARNING FOR EXOTICA

HUGH MACDIARMID, in the lines quoted at the head of this book, likened himself to the ancient Greek poet Pindar when 'seized by honey-sweet yearning' for the trees of his native land. What trees had MacDiarmid in mind? Scots pine, possibly, the tree of old Caledonia. I don't know what trees Pindar marvelled at. Pine again? Maybe the Mediterranean variety known to us as maritime pine or pinaster. Or it could have been something more exotic (to us), like cedar or cypress. Whatever. Heather and myrtle honey yearnings both, in lands far apart.

Throughout recorded time exotic trees have been imported into Scotland. Some of them seem old familiars now, so long established that they're part of the family. Sycamore, native to the mountains of Europe, has been acclimatised for many centuries. It may have crossed from France at the time of the Auld Alliance, or even further back when the Romans came. Beech, a tree that failed to reach much beyond the English Midlands in its prehistoric invasion, is perfectly at home. Among others are the Spanish or sweet chestnut, which probably came to England with the Romans and in time appeared in Scotland; its near namesake the horse chestnut, the conker tree, was introduced from Greece in the 1600s, the cedar of Lebanon was brought from the Middle East probably in the same century. There are others.

We park in a side road, cross an old stone bridge and tramp along a lane that ends abruptly in a field somewhere on the outskirts of Drummond Castle estate in Perthshire. It's no ordinary country lane, lined as it is not with beech or sycamore trees but with huge sweet chestnuts – ancients with vast ribbed trunks and mighty upreaching boughs.

This must have been a noble avenue in time past, but now it's ragged and gapped and leads nowhere. These remaining trees are in rude health – still producing seed in quantity every few years (and the nuts are good to eat, says the factor, who has tasted them). So presumably, given a chance, they could reproduce.

How old are they? All of an age? No one knows how many centuries ago they were planted. And wherever their homeland, here in rural Perthshire they flourish like natives.

A recent incomer is the Norway spruce which grows in profusion all over northern Europe and has become established in the Scottish landscape as a staple of modern forestry. It arrived in this country four centuries ago, somewhat earlier than larch.

The greatest influx of new species came in the nineteenth century when curious travellers and bold botanists scoured the remote places of the world and brought or sent back seeds and plants of hundreds of new species. Some failed, others flourished. Trees native to the Himlayas, the Andes, the Americas, China and Japan took root in Scottish soil and in time transformed the landscape. Plant hunters roamed far and wide to satisfy the demand for exotic, exciting new species. Western Europe reached out over the sea and took its pick of other people's trees.

Some of the trees that were eagerly tried out by experimenting landowners in the seventeenth and eighteenth century came from north America where the old growth forests were being relentlessly pushed back by the settlers. Mostly the trees introduced from the eastern side of the continent failed to live up to their promise as forest trees in Scotland. But when the Rockies were reached and the Pacific coasts explored it was another story. This was a bonanza.

Scots collectors, several of them sponsored by progressive Scottish landowners who inspired much of the nineteenth century's plant-hunting activities, were prominent in the search for new and promising species. First to make his mark as a naturalist was Archibald Menzies who sailed (uncomfortably) as ship's surgeon with George Vancouver on his exploratory voyage to the Pacific coast where, botanising on his trips ashore, he 'discovered' (which is to say he recognised, identified and described) the coast redwood and, around Nootka Sound on the west coast of Vancouver Island, gathered seeds of

Archibald Menzies, plant-hunting pioneer.

the glorious western red cedar and came upon the funereal Nootka cypress. Notably, he also chanced upon that relic of primeval woodlands the Chile pine, alias the monkey puzzle. The trail blazed by Menzies was followed by David Douglas, greatest of all plant collectors, and in turn by the hapless John Jeffrey. Jeffrey sent home a first, small packet of seed from the western hemlock, a tree that happily defies the deepest shade, a resilience not always welcome to modern foresters or to native tree enthusiasts. It grows where they don't want to see it. In the mountains near the Sacramento River he collected seed of the incense cedar and nearby, in the Shasta valley, discovered the tree that bears his name, the Jeffrey pine. Jeffrey also found the lodgepole pine, a tree once much favoured by the Forestry Commission in Scotland, but less so now.

The hunger for new and promising kinds of trees reached its apogee in the middle years of the century among tree-planting landowners, with Scottish lairds, aristocrats and lesser gentry in the lead.

Oddest-looking of all introduced trees is the monkey puzzle – for the most part fine, long-established trees planted in Victoria's reign, the era when the species, more formally known as the Chile pine, took the nation's fancy. All over Scotland they can be seen raising their weird domes on shaft-like stems, in the policies of stately homes, beside suburban villas, in churchyards, in cottage gardens. A bizarre fancy this, to translate an exotic tree from Andean slopes to the kailyairds of old Caledonia.

How came it here? Archibald Menzies, a Scots gardener turned botanist, protégé of the naturalist Sir Joseph Banks, toyed with a dish of large, glossy nuts at dinner in Valparaiso, curious as to what they might be. No doubt he was pleased to be ashore after the discomforts and distress he suffered as ship's surgeon on board the converted collier *Discovery* with the explorer Vancouver. Valparaiso, a red-tiled town of one street built on the edge of a ravine, offered Menzies a chance to botanise in the surrounding country. But it was when he was invited to dine with the viceroy that he made his great find. There were nuts for dessert – in fact the seeds of the Chile pine, large (about two inches long), shiny, brown and edible.* The story goes that Menzies stuffed a number of these seeds into his pocket and later sowed them in pots on board the *Discovery*. On his return in 1795 he gave one pot to his patron, after whom the plant was called (for a time) the Joseph Banks Pine, and the remaining five to Kew.

Possibly Menzies wasn't the first to introduce the tree to Europe, since there is an engraving in the museum at Cologne showing what appears to be a pair of young monkey puzzles growing in an eighteenth-century park at Kleve (seed or plants may have been brought back from a Dutch expedition to Chile in the 1640s), but it was his pot plants that roused interest in the strange species. By the middle of the nineteenth century it had become quite a favourite as a show-off ornament. The tree, botanically *Araucaria araucana*, looks like no other pine, and with reason. It's a true primitive, the direct descendant of trees that grew on earth millions of years ago in the Carboniferous age, trees that died only to survive in another form as measures of coal. When the makers of the BBC's television series *Walking with Dinosaurs* needed a landscape for their dinosaurs they found it in the araucaria forests of Chile.

Menzies had other successes, particularly further up the Pacific coast where he identified – and occasionally collected and brought back – several species that would become staples in nineteenth-century gardens and plantations.

Northwestern America was a land of mystery and dread. Europeans had touched its shores and built small trading settlements in bays

* 'Preferably roasted,' says Alan Mitchell in his guide to the trees of Britain and Northern Europe.

David Douglas, who gave his name to the Douglas fir, one of the fine conifer species introduced from northwest America in the nineteenth century.

and river mouths where native Indians inhabited cedar lodges between the Pacific rollers and the green margin of the continental forest. These were old-growth forests, self-renewing, established from time immemorial, in whose depths grew ancient trees of giant proportions – a wonder of the world.

In the year 1826 David Douglas was rowed ashore at the mouth of the Columbia river. Douglas, a stonemason's son, gardener's boy turned botanist, was prospecting in North America for the Horticultural Society of England. At a place called Cape Disappointment he found the shore pine and in the forest growing thick and wild across the landscape he saw spruce and hemlock. Dominating all there grew a huge, rough-barked, stately tree first seen and described by Archibald Menzies a quarter of a century earlier. Douglas collected its seed and dispatched a packet to his employers in London, and in due course there sprouted from this source the tree that bears his name, the Douglas fir.

It was taken up eagerly, Douglas himself distributing parcels of seed to friends and supporters. Some went to Drumlanrig Castle in Dumfriesshire where his brother was employed by the Duke of Buccleuch. A tree raised from this seed and planted in 1832 still stands in the castle grounds, described erroneously on a tablet as the first to be grown in Britain. Another who received either seeds or plants from Douglas was Thomas Graham, Lord Lynedoch, one of Wellington's commanders,[*] who had them planted out at his estate near Crieff.

---

[*] Otherwise notable as a participant in the first cricket match played in Scotland.

A section of the American northwest where tree hunters were active. David Douglas landed at the mouth of the Columbia River and journeyed inland. Most of the virgin rainforest and much of what remains is under threat – Clayoquot Sound on Vancouver Island, for example, has recently been the scene of angry confrontations over logging. (From Stanford's map of the United States, 1861.)

Later, travelling upriver with a small flotilla of boats, Douglas scaled the heights above spectacular falls then known as the Grand Rapids and found himself among trees unseen and unrecognised before by any but the native inhabitants. The fruits of his journey included a trio of silver firs aptly named as the lovely, the grand and the noble firs. Another introduction by Douglas cast an even longer shadow (often literally). Archibald Menzies discovered it flourishing on the margins of the Puget Sound, a long arm of the sea reaching deep into Washington State, but again it was Douglas who collected and sent the first seeds home. In due course this newcomer would prove to be God's greatest gift to Scottish forestry and in the same breath the plant most vilified in all the land – the tree now known as Sitka spruce.

George Patton, later Lord Glenalmond, knew of the great trees flourishing on the far side of the Rockies and longed to try how they might grow in his own policies. Patton, besides being a laird in Perthshire, was a successful lawyer and aspiring politician. Among his acquaintances was John Hutton Balfour, professor of botany at Edinburgh University, regius keeper of the Royal Botanic Garden at Inverleith, Queen's botanist in Scotland and founder of the Botanical Society of Edinburgh. Patton broached his idea and as a result Balfour took the chair at a meeting of 'gentlemen interested in the promotion of arboriculture and horticulture of Scotland' at the botanic garden in November 1849, when it was decided to form a body to be called the

Oregon Association, to bring plants and seeds from the great Pacific forests. By the end of January a committee was in place which included Balfour, Patton, a number of aristocratic landowners and James McNab, the head gardener at the botanic garden.

McNab was the professional, a key figure in the association's business and a collector himself. In 1834 he had made a lengthy botanical trip through North America accompanied by his friend the Perth nurseryman, where numerous plants, seeds and other specimens were collected and their descriptions published by Balfour's new botanical society. He had not long succeeded his father in charge of the botanical garden. From the experience he gathered in Edinburgh he was able to write extensively on the new conifers (he was particularly interested in how they should be pruned). An engraving shows an alert, strong, handsome face, prominent nose, keen eyes, a mane of hair, a lush moustache and a beard fringing his chin in the fashion of the time.

McNab's disciple was a young gardener recently appointed at Inverleith, John Jeffrey. The story goes that when the branch of a tall tree was broken by the wind Jeffrey volunteered to climb to the top and remove it. He'd also won a prize for his collection of plants found in the Edinburgh area. He was soon to be given the chance to put this talent to wider use.

When the Oregon Association decided to send a collector to America McNab put forward Jeffrey's name and he was appointed in February 1850. The Hudson's Bay Company, trading with the northern region of Canada, agreed to ship Jeffrey across the Atlantic and give him an escort through the northern wildernesses. He was instructed in taking latitude and longitude before setting sail from London on board the Hudson's Bay vessel *Prince of Wales*. A call was made at Stromness in the Orkney Islands and eight weeks later the ship dropped anchor at Five Fathom Hole off York Factory, the company's station on Hudson Bay. By March the following year he had covered more than eight hundred miles across the inhospitable swampy wilderness of what is now northern Manitoba, then followed the Saskatchewan River to the Edmonton House station (where the city of Edmonton now is) and on again to reach the Athabasca River, from where he started out with a hardy band of men carrying the 'winter packet' from post to post, reaching Jasper House in the Rocky Mountains on 21 March. From there he wrote to his employers in Edinburgh informing them of his progress thus far. It had not been an easy trip:

> All this distance I walked on snow shoes, the snow being on average two feet deep... During this journey I slept with no other cover than that found under the friendly pine, for the space of forty-seven nights, on several occasions the thermometer standing from 30° to 40° below zero... Once or twice I got slightly frost bit.

As the snow deepened, horses and Indian porters had to be left behind and Jeffrey and his companion, a man called Clouston, packed their necessary belongings in knapsacks and, carrying their rifles, trudged on alone.

Meanwhile he had been able to dispatch the first fruits of his collecting activities, made in territory east of the Rockies. The box, eagerly opened at a committee meeting of the Oregon Association on 6 November, was found to contain some cones of eastern conifers, a few bird skins and some beetles. There were only a few seeds. It was nearly a year later before the next box arrived, but it came from San Francisco, showing that Jeffrey had reached the western seaboard where it was hoped his discoveries would be most fruitful. Along with plants, seed packages and more beetles retrieved from the box on 24 August 1853 was some gold dust (it was the height of the Californian gold rush) but there was no sign of Jeffrey's more precious and eagerly expected journal. The association was dismayed to be billed for postage of £135 though in the end the Post Office waived the fee. More specimens followed shortly afterwards, including a small cloth bag containing the first seeds of western hemlock, one of the tallest trees in the world. Western hemlock grows all along the Pacific coast from Alaska to California and in the wetter parts of the inland mountain areas.

The tree was soon taken up. George Patton grew it enthusiastically on his estate, the Cairnies. Queen Victoria, mourning for her Albert, saw a photograph of two of Patton's young trees in 1862 and was so attracted by their drooping foliage that she wished it to be named in honour of her late consort. So it became popularly Prince Albert's Spruce and botanically *Abies albertiana*. Neither name has lasted. Now western hemlock is never called a spruce, its botanical name has been changed to *Tsuga heterophylla* and Albert has lost a memorial.

A Wellingtonia (or giant sequoia) overtops Melville's column in St Andrew Square, Edinburgh. The scale of this imagined transplant was based on measurements of a sequoia seen in the wilds of North America by the transcontinental explorers Meriwether Lewis and William Clark.

After that, nothing more from Jeffrey, not a word, not a note, not a box or a bag. He disappears from view. The Oregon associates instructed a contact in San Francisco to track him down but without success. Several letters addressed to him lay waiting collection at the British consulate. But Jeffrey had ridden into the western sunset. The mystery of his fate has never been solved. James McNab offered the explanation that he had been killed while trading with Indians, but that seems to be speculation. Another rumour had it that he disappeared northwards, lured by the gold rush. In due course Jeffrey, dead or alive, was formally dismissed *in absentia* for neglect of duty.

It seems a hard fate, and Jeffrey's reputation has suffered in consequence. He had the misfortune to be overshadowed by his predecessor David Douglas. But he made many valuable introductions and his achievement should not be underestimated. 'No one could have worked more conscientiously and more perseveringly than Jeffrey did during the first two years of his appointment,' an associate wrote. 'His collections do him no discredit'.

'Another of those indefatigable Scots' (Alan Mitchell's words) introduced the world's biggest tree to Britain, though it was a close-run thing. William Lobb, collecting for Veitch the English seedsman, thought he had it in the bag. At a lecture in California Lobb heard of vast trees growing beyond all imagining in what we now know as Calaveras Grove and immediately set off to see for himself. Having found the trees and gathered seed and a couple of seedlings he set off poste haste through Mexico en route for England.

But John Matthew, laird of Gourdiehill, a small property in the Carse of Gowrie, had somehow arrived on the west coast of America and got wind of the same trees. Unknown to anyone, including Lobb, he reached Calaveras, gathered seed, bundled himself and his baggage across the continent, embarked on the first transatlantic steam packet and was safely back at his Perthshire home in August 1853, five months before Lobb reached England. In the interval Matthews had been busy distributing seeds among his neighbours.

What to call it? In the States they use capital letters – it's simply the Big Tree. To native American Indians it was *wawona*, but that could be ignored. In Britain someone named it Wellingtonia after the recently deceased duke, victor at Waterloo and later prime minister, and the name stuck – a green obelisk for the Iron Duke. Wellingtonia it remains in popular parlance, also known as the giant redwood and botanically as *Sequoia giganteum*. Soon Wellingtonias raised from both the Matthew and Lobb seed parcels were growing in Scottish soil. These giant redwoods became the rage, and as demand outstripped supply the price rocketed. A pot-grown tree was bought by Sir Robert Menzies for the astonishing sum of three guineas and planted out in 1858 in his castle grounds in Perthshire where it prospered. The journalist Thomas Hunter recorded the curious case of a fine young specimen at Dupplin, seat of the Earl of Kinnoul, which 'was said to have, like Jack's famous beanstalk, grown up in a single night, at a time when a Wellingtonia could not be got for love nor money'. The plant made its sudden appearance at Dupplin early one morning in July 1859 – apparently after a clandestine night visit to neighbouring territory where several specimens grew. A few drams of whisky to the gardener facilitated the transfer from one estate to the other.

Tree fanciers who hoped for a financial return from their Wellingtonias were disappointed. There is no market for the timber, which shatters easily. The giant redwood is purely an embellishment to be seen and admired, the outdoors equivalent of a Raeburn on the drawing room wall.

*

Pinetum: 'a collection of pine trees for botanical or ornamental purposes' (Chambers Dictionary). Any self-respecting landowner in the mid nineteenth century set about planting experimental groves of the new conifers. A century and a half later many still flourish, with the trees grown tall and handsome and often labelled according to species (though the classification may be outmoded) and possibly also with date and details of planting. Great estates like Scone and Atholl boast fine examples.

At Highfield on the Scone estate 'thirty-two varieties of the newer coniferae' were planted out, at first with a protecting hedge of common-or-garden spruce trees to shield the precious introductions from the elements. Thomas Hunter noted that among the rarities sitka spruce were doing best of all. He also remarked on a very fine noble fir, somewhat mutilated because twelve years earlier its top had been cut off to make a walking stick.

The Earl of Kinnoul, 'well known for his arboreal tastes', laid out ten acres of excellent, well sheltered land at Dupplin as a pinetum about 1870. His collection of conifers was intersected with grassy walks twenty feet wide to allow for bosky ramblings and easy inspection. After twelve years all were reported growing sturdily, dominated by a sixty-foot Douglas fir that clearly had been planted long before.

Pineta and arboreta were seldom merely pleasure gardens raised for the enjoyment of wealthy proprietors. There was often a serious purpose behind the planting, a curiosity as to how these introduced trees would adapt to the soils and climate of Scotland, and whether they would prove a boon in terms of forest products. There could be money in them.

In the early 1850s Sir William Stirling-Maxwell laid out his pinetum next to the kitchen garden at Keir with the express purpose of testing the value of the new introductions. He worked on the Noah principle. Each kind was planted in pairs, so that if one sickened or died another would carry on the line. Thomas Hunter saw a thriving noble fir that had been blown down in the great gale of 1879 and then hauled upright again.

Patton planted in groups rather than pairs, with the purpose of putting different varieties to competitive trial. His Pine Haugh at the Cairnies was laid out over two or three acres of gravelly soil some ten

The young Douglas fir planted at Scone in 1999 to celebrate the bicentenary of David Douglas's birth. Douglas had been employed as a gardener at Scone.

feet above the River Almond, benefiting from full exposure to the afternoon sun. As at Scone, Hunter found the sitka thriving best of all, noble fir doing very well, grand fir promising to be – as he wrote – grand, Douglas fir surviving well enough but rather parched in the gravel, Weymouth pine and others, including the monkey puzzles, affected by frost, and of course western hemlock growing splendidly and quite at home. (You can't keep a hemlock down.)

Patton was not alone as a planter of forest trees. At Strathallan the Birks Wood, in spite of its name, was planted out with 'a promising crop of the newer trees', chief among which were between seven and eight acres devoted exclusively to Douglas fir. At Scone, a plantation of Douglas firs planted in the 1850s covered about thirteen acres. At Monteith the Douglas fir flourished exceptionally, 'rearing its head about eight feet higher than any of the other kinds planted at the same time'. Steuart Fotheringham scattered new conifers liberally in a forty-acre plantation at Murthly already carrying old oak, ash and other broadleaves, Scots pine and Norway spruce. His enthusiasm overcame discretion, and the trees were planted so thickly that his foresters soon had to go through the wood felling every second tree to give breathing space. That done, most of the new species soon grew handsome and large for their age.

> *A small tree planted in the lawn at Scone Palace in the summer of 1999 commemorates the 200th anniversary of the birth of David Douglas, who was born in the parish and worked as an apprentice gardener on this estate. Not far from it I see a ragged wall of assorted tall conifers,*

marking the edge of the Scone pinetum. None of these giant trees were there – few were even known to Europeans – when the boy Douglas learned his trade.

Douglas was in his early grave by the time the fourth Earl of Mansefield planned his pinetum at Scone in the 1840s. Now the originals that remain have grown massively. I pace round the base of a giant redwood, close as I can get to the bole, and it takes seventeen good strides to complete the circle. I wonder if it grew from one of those first seeds brought to Perthshire in 1853. There are other redwoods here and there, not as big, but monsters all the same with the deep spongey, rusty bark typical of their kind. They look ready to slough off their shaggy skins, snakelike.

At eye level in such a place it's the trunks of the trees you see first. Mostly you have to lift your head to look at the foliage, for the lower trunks are so often bare, stripped by nature or the forester's pruning knife. Dwarfed among many stems, I search for patterns. If the fourth earl and his woodman laid out a precise chequerboard their neat formulas have been disrupted by the effects of time, decay, disease, gales of wind and the unpredictability of natural growth itself. What may have been conceived as a uniform row of giant sequoias is interrupted by gaps and other species. Some rows strike off at an angle.

Seven noble fir trees proceed in line ahead like Nelson's ships at Trafalgar. Their trunks rise straight and true, silvery and scarred by long vertical cracks, perfectly round, clean and barely tapering till the tops are lost to sight in swatches of bluey-green foliage. They could be columns in a Wren facade. More practically, they'd make masts for a three-decker. But the wood manager at Scone declares that the planters got it wrong. The noble fir is a high level tree in the wild, flourishing on the Cascade and Siskiyou mountain ranges of northwest America, and when we grow it in richer soils it tends to outpace its strength and the timber splits. But who'll talk timber in the presence of such marvels?

Scattered around are their cousins the grand firs, tall and straight as the noble firs but dark and seamed in the stem. A cluster of brown fungus at the mossy roots pokes through a bed of dead twigs and cone scales. A thicket of branches swirls round the upper stem. Next to these, the Caucasian firs are untidy things, inelegant – from my ground perspective – with fractured bark on knobbly stems. But the October sun strikes through the greenery and makes all well. A Professor Nordmann from Finland (hence the botanical name Abies Nordmanniana) first noticed them on the Black Sea coast in 1837 but it was later that seeds and plants were distributed from Edinburgh by the famous firm of Lawson – Lawson of the cypress.

An avenue of western hemlock – nine on each side – encloses a world of darkness, shrouded by heavy, down-sweeping fans of foliage. In the gloom I crunch over a carpet of dry twigs, needles and tiny crinkly cones, the accumulated fall of many seasons, so soft and springy you could lie down and sleep on it. When my eyes adjust to the gloom I discern a sprinkling of inch-high spikelets of new growth, some of which would make future trees if left in peace; hemlock will flourish in deep shade where seedlings of almost any other sort would fail.

The best is last. At the far end of the pinetum two pairs of sitka spruce explode into view, guarding the corners of the ground: huge trees, each thrusting from a massive swelling base like a sea monster rising from the deep.

These Sitkas were already 'fine specimens' when Thomas Hunter observed them at Scone well over a century ago during his visits to the great estates of Perthshire. Hunter's book *The Woods, Forests and Estates of Perthshire*, respectfully subtitled 'with Sketches of the Principal Families of the County', contains detailed descriptions of the parklands and plantations of the local aristocracy and gentry at a flush time when the newly introduced species were beginning to grow tall and show great promise. His claim that a history of forestry in Perthshire during the previous hundred years was essentially the history of forestry in Scotland is not quite unreasonable, given the size and varied nature of the county, the number of its wealthy landowners, the extent of their estates and their enthusiasm for trees and woodland. Nowhere else could such a microcosm of the Scottish countryside be found. In the eighteenth century, he wrote (in reference to the estates of the earls of Mansfield), most of the country had been 'simply moorland, with a great extent of waste land partly occupied by barren woodbrush such as hazel, birch, elder etc'. But now! – 'As far as the eye can reach, forests of every variety of timber suitable to the climate wave to the passing breeze, while here and there a huge arboreal giant raises his head proudly to the sky.'

Unfortunately his volume is dry. Hunter was no poet, though he tries in a plodding late Victorian way. No vivid images spring from the page. But he was conscientious and painstaking. Not an ancient oak or a young specimen of a new exotic escaped his eye or his measuring tape, and so much the better if there was an interesting tale to tell. At Gask, for instance, he finds a splendid row of beech trees under which Jacobite soldiers were 'regaled' (i.e. given a dram) while the laird entertained Prince Charlie indoors. The grandest of these trees, the one nearest the Perth road, measured eighteen feet round the trunk at five feet from the ground. At Kinfauns on the Carse of Gowrie he found 'a most promising' Wellingtonia which Mr Macdonald the gardener received as a present in a pot in 1860 'when it was no larger than a man's finger' and which had now, some twenty years later, risen to a height of nearly forty feet. A Douglas fir planted at roughly the same time was seventy feet tall despite the loss of its leading shoot a few years before. At the Cairnies, George Patton's preserve, he observed an interesting larch growing in not more than a few inches of soil on a rock overhanging the River Almond within view of the picturesque waterfall known as the Buchanty Spout (dire spot – more of which later). 'The workmen engaged in planting this spot were one day enjoying a smoke after dinner, when one of them, who did not indulge in the weed, was seeking for recreation in some other form. Taking a spade in his hand, he cut out a piece of turf, and, laying it upon the rock, it occurred to him that he might stick in a plant, just for the fun of the thing.' There it prospered, was now nine feet two inches in girth one foot from the rock, with an estimated seventy or eighty cubic feet of timber in it. 'It is marvellous to see the exertions the tree has put forth to draw sustenance for itself, the roots stretching over the rock in a most wonderful manner in order to fasten its radicles in the rich soil on the bank of the Almond.'

Hunter was one of the first to catalogue notable trees by size. Others followed, notably Elwes and Henry whose seven-volume *The Trees of Great Britain and Ireland* came out between 1906 and 1913, and recently Alan Mitchell, whose enthusiasm led to the foundation of a national tree register. Hunter used time-honoured and somewhat rough and ready methods – a tape measure for girth and, for gauging height, either a stick or calibrated rule held up at arm's length and aligned with the tree. Nowadays more accurate instruments are used.[*]

---

[*] But how accurate? When the Forestry Commission decided in 1999 to check the progress of what was confidently thought to be the tallest Douglas fir in Britain (at the Hermitage, near Dunkeld), a tree climber dropped a line from the top to the ground under the eyes of invited guests. When the line was measured the tree was found to be a fraud – thirty feet shorter than its supposed height of 220 feet. A crestfallen Forestry Commission official commented: 'Most trees have been measured using trig points and this must throw the accuracy of those readings seriously in doubt.' Since then the title has gone to a Douglas fir near Beauly, measured by laser in 2002.

Woods, Forests etc. was expanded from a series of articles written for the newspaper Hunter edited, the *Perthshire Constitutional.* Hunter's origins were humble. Born in a mean street in Glasgow, the son of a tradesman (a cousin of the explorer David Livingstone), he was apprenticed to a printer and studied English, French and other useful subjects such as shorthand in the evenings. Branching out as a journalist he came to Perth in the early 1870s, was offered a joint partnership in the *Constitutional* and shortly afterwards became its sole owner.

In the days when grandees jealously guarded their privacy and the common people were seldom welcome on their ground Hunter had ready access, no doubt because newspaper editorship had a certain status. In return he treated his distinguished hosts deferentially while recording their family histories in tedious detail. Whether he ever met them, even if only professionally, is not clear. No backstairs gossip leaks on to his pages. The people he did meet and talk with were men like William McCorquodale, long-serving head forester at Scone. 'We had not proceeded far till Mr McCorquodale pointed out a very interesting experiment' – it concerned the preservation of fence posts with tar – and, apropos of the virtues of Douglas fir, 'Mr McCorquodale says that in filling up vacancies in old plantations the *Douglasii* can be recommended above all others'.

Driving along the estate paths – I assume, by pony and trap, and walking among the trees for a closer look – he covered a vast amount of territory. Perthshire is a big county. What stimulated his interest in trees? He doesn't say, though he went about his task with evident enthusiasm. After woods it was on to pastures new; a later series of articles in the *Constitutional* covered *Farms, Farming and Stock in Perthshire and the North.* His woodland book earned him the 'highest honour' at the great international forestry exhibition in Edinburgh in 1884, the year following its publication.

While Hunter roamed the great estates looking at trees Magnus Jackson captured their images on glass plates. Jackson was a photographer. He would set off from his small premises (not much more than a wooden hut) in Marshall Place, Perth, with a six-foot-long trunk in which was carried his portable studio or tent along with the camera, plates and chemicals he needed – and as often as not, 'a good-sized pruning knife'.

The last survivors of 'great Birnam Wood' – the frontispiece to Thomas Hunter's compendious *Woods, Forests and Estates of Perthshire*. An engraving from the 1880s.

Since he makes a passing reference to an assistant perhaps he'd have a lad in tow to carry the heavy trunk. Jackson conceded that he might have been better served with a small omnibus or horse-drawn cab fitted up as a mobile studio, but the trunk had distinct advantages. It was very convenient for lugging deep into woods along narrow paths, it could be put in the luggage van on rail journeys, and it fitted very nicely on the back seat of an ordinary dog cart. Once in the policies or woods where Jackson proposed to take his tree portraits the tent could be swiftly erected by the lad while Jackson scouted around for the best angles. Sometimes he might have to tie back or lop branches from other trees close by which interrupted his view through the lens, which is where the pruning knife came in: 'I have frequently to call in the assistance of a forester or a gardener to assist in this operation.' Then he might have to wait for perfect stillness in the air. Working with collodion plates and long exposures, he couldn't risk any breath of wind causing movement in the foliage. 'Trees require very careful watching. If attention be not given to take advantage of a lull in the wind the plate will be lost.' For Jackson, recording trees was a matter of aesthetics as well as skill; shots of single specimen trees 'unless sharp, clear and well defined, are worthless as works of art'. Light was important too. Thus at Dunkeld he was once found setting up his equipment at four o'clock on a summer morning.

Jackson liked to include a human figure, judiciously posed, to enhance the artistic effect of his plates. It might be a small boy in a cap sitting on the roots or an old woman in mutch and black skirt leaning on her staff, or gardeners and foresters pressed into service as models. Artificial and stiff as these Lilliputians posing under the great trees are (had to be, because of the length of time they were required to stay still), they have curiosity value. Below a huge leafless oak sits an elderly forester looking straight at the camera, his expressionless face fringed by an off-chin beard. Under a spreading Douglas fir at Lynedoch a shirt-sleeved labourer with scythe on his shoulder stands in conversation with a superior person in jacket, waistcoat and hat, hand nonchalantly on hip. Nameless people all; gone, while the trees live on.

Jackson was of an age with Hunter and one often followed in the other's footsteps – in fact Hunter used engravings from Jackson's plates to illustrate his book. Jackson's photographs show the new trees growing impressively though still far from full stature. Now they provide a graphic commentary on past and present. The sweep of young 'Douglas pines' at Murthly can be compared with the same trees today. 'Trees, Murthly' shows tall conifers ranged in descending order down a grassy walk, seen from a stone stairway flanked by urns – still recognisable though the terrace is untidier. A gent impeccably dressed in light suit and straw boater reclines on the bank below a line of youthful deodar trees – the Deodar Avenue, famous in its day but felled long since.

Sir William Drummond Stewart was the most eccentric of the nineteenth-century gentleman planters. In the ornate ballroom of Murthly Castle, Perthshire, in the wing rebuilt in fashionable Victorian Gothic style after a fire, hangs a full-length portrait of Stewart as a young officer in the Hussars. He's a handsome bucko, Byronic even, in his pelisse and fur shako, posing with hand on sabre beside a shattered tree and splendidly indifferent to the war that rages behind him – for in the background can be seen a smoking cannon and small agitated figures silhouetted in the glare of battle. This purports to depict Sir William on the field of Waterloo, aged nineteen.

After these military exploits Sir William's taste for adventure led him to America where he lived with a tribe of Indians, some of whom he brought back to Murthly, where they roamed the estate and alarmed the natives. He also imported buffaloes to keep the Indians company. Hunter, aware of domestic ill will – the late Sir William had attempted

Professor John Hutton Balfour, a founder of the Botanical Society of Edinburgh and – along with the ill-starred George Patton – of the Oregon Association dispatched John Jeffrey on his final (and finally tragic) mission in search of new conifers.

both to bilk and to disinherit his family – contented himself with the bare statement that he 'embellished the grounds by planting fine pines etc'. This is niggardly. Stewart laid out the extensive grounds at Murthly in sweeping drives and stately avenues, to be shaded in the course of time by noble trees. He was fond of parallel terraces, seven of which marched side by side down towards the Tay, including a great series of Douglas firs planted around 1850. Within thirty years some had already reached a height of seventy feet. In 1945 the national timber shortage led to the felling of every second fir tree, but even so they are still impressive. An even more exotic look was imparted by the double line of monkey puzzles called the Araucaria Avenue leading directly to the new private chapel which Sir William built adjoining the old: 'This avenue is said to be the finest of the kind in the world, and one can readily believe it,' wrote Hunter. We look in vain for it today. It fared worse than the Douglas Avenue in the post-war onslaught and today not even a stump remains. Still standing, however, is the narrow walk of old yew trees between house and chapel by which the present laird returns from prayer. It's a one-way trip, since he goes to his devotions by another route. Traditionally the laird must pass under the yew archway on his way to chapel only in his coffin. There is a Sunk Terrace, a wide grassy swathe formerly bordered by splendid deodar cedars. Those too have disappeared.

Sir William himself was uprooted. The Stewarts were not a happy family. Hunter reports that 'in his latter days he became entangled by a Texan adventurer, to whom he tried to leave the estates'.

He was unsuccessful in this but the family resentment was so strong that his successor disinterred William's remains from the chapel and dumped them in a cave excavated in the embankment at the foot of the Sunk Terrace. The cave can still be found under a screen of hanging ivy but the bones have gone, dug up again by a later laird and magnanimously restored to the vault.

In May 1859 the Oregon Association received a huge batch of Caucasian fir seeds sent from the shores of the Black Sea, a part of the world far from its usual source of supply, for which it paid £50. It was the association's last fling. Four days after receipt and distribution of this consignment the association, long since deprived of the services of its ill-fated last collector, was wound up (though some former associates later sent another Scot, Robert Browne, on an expedition to British Columbia in 1863).

The Oregon Association predeceased its founder by ten years. George Patton continued to combine a burgeoning legal and political career with the obsessive planting of exotic trees. It was reported that 'from time he succeeded to the Cairnies in 1831 he displayed the spirit of an enthusiastic arborist, and spared neither trouble nor expense in securing specimens of the rarer varieties with the view of testing their adaptability to the climate of this country, either as ornamental or forest trees'. At the Cairnies and on his elder brother's estate of Glenalmond, where he had a free hand, he grew 'almost every tree belonging to one or other of the finer varieties of the fir tribe'.

Alas, George. In public life, after a rewarding career at the bar specialising in railway litigation (hence the sobriquet Railway Patton) he became a judge, Conservative MP for Bridgwater, and in 1866 Lord Advocate, the senior law officer in Scotland. Sleaze was to prove his downfall. Allegations of election bribery led to an official inquiry, at which he escaped the humiliation of a personal appearance by deftly appointing himself Lord Justice Clerk, with the judicial title of Lord Glenalmond. It was a futile gesture. Four days after presiding in court at Ayr, his last appearance in wig and robes, he killed himself.

An obituary speculated tactfully: 'How far his brother's recent death, the rash and consequent erroneous public announcement of his own [a journalistic faux pas], and the oblique, but offensive accusations in the course of being made before the Bridgwater Bribery Commission, may have broken in upon the natural timidity of his mind, and overset it, God alone knows. We do not pretend to judge him in his last act.'

On the bank of the River Almond above the Buchanty Spout gorge a necktie and a cut-throat razor were found. The Perth boatman, a man called Malloch, was summoned to drag deep pools below the torrent and in the dark waters he found Patton's body, dressed all in black. His throat was slashed. It was observed that an ash sapling hanging over the gorge was streaked with bloody finger marks. George Patton's last hold on life had been to clutch at a native tree.

The towering Wellingtonia avenue at Benmore Botanic Garden in Argyll. It was planted in 1863.

11

GRANDEES, TALL TREES, GREAT EXPECTATIONS

MULTIPLE MILLIONS of trees were planted by the great landowners of the nineteenth century. James Farquharson planted fourteen million, mainly pines, on his Deeside estate at Invercauld, opposite Balmoral (before it was royal). Nobody, it was said, was able to count the millions planted by Sir James Grant of Grant (known by some as Sir James the Good) in Speyside. He began modestly enough with twenty-eight acres of pine trees around a little place he built on moorland near the Spey river and named Grantown after himself. In time he added a plantation here, another there, until both sides of the Spey were covered in growing forest.

When James the Good died in 1811 there was a cloud over the succession. His eldest son Lewis-Alexander suffered from a gentle madness that left him incapable of handling his affairs. A sad case. Lewis had been called to the English bar and was a coming man in the Westminster parliament. But a taste for loose women led to syphilis and while the treatment (mercury) cured the ailment it addled his brain.[*] It was tacitly arranged that his younger brother Francis should manage the estates in his stead.

Francis responded enthusiastically. Francis had been a military man, MP for Banff and Elgin – he was a Peelite – but once he took over from his brother (acquiring on his brother's death a title as the sixth earl of Seafield) he eagerly embarked on agricultural and other domestic

---

[*] The ministrations of Dr Francis Willis, who had attended the madness of George III, failed to alleviate the condition. Thereafter Lewis whiled away his time amiably playing whist, hare coursing and ambling between family seats.

improvements. He relocated and rebuilt the town of Cullen, then but a single street of thatched cottages fronting an open drain, and gave Portsoy a new harbour. Between taking over the vast Grant estates and his death in 1853 he was said to have had planted precisely 31,686,482 trees, including pine, larch and various hardwoods, over more than eight thousand acres of his lands. For this labour he was awarded the gold medal of the Highland and Agricultural Society.

Francis' son John, the seventh Earl of Seafield, became equally devoted to forestry and farming matters. He had new farm steadings and houses built, reclaimed waste land and bred Highland cattle. At agricultural shows he would appear in full Highland fig, sporting a big curly beard and a feather on his bonnet. Being a stickler for this 'garb of old Gaul' he would make his displeasure known if a tenant attended a show trousered instead of kilted. John, too, was a tireless tree planter. In just one of his projects some 14,000,000 pine trees were planted on the moor at Duthil, near Carrbridge. Bronchitis carried him off in 1881 at the age of sixty-six, and three years later his only son Ian went to an untimely grave, leaving Countess Cathleen, old John's widow, to reign over the spreading Seafield pinewoods.

Yet for all the effort of the planting lairds the results often disappointed. Such records as exist imply that the tree cover of Scotland actually declined in the middle years of the nineteenth century. Too much timber was felled and new woodlands often failed. Neglect was 'strikingly visible' everywhere, according to one report. Mark Anderson wrote that 'few owners if any had a clear conception of the objective they had in view', and that 'large areas were planted with unsuitable species and few planters knew what to do with the plantations they had created'.

New money came on to the scene and coupled with a new approach to forestry helped to reverse the trend. In 1869 the Macphersons of Cluny let out their lands on the south side of Loch Laggan to Sir John Ramsden. Ramsden was a man for trees. He bought Scots pine from Deeside seed and introduced exotic conifers from America on the estate at Ardverikie. He has been credited with liberating the noble fir from its ghetto among the ornamental trees of the pinetum and planting it in great numbers as a forest tree. He built forty miles of road, and put up forty-five miles of deer fence and

Sir John Ramsden, who planted trees on his Ardverikie estate at the rate of a million a year.

thirty-five miles of sheep fence in order to protect his young plantations, and in the course of the next fifteen years he planted at the rate of a million trees a year. It was a huge investment for a tenant but it paid off. There was a compensation clause in the lease and when Cluny died the family couldn't pay for Ramsden's improvements. As a result the estate passed into Ramsden's hands.

On the Cowal Peninsula of Argyll the sugar magnate James Duncan bought up land around Benmore until he had 11,000 acres stretching from the village of Strone in the south to the head of long Loch Eck. He straightened the winding river Eachaig, drained boggy fields and opened up a silver mine above romantic Puck's Glen. He also set up as a man of taste, building a gallery beside Benmore House, where visitors could admire his collection of painting and sculpture. Among his guests was Stanley the African explorer. Above all Duncan became an avid planter. In a dozen years from 1870 he planted 6,500,000 trees over the bare knobbly hills of the area – 'he cloaked the hills in the mantle of conifers', as described in the words of a poster in the tearoom at Benmore, the estate now being an outstation of the Royal Botanic Garden of Edinburgh. As it happens, the most eye-catching trees – a regiment of giant redwoods lining the entrance drive, unmissable from the roadway – are not the sugar magnate's. These huge Wellingtonias were planted in 1863 by a previous incumbent.

In spite of nouveaux riches, the old order still had possession in much of the countryside. Lord Lovat held sway over territories that stretched up the valley from his castle at Beauly, along Strathfarrar to

Benmore in the 1870s, with the bare hill A'Cruach behind – soon to be thickly wooded thanks to the planting landowner, sugar magnate James Duncan. Note the avenue of miniature trees which would mature into the magnificent Wellingtonias pictured on page 130.

the bare mountains, down the Great Glen to Fort Augustus and across the wilderness to Morar. After a misspent youth (his father died when he was seventeen and money went to the boy's head) he settled down to planting trees and tending his forests according to the best modern principles. Meanwhile his friend Sir John Stirling Maxwell was steadily pursuing an obsession on the bleak inhospitable slopes around Loch Ossian, bent on proving that a forest would grow in the most dreadful wilderness, given time, patience, drains, dollops of fertiliser and the right kind of tree.

Stirling Maxwell seems to have been a quiet, modest man. Orphaned at the age of eleven, he was sent to Eton and went on to Cambridge. He owned two estates, at Pollok on the outskirts of Glasgow, and Corrour which extended to more than 50,000 acres of high moorland, swept by winter gales and snowstorms. 'There is no more desolate region in Scotland', wrote his father-in-law Sir Herbert Maxwell, wondering at Johnnie's devotion to the place, where he laboured against the odds to create an alpine garden, indulged his passion for rhododendrons and experimented doggedly with growing trees.

Before the road was made the only access to the shooting lodge at the far end of the loch was by boat. The first lodge was no more than a cottage on the hillside.[*] A new lodge was built close to the water's edge

---

[*] At 1700 feet above sea level the garden was too exposed for the growth of potatoes, 'although rhubarb, a true alpine, flourished'. So we learn from the garden historian AA Tait.

Loch Ossian before Sir John Stirling Maxwell fringed it with trees.

after the railway came in 1894 and much was altered and extended in later years. Its ten bedrooms (not including the servants' quarters) meant that there was ample room for guests. Maxwell was a sportsman, which was part of Ossian's attraction. There are atmospheric photographs of stalkers on the misty heights above the loch – and significantly the hills are bare. Other photographs show the family in the sitting room beside a ponderous stone fireplace decorated with heraldic shields.* A large window gives on to the loch. Shelves stuffed with books indicate Maxwell's literary tastes – what other Highland shooting lodge catered so well for the serious reader?

Maxwell's first trees were planted by the shoreline in 1891 and as time passed he extended the plantations on to higher ground. Much of the soil was acid and peaty and there the trees failed. He was undeterred and continued experimenting. The turning point came when he visited Belgium in 1906 to investigate how they grew trees on heavy peatland there. In the Hertogenwald, a high boggy area east of Verviers, he watched spruce seedlings being planted in lines of upturned turfs dug from the drains and ditches. He came home to Corrour, had his men try out the system, refined it over the next seven years, tried giving the infant trees a boost with a dash of fertiliser, and in the course of time the trees survived the storms and a forest flourished where no forest should. 'The real point of Corrour,' declared his father-in-law, 'was the idealistic creation of a Scottish landscape for the twentieth century.'

* Big hearth, sma' bleeze. Maxwell was stingy with fuel.

The only way to get to Corrour today short of hiring a helicopter is by train, snaking among the bog pools and rocky outcrops of Rannoch Moor. Or you could tramp across the hills. From the station – a High Noon sort of place with two or three buildings and a single line of track – it's a mile or so to the foot of Loch Ossian, a freshwater loch now partly fringed with conifer plantations. Before Stirling Maxwell set to work a century ago its windswept shores were as bare as the surrounding moorland, and only a few hardy native trees struggled to survive.

Corrour halt was built as a private stopping place for the convenience of visiting landowners and their guests and didn't appear on the timetable until many years later. Here Johnnie Maxwell and party would alight for the shooting season, wrapped up well, to be met by pony and trap, or later by motor car, for a journey to the lodge at the far end of the loch.

An ornamental iron gatepost (no gate now) topped with a ball and spike indicates to me that all beyond was Stirling Maxwell's. Rough birch straggles over the hummocky ground – no doubt the original cover on all these slopes. In a cove two gaunt rowans put out their first springtime fingers of leaf.

A mossy path leaves the track and climbs to a grove shaded by stately conifers, a brooding, sun-starved, eerie place. One or two trees brought down by storms lie dead in a ruck of broken branches, and moss-covered stumps show where others have been felled. The survivors are big – a Sitka raised on heavy buttress roots, with speck- les of light piercing its topmost foliage. Some trees have numbered metal labels on their trunks. Nineteen is 'Picea orientalis, oriental spruce, Asia Minor, Armenia, Caucusus'. From the Black Sea to Ossian's loch.

At the top what once was a hand-crafted wooden gate hangs open, broken and askew, and in the mud below it are hoofprints of deer passing through. The little path contours along the open hill, supported here and there by low retaining walls, towards a formal, well-grown plantation and another gate – this one quite a grand affair, with a fleur-de-lys pattern below the handle (which has lost its knob).

Near the head of the loch are overgrown pleasure gardens, a wilderness of trees – spruce and birch – with banks of fat-budded rhododendron among them. Though it's late in May it's too early for most of them to flower at this height and exposure. Stirling Maxwell was a connoisseur of rare rhododendrons; I guess these terraces were

Ronald Crauford Munro-Ferguson – landowner, politician and 'missionary of forestry in Parliament'.

designed to be seen across the water from the lodge windows. High up, I sit where I'm sure Johnnie Maxwell sat, on a bench of split log, grey with age, a viewpoint on the unfolding length of loch.

A small boat is moored at a stone jetty. The house is hidden behind a high wall. Granite crow-stepped out-houses are original, but not the timber holiday chalets. Nearby is a plaque set in a boulder – unveiled, it says, in the presence of the Society of Foresters of Great Britain – dedicated 'to the memory of Sir John Stirling Maxwell, 1866–1956, whose pioneering work on the planting of peat at Corrour led to the successful afforestation of large areas of upland Britain'.

As the nineteenth century drew to its close Ronald Crauford Munro-Ferguson had a twenty-five-year plan for his forests at Raith in Fife and Novar on the Cromarty Firth drawn up by Colonel Frederick Bailey, late of the Royal Engineers and the Indian forestry service and now lecturer in forestry at Edinburgh University. Munro-Ferguson, a Liberal MP and a progressive in the matter of growing trees, was described by Stirling Maxwell as 'the missionary of forestry in Parliament who has steadily practised what he preaches'.[*]

In his introduction to the grand plan Munro-Ferguson regretted that forestry provided such a scant living, wryly illustrating the plight of such a landowner struggling to raise cash by using his woodland as collateral: 'We make our pilgrimage to the family writer [lawyer]

[*] Munro-Ferguson became Governor General of Australia in 1914 and then Secretary for Scotland in Bonar Law's cabinet of 1922, by which time he had been ennobled as Lord Novar.

A case of the wind blowing 'where it list' – woodland near Dunkeld devastated by the great gale of December 1879 which brought down the Tay Bridge. It was recorded that 'many centenarians of great size succumbed to the force of the gale'.

where we may obtain a surprising amount of money upon a parcel of feus, a respectable sum upon a pit, or farm land, something even on a sporting rental; but try to pawn woods for a number of years and the man of business will change the conversation.' Poor forest management (which he saw all around) only exacerbated the many natural hazards to which woodland was subject – 'where man cuts, fire burns, water rots or the wind blows, as each lists. . . the squirrel reigns at the head of the tree and the rabbit at the foot'. The phrases are almost biblical.

Munro-Ferguson knew all about the wind blowing where it list. His corner of Cromarty lay open to the storms blowing across the North Sea. The gale of 1879 which tumbled the Tay Bridge felled many Novar trees and another gale in 1893 caused equal havoc. Instead of wringing his hands he set about selling the fallen timber and planting more trees on a timescale due to end in 1924. Not the wind but a world war was to cause the next upset.

Lord Lovat also had a plan in mind (the *fin de siècle* and early twentieth century was a great age for planting trees on paper). Like Stirling Maxwell and Munro-Ferguson, Lovat was a leading light in the Royal Scottish Arboricultural Society, a prestigious lobby for progressive forestry – more influential, as its members liked to think, than the younger English society. Under the aegis of this august body Lovat and his future son-in-law Captain Archibald Stirling, owner of the Keir estate in Perthshire, undertook to draw up (at their own expense) a detailed plan to serve as a model for a great expansion of forests in Scotland.

Emblem of the Royal Scottish Arboricultural Society, a driving force for afforestation after the lean years. Modernised as the Royal Scottish Forestry Society, the organisation retains the old-fashioned pine-tree logo and the motto 'Ye may be aye sticking in a tree.'

Where to start? Where better than on home ground? Lovat had long surveyed his native hills and imagined them richly wooded. Looking for a suitable slice of country he and Stirling hit on the Great Glen – Glen Mor as they preferred to call it – a significant part of which was Lovat territory.

The Great Glen bisects the Highlands on the line of a geological fault. For fifty miles it cuts a diagonal trench between Fort William and Inverness, dividing the northern Highlands from the Grampian plateau. Loch Ness and two lesser lochs lie in line ahead on the valley floor, linked by the Caledonian Canal.

It was well served by transport. The canal allowed sea-going vessels to travel coast to coast between the Atlantic and the North Sea. A stretch of almost thirty miles was served by rail. A recently constructed (and now demolished) railway spur from Spean Bridge linked the western half of the glen to the Caledonian Railway main line, giving direct access to Fort William and thus to Glasgow and the Clyde.

Diversity of climate, soil, terrain and land use added to the appeal of the Great Glen – making it virtually a micrcocosm of the Highland region. And the land was cheap. Lovat and Stirling calculated that the lot could be leased for an average of two shillings and threepence-halfpenny an acre. Yet, as they pointed out, it contained 'some of the best larch ground in Scotland'. They had this on good authority. The late Professor Mayr of Munich, no less (one of the fashionable German scientific foresters), had declared it to be the best planting ground in all Europe.

Nowadays the Great Glen is wooded, at first glance much as Lovat and Stirling imagined it. Trees shade the roads and clothe the steep slopes on either hand. When Stirling and Lovat looked at it nearly a hundred years ago the landscape was relatively bare.

First the ground had to be surveyed, a task which took from August 1910 (when the guns were out on the moors) until the following January. Friends and neighbours were roped in. The Countess of Seafield lent her woods manager and Mr Munro-Ferguson his head forester at Novar. These two, 'aided by foresters of great local experience', reconnoitred the ground with an eye to the soils, climate and exposure and suggesting what trees should be planted and where. On knolly ground there might be a spread of pine while a wetter slope below should be dedicated to spruce. The final report (with maps) summarised the planting principles. Blocks would be modest in size and no single species would dominate (as Sitka Spruce does today). Larch was favoured with Scots pine and Norway spruce. There would be room for Douglas fir.

With trees would come jobs, for shepherds and stalkers do not fill the glens. Men like Lovat sought to create rural employment and reverse the drift from the land. Jobs would multiply as the trees grew. According to his biographer Lovat constantly aimed to better the lot of the crofter by 'enabling him to extend his holding, improve his home and supplement the income from his land by some subsidiary industry in the off season' (but not, of course, at the expense of the proprietor – there was a limit to Lovat's altruism).

As proof, Lovat and Stirling totted up the jobs required in the Fort Augustus area in the first twenty-five or thirty years of the new forest: a head forester plus three assistants; thirty planters and six boy helpers; ten woodcutters; three rabbit trappers; seven men to patrol the woods, kill foxes, stoats and crows and other creatures classed as vermin, and to keep a lookout for fires; three fence builders and menders; also an unspecified number of part-timers – mainly women and boys – employed in the tree nursery. More would be needed as the trees reached felling age.

Since much forestry work was seasonal, labourers and their families would have time to tend smallholdings, and it was hoped that the prospect of steady winter work in the woods might lure ambitious

Forest workers with axe and crosscut saw, the traditional tools of their trade throughout the nineteenth century and beyond.

able-bodied men back to the land. 'The five-acre croft, which of itself cannot maintain a family, constitutes an attractive home if outside labour is assured in the neighbourhood.'

Thus, guaranteed work for men and some for women and children. Families would be raised, communities flourish. There would be new homes, shops, schools and village halls. By the time the whole of the Great Glen had been planted – by, say, the 1950s – six hundred families, more than two thousand people in all who depended on forestry, would live and work in an area inhabited by only a fraction of that number as Lovat and Stirling penned their report. Life would return to empty glens. This alluring vision, applied country-wide, continued to be held for three-quarters of a century, all through the triumphal years of the Forestry Commission until the advent of new machinery, new silvicultural ideas, new harvesting techniques and abrasive politicians killed it.

Lovat and Stirling's call for an over-arching forest authority, free of government control but answerable to parliament and financed by fixed grant, was a harbinger of things to come. In some ways it foreshadowed the Forestry Commission called into being after the Great War. If it meant some intervention in the way landowners ran their woodlands, so be it. It worked in Europe – why not in Scotland?

The plan was drafted in Archibald Stirling's house at Keir, where a guest was amused to see Stirling and Lovat, along with Colonel Bailey, the retired Indian forester and editor of the arboricultural society's journal, wrestling over the wording. He recounted that Lovat produced purple prose which Stirling rigorously pruned, dismissing it as 'that *Daily Mail* stuff'. On publication in 1911 the report filled a special edition of the arboricultural society's journal, preceded by an editorial calling urgently for a country-wide survey similar to that of the Fort Augustus area. It was the duty of the government to instigate this at once, and planting should begin as soon as suitable areas had been identified. 'There will be a great waste of time and public money if the survey and the first comparatively simple stages of afforestation are delayed,' the editorialist declared. In vain – for the moment. The plan was read and shelved.

12

THE ARBORISTS' OUTING

WAVERLEY STATION at first light on a summer morning. Boarding
special carriages attached to the 4.28am train for Perth is a motley
group of men, both whiskered and clean-shaven, dressed in tweeds and
some wearing knickerbockers, stout stockings and boots, watch chains
looped over paunched waistcoats, coats and capes at hand in case of
inclement weather. A whistle blast, a wave of the green flag, a billow of
steam and the train departs; great excitement as it rumbles over the
Forth on the girders of the great new bridge. At 5.33am on the dot they
reach Perth for breakfast at the Station Hotel. Already the sun is
shining, a propitious start. The arborists are agog. The 1894 annual
expedition of the Royal Scottish Arboricultural Society is under way.

That year it took them north. En route they crowded the
windows on the left-hand side of the train to admire the fine Douglas
fir plantations established at Scone by the late Mr McCorquodale, a
man well known to many of them. Shortly afterwards, at Birnam and
Dunkeld, they entered larch country. 'Immense plantations reared their
head on every side,' and at the next stations larch logs were seen stacked
in huge piles awaiting transportation. At last they reached Aviemore
village (no sports shops, diners and ski hotels then). Here they alighted,
to be welcomed by Mr Grant Thomson, wood manager to the Countess
of Seafield, before being trundled away in a convoy of horse carriages.

Mr Grant Thomson had sketched out an itinerary for the day:
10am, Loch an Eilein, ruined castle, osprey's nest, echo, fine scenery,
old Scots firs; 12.30am, entrance to Glenmore forest, Glenmore Lodge,
picturesque loch in midst of forest, and so on – a full day until they
were due at 8pm to board their train again at a point further up the

(now dismantled) line. Light refreshments were served at Inverdrurie school – a school no more but the information office for Rothiemurchus estate – and the drive resumed through enchanting forests of Scots pine 'diversified here and there by glades of enticing beauty'. At Loch an Eilein they strolled amid pines and birches, observing that the slopes of the mountainside opposite were thickly studded with large and venerable holly trees. Even more exciting was a clear sight of a hen osprey perched on the ruined castle on the lochan's islet. It was the only site in the country where ospreys still nested but the anonymous writer of the excursion report was confident that the bird sat 'in perfect security in her rudely constructed nest, beyond the reach of all prowling enemies'. He was too sanguine. Five years later the nest was robbed and ospreys abandoned Scotland for the next half century.

Giddy-up again. The excursionists returned to Coylum Bridge and took the cart track – now superseded by the ski road – to the shooting lodge at Glenmore – a youth hostel now – and the shores of Loch Morlich, from where they viewed Cairngorm and its neighbouring mountains, with snow still visible in the corries of Braeriach. Then it was off on the climb to the Sluggan pass. Numerous tall ant hills, some of them five or six feet high, were seen on the way. At the high point of the road the group clambered from their carriages intending to walk up to the Cobbler's Rock, a craggy eminence above them.[*] Tangled undergrowth soaked by recent rain soon deterred them and they embarked again for the descent. Off went the horses at a fast pace while the coaches lurched uncomfortably close to the edge of a steep fall down to the Milton Burn in the gorge below. It was a palpitating moment for the faint-hearted 'as the carriages swayed to and fro in a rather alarming fashion, threatening each moment to precipitate their occupants to the bottom'.

After the terror the reward, a panoramic view of the Spey valley extending to the Monadhliath Mountains on the horizon. Loch Morlich peeped through trees. In the foreground rose a hill whose slopes had been afforested a quarter of a century earlier by the seventh Earl of Seafield – 11,000 acres covered by nine million new trees planted among surviving old Caledonian pines.

---

[*] Gaelicised by the Ordnance Survey as Creag a'Ghreusaiche, which means the same thing. It is now topped by a tall communications mast.

Excursionists and hosts (including ladies) assembled at Christie's nursery in Fochabers, where they admired Mr Christie's 'many rare and choice exotics'.

At the entrance to Abernethy forest they passed under a flag-bedecked archway of native evergreens (a piper playing popular airs) and on the shores of Loch Morlich they sat down in the shade of old pines to an alfresco luncheon provided by the Countess of Seafield. Here was drunk the health of the Queen, the Prince and Princess of Wales and other members of the royal family, and success to the Royal Scottish Arboricultural Society.

Lunch and speeches over, the drive continued among elderly pine trees that became increasingly fine until at Torehill 'Nature seemed to have outlavished herself'. The arborists stretched their legs by ascending the hill where in spite of a wrecking storm twenty years before and an earlier devastating fire – evidence of which was still visible in a layer of charcoal and burnt soil – young trees were growing sturdily and some juniper shrubs reached a height of twenty feet. Tapes and 'various instruments of measurement' had been much in use throughout the day. A pine 'with the habit of an oak' was found to girth twenty feet at its base and nearly fourteen feet at chest height. Another pine 'in shape curiously similar to a Prince of Wales' feather', reached a height of seventy feet.

Another beflagged arch to pass under at the Dell close to 'the pretty rural village of Nethy Bridge, fast becoming a favourite resort for health seekers' where all were invited to choose a pine seedling potted at the nursery as a memento of their visit. And then by train across bleak Dava Moor (no railway crosses it now) via Forres, 'a Montpellier of the north', arriving at Elgin in the dark just before eleven o' clock for accommodation in various hotels and a good night's sleep.

But no long lie. 'The members were early astir and left Elgin by train at 7.35am.' At Fochabers they breakfasted at the Gordon Arms. Gordon was the big name in these parts; the Duke of Richmond and Gordon (the same who owned Glenmore) was to be their host for the day. After breakfast a visit to Mr Christie's tree nurseries – a hundred years later Christie's of Fochabers is still in business – and his 'many rare and choice exotics growing with a rich luxuriance'; a photographer recorded the scene. Next on to Cullen Wood, whence vistas to Gordon Castle and its gardens, Fochabers rooftops embowered in foliage, and the Moray Firth; 'grand ancestral trees of the stateliest dimensions'; Cotton Hill whose summit was topped by a picturesque summer house and, in a grassy hollow below, many fine specimens of park trees – gigantic spruce, silver firs and larches; an old freestone quarry transformed by the duchess into a tiered garden with ornamental trees and shrubs. Here a heavy shower came on but 'a neat tea-house' gave shelter. The shower became a downpour and the party proceeded 'at a sharp pace' to luncheon provided by his grace the duke, punctuated by the usual toasts to the Queen and royals, the duke, and the duke's helpers.

An early train back to Elgin for the society's annual dinner at the Gordon Arms (overflow at the Palace Hotel); loyal and patriotic toasts – 'a pleasant evening was spent'.

Train at 6.40am to Cullen. Breakfast at the Seafield Arms – where else? This is Seafield country again – followed by a lengthy drive, with Cullen's forester Mr Michie and gardener Mr Smith seated in the leading carriage, in themselves 'a veritable encyclopaedia of arboreal lore'. Through an avenue where sixty-year-old elms, limes, horse chestnuts, purple beeches and ash trees mingled in a canopy, to the village of Lintmill, 'quite the *beau idéal* of a rural village' with its neat flower and vegetable patches, its cottage walls clothed with roses, clematis and other pretty climbers, and for good measure a display of flags and sprays of evergreen. Estate workers and their families living in this paradise turned out to cheer. Another 'lusty cheer' (returned by the arborists) rang out from the thirty workers at the estate sawmill. Past the pinetum – Douglas and other firs, Menzies (i.e. Sitka) spruce, cedars, Lawson cypress, Wellingtonia etc. – to the Low Glen with its Norway spruce dipping pendulous boughs in the burn at their base, the High Glen, the Grand View Drive and the five-mile length of the

Workers at the tree nursery, Fochabers, in the late nineteenth century.
Men such as these turned out to cheer the visiting arborists on their way.

Rannas Drive. In the fruit garden figs ripened in the open on the walls, and near the mansion house a large monkey puzzle blown down in the winter's gale had been propped up again and seemed to be thriving.

From a hilltop the Laigh of Moray golden with grain – an early harvest in prospect – came into view but by now the rain was incessant and woods had to be left unexplored because of the deluge. Shelter and refreshments were found in a roofed part of the semi-ruined Pluscarden Priory, with an interlude in the chapter house where Mr James Kay of Rothesay led a rendition of the 'Old Hundredth' Psalm: seventy male voices in chorus singing to the Lord with cheerful voice.

On the fourth and last day the arborists made their usual early start, on the 6.15am train heading for Grantown and a last look at Seafield country, this time in the woods around Grant Castle, seat of the countess. Once again Mr Grant Thomson met them with his string of carriages. Sweeping views of Strathspey and its dark pine forests were visible (the sun having returned) from the top of Ballieward Hill, but it was a stand of young larch that caught their eye, chance growth sprung from seed fallen randomly on the ground. Some fifteen years growing, the trees covered the ground 'as regularly as if hand-planted'. On the opposite side of the road the same message was repeated, where both naturally-sown larches and Scots pine mingled amid a thin spread of older trees. Almost everywhere they looked on this day – and indeed throughout the whole tour – there was abundant natural growth, trees springing up of their own accord and thriving on receptive soil. What the writer saw caused him to suggest that 'the exotic larch may be said

The old pine tree called 'Peter Porter' admired by the more energetic excursionists (who climbed a heathery hill in the heat of the sun to view it).

to be now completely naturalised in these woods' – an eclecticism not universally favoured a century later.

There were more trees to be observed and measured, and a drive back to Grantown past the golf course 'where keen players, both male and female, were busily displaying their deftness with the clubs and trying their best to win a hole'. Near Mr Grant Thomson's residence and the offices of the wood manager's department more employees turned out to cheer the excursionists on their way.

Lunch was taken early, with much still to be seen. On Curr Hill, cleared of its mature timber twenty-five years before, they saw abundant new growth of pine and larch, a 'fine example of a self-reproduced wood which afforded them an object lesson worthy of careful study'. Onwards. They crossed the Spey by a rumbling wooden bridge due to be replaced; construction had already started alongside. Here they learned that the old bridge built of untreated native timber from Abernethy forest showed little sign of decay after almost thirty years, and were aghast to hear that its replacement would be made of creosoted timber from abroad – 'somewhat out of place in the midst of plenty of native timber close at hand'. Dinner was taken early, hall and tables decked with fir and heather, last healths were drunk. Members were informed that their colleague Colonel Bailey, lecturer in forestry at Edinburgh, who had recently been badly hurt in a railway accident at Newtonmore, twenty miles or so down the line, had been visited at his sick bed and was progressing well.

At Grantown station the arborists boarded a special non-stop for Perth, and at half-past ten they reached Waverley where they dispersed, each clutching his gift of potted pine.

Timber squad at work in the woods near Crawfordjohn in the 1890s.
Women and girls had a traditional role in forestry work.

13

EYES ACROSS THE OCEAN

W HEN THEY were greeted by John Grant Thomson on the platform at Aviemore station the arborists were meeting a man important in the affairs of the Seafield estates. Huge forest areas in the northeast of Scotland were under his charge. Such men as he guided the hand of their planting masters (or mistress in the case of Seafield) – a long line of capable men stretching down through the years, whether dignified as wood managers, foresters or merely gardeners – as they often were in the early eighteenth century when their role was less specific.[*] Often they were literate as well as practical men. Thomson's predecessor as wood manager on the Grant estates was James Brown, author of *The Forester*, a standard text for most of the later nineteenth century. Brown had a doctorate. He and contemporaries like William Gilchrist, forester at Cluny Castle in Aberdeenshire, or Thomas Wilkie, forester at Tyninghame in East Lothian, contributed to the journals, giving readers the benefit of their own experience. Daniel Dewar, the Lovat forester at Beaufort, was both a practical man and a diligent student of forest literature. His reading went far beyond the texts of his trade. Ranked beside the forestry books on his shelves were works by Matthew Arnold, Adam Smith, Darwin, Huxley, the historian Froude and 'many in lighter vein'. He could quote accurately and at length from his favourite poets.

---

[*] And not always adequately rewarded, according to Thomas Boutcher the nurseryman of Comely Bank, Edinburgh, who grumbled in 1775 that 'a great man bestows from £50 to £100 a year on a French cook; for a British gardener, seldom more than from twenty to forty'.

'Scientific forestry' as practised in continental and imperial forests much impressed late Victorian woodland owners – an interest heightened by the great International Forestry Exhibition of 1884 held in the grounds of Donaldson's Hospital, Edinburgh.

It's not surprising that many long-serving foresters came to be treated by their employers as friends, if not equals. Daniel Dewar was said to have been as much a friend of successive Lovats – three generations of them – as their trusted servant. Sir Walter Scott, always a generous spirit, treated his blunt 'wood-forester' Tom Purdie with warmth and affection. Purdie had joined Scott on his farm at Ashestiel in 1804 and continued in his service until his death at Abbotsford twenty-five years later. Scott would walk round the woodlands amicably chatting with Purdie, 'who carries my plaid and speaks when he pleases'.

When old Daniel Dewar died after a lifetime of service at Beaufort his obituarist noted approvingly that he had been one of the first to adopt German methods of growing forest trees. German ways, and French too, were all the rage. Progressive foresters beat a path to source. James Michie, Queen Victoria's forester at Balmoral, reported glowingly on a visit to Thuringia in central Germany. Others described what they saw in Prussia and in the Basses Pyrénées. Colonel Bailey spent time in the Belgian Ardennes where he toured the wooded estate of Mirwart owned by the illustrious Dr William Schlich, a man erudite in the ways of managing woods.

It was equally enlightening to learn what foreigners thought of Scottish methods. Usually they were critical, though there were exceptions. Lucien Boppé, professor of forestry at Nancy, made a

James Brown, practical woodman and learned author of
The Forester.

whistle-stop tour through Perthshire, the Cairngorms and northeast
Scotland in the 1880s. Accustomed to the balanced variety of the old-
established forests in his native France, he was disappointed by the
monotony of the plantations he saw on either hand in Scotland,
composed as so frequently they were of trees all of an age and all of one
species (the same criticism would be levelled at the much larger
Forestry Commission plantations in the following century). It pained
him that clear-felling seemed to be the rule when trees were harvested,
and so little attempt was made to husband the woodlands more
sensibly: 'When a gust of radical exploitation or that of the tempest
happens to pass over a block it disappears with no bond between the
forest of the past and that to be reconstituted for the future.'

This struck him forcibly when, glowing with pleasure at the
reception he had received at some castle on the way, he came upon the
wreckage of what had once been a great forest. 'Twenty years earlier the
forest had been entirely converted into railway sleepers; today nothing
of it remains but the bare roots which bestrew the soil giving it the
appearance of an immense charnel house. What a heart-rending
spectacle of the forest in ruins.' This lament, too, has a modern ring
about it.

It was not only the clear-felling regime adopted by Scottish
woodland owners that distressed the continentals. Schlich, who had
settled in England, explained in his multi-volume *Manual of Forestry*
that 'Conifers generally grow too quickly in Britain because the woods
are too heavily thinned when young; hence the individual trees

increase too rapidly and produce timber inferior to that of the same species imported from the Baltic, and grown in crowded woods.' Crowded woods were the thing. Trees densely packed would grow tall and straight, shorn of troublesome side branches without the need of a pruning knife, and reaching for the sky with their foliage reduced to a topknot. This is not what orthodox Scottish foresters aimed at. They thinned early and often, taking out surplus trees in stages so that the best stems left in place would thicken fast and produce timber quickly.

It did not please Dr Adam Schwappach, professor of forestry at Eberswalde in Prussia, who sailed up Loch Lomond in August 1893 and made a swift tour of various woodlands. He, too, thought that Scottish woodlands were over-thinned and 'too much managed like trees in a park'. Such trees 'might beautify a landscape or please an artist' but would give a poor return when felled and sold. Profit mattered more than pleasure.

But Schwappach gave praise where it was due. When he sailed from Leith for Hamburg he could reflect in his cabin on finding at least one example of sound practice: 'The most extensive as well as the most scientific system of forestry according to German notions was met with in the large pine forests belonging to the Countess of Seafield.' Here he was pleased to find the Seafield pinewoods seeding themselves profusely and young forests growing up around the old. This reminded him of the agreeable facility of French and German woodlands – aided by shrewd management – to reproduce themselves. Even on Seafield ground all was not as it might have been, for the cover was often patchy. Dense clumps alternated with more open ground with scattered trees which developed the bushy form he condemned.

The best that he saw was at Curr Wood to the south of Grantown, a wood that would also attract the arborists on their tour. Seed trees left when the slopes of a small hill above the Spey had been felled for estate use had been prolific and within two or three years the next generation was emerging thickly on the ground. Forty thousand small trees per acre were counted and within fifteen years the growth was so dense that a man might not force his way through. The arborists had found 'a fine crop of larch and Scots pine, the latter predominating. In the whole wood there was very little space seen entirely bare of seedlings'. Schwappach, following in their footsteps a year later, remarked with some surprise that even in Germany such density could not have been achieved without filling in the gaps by hand. Lucien Boppé had been equally impressed by such examples, which indicated (to his eye) that the forests of Scotland might easily be regenerated 'by natural means alone'.

Perhaps they were too optimistic. The dry climate and loose morainic soils of the Strathspey glens encourages rich regeneration. Elsewhere in Scotland chill, wet and boggy soils are less receptive. And in the windy regions of the west close-grown trees with their spindly shanks, shallow roots and tufted tops can blow down like a pack of cards once a gap is opened. Furthermore, the Europeans inherited forests which had been carefully tended for centuries, whereas Scottish foresters were starting virtually from scratch. Having paid to establish his forest, a landowner wanted to get his return swiftly. The temptation to clear the lot once the timber reached marketable size was great. Textbook 'German methods' were all very well, but there were drawbacks.

The doyen of wood managers in the later years of the nineteenth century was William McCorquodale – 'the late Mr McCorquodale' – whose Douglas fir plantings at Scone had been admired from the train windows by the arborist excursionists. McCorquodale had been taken on as a lad at the Duke of Montrose's home farm at Buchanan in 1827, after which he became one of the first forest pupils to be given five years' training on the Montrose estates. This included attendance at classes over winter at the Edinburgh Botanic Garden and a spell at tree nurseries in the same city. Sixty years after starting work at Buchanan, McCorquodale, by then long established as wood manager for the Earl of Mansefield at Scone, reflected kindly on his first employer. Montrose – 'himself an enthusiastic forester' – evidently encouraged his protégés to seek advancement even if it meant leaving his own service. 'Young intelligent men belonging to the district, with fair education, after acquiring a pretty good knowledge of their business, obtained positions as foresters chiefly through the influence of the duke.'

McCorquodale was lucky. He had been born in the right place. Other promising lads may not have been so fortunate in their employment at a time when forestry was a tight little insular profession. Times had changed by the end of the century when organised groups like the

Stand of the Royal Scottish Arboricultural Society at the International Forestry Exhibition.

arborists of 1894 were able to compare practice in different woodland settings, but when McCorquodale was young foresters had little opportunity to do so. No up-to-date texts were available in the 1830s and 'the few old books on forestry were hardly worth perusing'. And while 'a new era is happily dawning', it irked McCorquodale that there was still no specialist education available to aspiring foresters at home. If they wanted a structured training they had to go abroad.

The science of the new British forestry was born in France, Germany and in the heat and dust of India. As early as 1850 the British Association, meeting in Edinburgh, had been concerned by reports that the forests of India were disappearing fast (reckless deforestation isn't new). With the extension of British power after the mutiny an Indian forest service was established in order to sustain these threatened forests and manage them sensibly. Early inspectors-general of the service were recruited from continental Europe and were steeped in the doctrines of scientific forestry current there. Dietrich Brandis, who hailed from Bonn, was knighted for his services to the British Empire. His successor was a fellow German, William Schlich – a man who was to exercise great influence on British forestry and who would become a naturalised Briton. He, too, was knighted. Schlich in turn was followed in the Indian service by a Herr Ribbentrop from Hanover.

An Indian forest school was established in 1878 at Dehra Dun in the still thickly wooded foothills of the Himalayas. To Dehra Dun duly flocked young educated men from Britain who were denied the opportunity of pursuing a career in forestry at home (where there were no forests to speak of) and who were eager to accept the challenge of Empire. There they imbibed forestry on the accepted European principles under the directorship of Frederick Bailey.

India was the place. When McCorquodale regretted the lack of a forest school at home he was not thinking of its potential benefit to forestry in Scotland. 'If a school of forestry were established in Edinburgh in connection with our new arboretum where forest science could be studied,' he wrote, 'it would be uneccessary to send forest pupils to France and Germany to be trained for the Indian service.' Apparently McCorquodale believed that if a smart lad wanted to get to the top in Scottish woodlands, all he needed was the sort of hands-on training he himself had received supplemented by a regime of self-education. When Schlich was persuaded to leave Dehra Dun to start Britain's first forest school at Cooper's Hill in Surrey the aim was the same. Cooper's Hill graduates were destined for the imperial service.

But in Scotland a movement was gathering momentum to put forestry on a proper footing, which included provision for thorough professional training. The Royal Scottish Arboricultural Society, always in the forefront, offered £400 to establish a chair of forestry at a Scottish university. The chair did not immediately materialise but a lectureship in forestry was created at Edinburgh and Colonel Bailey, back from Dehra Dun, was head-hunted for the post. When the course was later expanded he was duly appointed professor.

Distinguished foreign foresters added weight to the argument that a school of forestry should be founded in Scotland in a district with access to substantial woodland where theory could be combined with practice. It was pointed out that schools in France and Germany were set in the midst of local woodland. For example, demonstration forests covering thousands of acres were available within a few miles of the French École Nationale des Eaux et Forêts at Nancy. Something had to be done.

It so happened that Lord Lovat and Sir John Stirling Maxwell had just such a place in mind for a native forestry school. It was at Ballogie in Aberdeenshire, where extensive plantations were stocked with trees of all ages and all practical forestry operations could be carried out from planting seedlings to the final felling. Ballogie was on the market and could be theirs.

But bureaucracy blew cool on the project. A development commission, set up recently by the Government with money to spend on such things as Lovat and Stirling Maxwell had in mind, decided that Deeside was too far from populous central Scotland and that something closer should be found. Whereupon in stepped the Marquis of Tullibardine, heir to the Duke of Atholl, offering the commissioners an alternative on his Perthshire estates.

Lovat and Stirling Maxwell were not amused when they got wind of his intervention. Letters addressed familiarly to 'Dear Bardie' were crisp in tone. Skirmishing continued between spring 1913 and the summer of 1914. Phone calls were made – 'Maxwell and Lovat have been ringing me up for some days wishing to see me,' Bardie complained. Meetings were arranged over the dinner table.

Tullibardine prevailed but his victory was Pyrrhic. It was agreed with the commissioners that part of the Atholl estates would become a demonstration area 'for the practical application and development of the science of forestry'. Terms were agreed and a contract made by which four thousand acres around Loch Ordie were to be leased for 150 years from Martinmas 1915. But even as the ink dried on the document Britain was sliding into war and by Martinmas 1915 all deals were off.

14

THE CRUEL YEARS

IN 1917 His Majesty's Secretary for Scotland Robert Munro travelled from London to his constituency in the far north of Scotland. As his train rolled onwards to Wick he was pleased to see from the carriage window, hurrying past, 'long lines of trucks, and every truck containing wood'. Nevertheless he allowed himself the rueful comment that the bare hillsides through which he was passing had once been thickly forested. Had they not been felled long ago there would have been timber enough to defeat Kaiser Bill.

April was the cruellest month. Three years into the war the U-boat onslaught had reached its height. In April 1917 some 900,000 tons of shipping destined for British ports went to the bottom. The nation was under siege, a situation inconceivable when Britain entered the Great War.

In 1914 the map was still thickly patched with red and the ports of the world were ours. So were the forests. Elephants dragged teak from the jungles of Burma and lumbermen laid the mighty Douglas fir low on Pacific shores, all for the benefit of a small crowded island on the edge of Europe. Trading Britain was hungry for timber and precious little could be had from the woodlands at home. Even when available, home-grown timber was considered inferior.

Who could have thought, in August 1914, that there would be famine? That an enemy blockade would bring the war economy to crisis point? At first the ships got through. Tall-funnelled freighters low in the water, with timber in the hold and decks laden with more, edged through the Panama Canal, ploughed across the Atlantic,

Before the onslaught – an early motorcade of foresters visit the pre-1914 pinewoods of Ballogie. In the looming Great War, trees and woodmen alike would fall.

buffeted their way over the North Sea (which was the German Ocean until patriotism forced a change of name). When the Great War broke out half our supply came from imperial Russia through Archangel and Riga, and most of the rest from Scandinavia, Canada and the United States. The world's greatest merchant fleet sailed under the red duster and much of it carried timber, the bulkiest cargo of all.

But the war needs were insatiable. Steam powered all industry, and the coal mines that fuelled it needed a constant supply of pit props. The shipyards, now under pressure, required huge quantities for scaffolding. Across the Channel the need for timber grew. Huts to house the soldiers. Timbers to shore up the long lines of trenches and dugouts, constantly needing renewal under the barrage, wooden stakes for the barbed-wire barriers in no-man's land. Duckboards to give safe passage over the mud of Flanders. Sleepers for the railway lines and carriageways built to carry supplies and men to the front. Everything from rifle bullets to tanks came packaged in wood. 'Every shell that is fired, every bomb that is dropped and every tin of bully that is eaten will have arrived packed in a timber box or crate' – the words were written during the second World War but they apply equally to the first.

Early random submarine attacks on merchant shipping increased in force until by the first months of 1917, when packs of long-range U-boats ranged the seas at will, all vessels heading to or from these shores faced sudden and unpredictable attack. The passage round southwest Ireland – the route to Liverpool and the Clyde – became, in Winston Churchill's words, the cemetery of British shipping.

Old weathered logs, carried as flotsam by the ocean currents, fetched up on distant shores, the sole survivors of many a sinking.

By the end of 1916 the yearly supply of timber from abroad had dropped by almost half (it would fall to one-fifth of the peacetime total by the final months of the war). The gravity of the crisis was evident. Shortage of shells at the front grabbed the headlines, increasing food shortages pinched stomachs at home (by then the public had been introduced to the delights of 'war bread', grey tasteless stodge), but the timber famine, though unsuspected by the public at large, was equally a threat to survival. From enjoying the pick of the world's forests, Britain now had to turn to her own meagre woodlands to fill the gap.

The government was aware of impending crisis. The first shot was a warning to woodland owners not to fell indiscriminately in the neighbourhood of coal mines, since plenty of pit props would be needed. With the price of timber escalating and a growing demand from the War Office for the small timber needed at the front, it was a necessary caution. But it was not enough. If timber could no longer be shipped in from abroad, home-grown trees must fill the gap. Was there enough? No one knew. A forester reflected that in 1914 'our home-based assets were the nucleus of a forest service, far too small to be effective, a conservatively minded and loosely organised home timber trade, and some three million acres of woods containing no one knew exactly what in the way of trees suitable for conversion to war-time requirements'. A home-grown timber committee soon proved inadequate to ensure sufficient supplies (which had increased only marginally after eighteen months of war) and as Asquith's Liberal government gave way to the more dynamic coalition led by Lloyd George, a War Office Directorate, swiftly followed by the Board of Trade's Timber Control, took over the task. Control it was called and control is what it did. The free market was gone. Home use of timber was rationed, fellings were determined and prices fixed so that owners should not profit from the war. According to Mark Anderson, the woods of Scotland provided far more timber than the rest of the United Kingdom. The onslaught spared neither age-old stands of pine nor the plantations of the previous century, including much woodland that was still immature.

The greatest losses were suffered in Strathspey and on Deeside where the greatest stands of marketable timber grew. Gilbert Brown, woods manager on the Seafield estates, recorded that more than 5000 acres of woodland had been felled, much of it in Abernethy. The great forest of Glenmore was heavily exploited in the last years of the war, as was Rothiemurchus. There were fellings in the woodlands scattered along the Great Glen and the glens leading off it. The woodlands of Drummond Hill at the eastern end of Loch Tay, where Black Duncan had first planted three centuries before, were laid waste apart from a few conifers left standing on the ridge. The politician HJ Scrymgeour Wedderburn, writing shortly before the outbreak of World War Two, recalled that most of the woodland on his own estate had been sacrificed in the previous conflict, leaving him little to do but plant hopefully again. Sentiment played little part. The writer and stravaiger Seton Gordon told how the site of a hut where Locheil had hidden after Culloden had been marked by willow trees until, when the woods above it were felled in the Great War, 'these guiding trees were cut down also'.

Sir John Stirling Maxwell was blunt. 'If the war continues for a year,' he told Secretary Munro, 'and still more, if it continues for two years [which at that time seemed very likely] the woods of Scotland will have been very largely swept away.' (And he would know. As chairman of the Control Committee in Scotland he was overseeing their destruction.) Some of those woods were saved only in the nick of time. The axemen were about to move into the Black Wood of Rannoch when the guns fell silent and the felling order was rescinded. Elsewhere the woods recovered as best they could. In some cases, especially where abundant seed fell on receptive ground, the damage might be repaired. Henry Alexander, who as a journalist had witnessed the wartime loggers in full cry in Strathspey, found it possible to write ten years later that in parts of Abernethy 'the effect is scarcely noticeable and one can wander for miles through magnificent forest'. Other areas were less lucky. And in the next Armageddon the fellers returned with a vengeance.

An unexpected flowering briefly mantled the devastated timber fields. In the wide acres where woodland had been felled and, often, the debris had burned by accident or design, a strange and joyful

Sir John Stirling Maxwell transformed the wilderness slopes around Loch Ossian with woodland and later became planter in chief of state forests. A modest, kindly man – virtues brought out in this 1917 portrait by William Strang.

phenomenon was observed. Acres of ground were invaded by rosebay willowherb, making the last days of war glorious. Poppies grew in Flanders fields; rosebay – fireweed by another name – flamed in the lost woodlands at home.

Many able-bodied estate woodmen volunteered for the trenches and more followed when conscription came. There were trees to cut but few men left to fell them. It dawned on the authorities that a useful pool of labour existed in the prisoner of war camps. Enemy soldiers captured in the killing fields of Belgium and shipped to this country for safe keeping could be armed with axe and saw and set to work in the woods. At first the censor tried to keep this activity hidden but it soon got about. People in the neighbourhood of Nethy Bridge, where there was a prison camp, saw squads of PoWs marching from their huts into the Seafield pinewoods. Others camped in the same neighbourhood at Inverlaidnam worked the woods west of Carrbridge.

As word got about in forestry circles it seemed to some that this use of forced labour might be cheap and profitable as well as patriotic. The Atholl factor cast envious eyes northwards and in July 1916 wrote to tell his duke in London that Lord Lovat was 'getting 120 German prisoners to cut his timber' beyond the Great Glen. He 'knew for a fact' that accommodation was being prepared for them. 'No one will grudge Lord Lovat his cheap labour,' he wrote (I hear the gritting of his teeth) 'but I hope it is intended to give every large proprietor equally reasonable facilities.'

At a railhead deep in some unidentified Highland pinewood (the place name censored, no doubt), men of the Canadian Forestry Corps rest from labour. The next consignment of logs lies ready for loading.

The war of the woods could not be won by captives alone. More manpower was urgently needed. Perhaps we could draw on Empire? Early in 1916 the colonial secretary Andrew Bonar Law cabled the Governor General of Canada to suggest the formation of a battalion of lumbermen – some 1500 men – to succour the motherland in her distress: 'Fellers, haulers and sawyers are urgently needed.' Canada responded faithfully, and swiftly. So did the offshore island territory of Newfoundland (still a separate entity; it did not join the Canadian federation until after World War Two). By the spring of 1916 the first battalion of the newly formed Canadian Forestry Corps had sailed for Britain, and it was soon to be followed by others.

When he was small William McGregor saw Canadian loggers arrive at the village of Kilkerran in south Ayrshire and eighty years later remembered their activities clearly. He watched them put up sectional huts in the field across from the one-teacher school, then a sawmill and a YMCA building, round which they made gravel roads from material excavated at the Burning Hill, where spoil from old exhausted mine workings still smouldered. He saw a team of horses drag the sawmill's boiler from the station, and when felling got under way observed the strange horse-drawn timber wagons – long, skeletal vehicles quite unlike the farm carts on Kilkerran estate, with a pair of rear wheels which slid back to accommodate the longer logs. He watched empty bogies being winched up tramway lines to the woods and then come jolting down laden with timber, and elsewhere logs rocketing down a timber chute to the roadside to be loaded on wagons and carted to the station.

The men of 110 Company of the Forestry Corps set up camp at the Sluggan late in 1916. The Sluggan is a narrow, steep, tree-covered pass on the edge of Glenmore forest, through which ran, at that time, the narrow road from Aviemore to Glenmore Lodge, the Duke of Gordon's shooting lodge beside Loch Morlich. It still exists as a rough forest road, traversed today mainly by walkers and mountain bikers, having been superseded as a traffic route by the new road to the ski slopes built in the 1960s. By May 1917 the Sluggan was 'in full go' – the timber was fast being felled and extracted, a tramway had been built to carry it out, and a sawmill was operating non-stop. The job was done swiftly. By the autumn of that year 50,000 trees had been cut down, the slopes were bare and the Canadians were moving on.

The woods of Strathspey were – and still are – extensive and much wartime activity took place there. The Canadians of 121 Company were based in Glenmore. Their territory covered a great sweep from the western end of Loch Morlich almost as far as An Lochan Uaine, the Green Loch in the narrow pass of Ryvoan, rising ground where an earlier crop of trees had been harvested a century and a half before. Unlike other areas which the Canadians clear-felled, the attack here was to some extent selective, due to the concern of the Duke of Gordon that the beauty of his glen should not be utterly despoiled and that sufficient trees should be left to produce seed for new growth when peace came. So they took out the best timber trees and left a good sprinkling of crooked, stunted or bushy specimens of the kind we now prize as true types of the Old Caledonian race. (The new Forestry Commission to whom the duke sold Glenmore shortly after the war was less concerned to preserve them and swamped the old trees with alien species.)

Having to pick and choose among the trees gave the Canadians trouble, but it was nothing compared to the difficulties caused by the terrain and the weather. Some of the ground was desperately steep and tracts around the Loch Morlich basin were swampy. The journalist Henry Alexander described the scene when he arrived on an official visit in 1917. The summer had been wet and he reached Glenmore just as the first storm of winter struck. The dome of Cairn Gorm was white

As pelting rain turns peaty ground to a quagmire, Canadian foresters man a donkey engine in the Highlands, dragging logs from the hillside.

with snow and fierce winds swept sleet and rain down the glen. 'Where logs were hauled the surface vegetation of heather and moss was churned up with the peat below it into a perfect slough. Horses and men were sinking, staggering and slithering as they dragged trees down the slopes.' The Canadians cursed the inhospitable weather and fate which had posted them to this miserable land. Is it surprising that seasoned lumberjacks accustomed to the Canadian wilderness should rail at the harshness of the Scottish weather? But by this time the Forestry Corps had been diluted, their ranks swollen by men disabled in the trenches or otherwise considered unfit for the front.

When the weather relented Alexander could find romance in the scene. There was a sense of fitness about it. In his eyes, the Canadian camp at Nethy, 'a charming site in the midst of the forest', had the picturesque appeal of the backwoods. It stood on an island of green turf, where old maps showed a building called Racoig, long since demolished. Everything was constructed with timber cut in the forest and the officers' quarters, admin buildings and stores were particularly rustic, clad as they were in 'backs' (outside planks with the bark left on) in the style of log cabins. Other ranks made do with huts lined in felt. The gangways between buildings were neatly outlined with white paint and the Union Jack fluttered on the flagstaff.

Nethy was a showpiece, but Alexander was also impressed by the camp at Glenmore, a 'lake-in-the-woods looking place' as he called it. It was built just beyond the loch, not far from the gabled Glenmore Lodge. Officers occupied the higher ground on a knoll. Below it the

Such a Canadian lumber camp in the Scottish Highlands appealed to a visiting journalist as a 'lake in the woods sort of place'.

rest of the camp formed a square with a sawmill on one side, office and stores on another, the YMCA on the third and the Finns' quarters on the fourth.

These so-called Finns were a polyglot squad of fifty or so foreigners who shared quarters uneasily with the Canadians – 'half a hundred Russians, Norwegians, Greeks and what not' – all being merchant seamen from ships stranded in British ports or rescued at sea and drafted into the forest service to give them something useful to do. There didn't seem to be any Finnish sailors among them when Alexander visited, but the name had stuck. They were an unruly lot. The day before Alexander arrived a Greek seaman knifed a camp mate for calling him a German.

If drink had inflamed the quarrel it wasn't bought on site, for the YMCA, like all canteens in the Canadian camps, was dry. Prohibition ruled. But there were other comforts. Apart from serving food and soft drinks the YMCA offered a sitting room, a piano for sing-songs, and a library. The sergeant in charge was a divinity student – hopefully a sufficiently muscular Christian to handle rough customers. Pigs were kept outside in a makeshift pen and the food scraps went into their trough.

Glenmore camp was home to two hundred men. They worked in the din of the sawmill, they crowded into the mess hall at night to wolf down meals after the day's heavy work in the open air, and every morning there was the clamour of men setting out for the felling slopes and the neighing and snorting of horses being led out to haul in the timber they cut. All this in the isolation of the woods, for eighty years ago Glenmore was a backwater, not the frequented place it is now. But at night their camp was bright with electric light, a facility rare in the countryside around, where most habitations were still lit by oil lamps. Once the mill shut down after the day's work the drone and whine of its saws gave way to a constant chuff-chuff as the steam dynamo provided power until lights out at ten o'clock, when silence fell and 'dark pines stand guard over the camp'.

> *Dark pines have encroached on the ground, all but obliterating traces of the past. A new forest grew. All that remains of the camp site now are hollows in the black peaty earth where the huts stood and, in deep shade, two mossed concrete blocks like sarcophagi, sole remains of the sawmill. One shows the imprint of brick cladding, since stripped away, and rusty bolts protrude from it. The other is a small obelisk which may have supported the sawmill chimney, for this is where the boiler and furnace stood. A metal plate half hidden in the ground may have been the fire bar. Until recently the site was hidden from view in dense growth, but Forest Enterprise has been busy; it has cut out trees deemed to be 'exotic', and the ground around is a tangle of stumps and brushwood which makes access difficult. Only the most alert passers-by on the yellow forest road will glimpse two relic monoliths between tree stems at the forest edge and wonder what they mean.*

The Canadians and Newfoundlanders – 'Newfies' in popular parlance – brought their own machinery to Scotland, plus a good deal of logging know-how acquired in the woods of the Old West. At Knockando, down river from Grantown, timber cut by the men of 106 Company on the steep eastern slopes of the Spey was hauled by high wire across the valley in cradles called blondins (after Charles Blondin, the Niagara tightrope walker) to the sawmill on the far side. At 2300 feet in length it was reputed to be the second longest span of logging cable in the world. The mill was strategically placed beside the main line of Great North of Scotland Railway (a line no more, now a long-distance footpath) so that the sawn wood could be loaded straight into the railway wagons. The network of railway lines laid down in Victorian and Edwardian days was a boon to the wartime logging operation. It was a simple matter to run a mile of standard gauge from the Canadian sawmill in the woods to the station at Nethy Bridge, giving direct access to the main line south.

There was a minor railway boom within the woods as a web of tramways and narrow-gauge tracks was laid from felling sites. Timber cut by the German prisoners was taken to the Great North of Scotland line at Carrbridge over the most primitive form of permanent way – simply slender trees lopped and shaved and laid end to end over which horse-drawn trucks with wide-grooved wheels jolted to the pick-up points.

The Canadians organised things more efficiently. Back home they were accustomed to their pulleys, high riggers, donkey engines, steam railways and trestle bridges, and they imported many of their techniques. In the deep cleft of the Sluggan a light railway two and a half miles long followed the line of the burn and in places straddled the river bed or crossed it on high trestles. The logs were transported on bogies – on the steepest gradients hitched to a hawser operated by a fixed engine – down to a specially built sawmill working on North American lines. The Sluggan loggers had a hard time felling and extracting the timber on difficult and often precipitous slopes.

Sawn timber could be taken by light railway to the Highland Railway station at the small country village of Aviemore once a matting of brushwood and slab timber had been laid over the boggiest sections of moorland to make a firm base for the track. The line spanned the River Druie on a trestle bridge sixty feet long and rails were laid across the existing road bridge (still standing but now reserved for pedestrians) to take it over the Spey at Aviemore. When the Sluggan was cropped bare and the loggers moved into Glenmore the top end of this railway was extended to Loch Morlich, where there was another sawmill, and from it spur lines branched off at tangents round the loch, up the glen towards the Green Loch and into the other felling areas in the forest. As in the Sluggan, hawsers attached to fixed engines eased the laden bogies down the steepest slopes, while on easier ground the horses took over. Timber was still being brought out of Glenmore in 1919 after the war had ended, and the line even became a tourist attraction. There were tales of adventurous visitors taking 'hurls' on the empty wagons from Aviemore to Loch Morlich and riding back perched high on the loaded timber.

New planting and the relentless advance of nature have obscured most of the tracks the Canadians laid, but evidence can still be found. At the eastern end of Loch Morlich there is a swampy patch of clear fell above which curves the unmistakable line of an embankment. The surface is overgrown with moss, grass and heather but here and there the outline of the log bed on which the sleepers lay can be distinguished under the vegetation. In places the soil has crumbled away to reveal the logs themselves, dark umber in colour, rotting and flaking, but intact. A rusted spike embedded in the timber can be easily withdrawn. Further along the route I spot a V-shaped piece of iron, purpose unknown.

Year by year more archaeology is lost. Bulldozed rocks now have to be surmounted to continue along the track as it enters the woods, looking much like any ordinary footpath except that here and there it plunges through high-banked cuttings. It's not hard to imagine horse-drawn wagon trains laden with timber rattling down the slopes, held in check by the brakemen. Twice the path dips into deep little gullies crossed by rustic bridges built for rambling tourists. Scattered greened-over timbers lying on the banks were part of the original trestles which carried the line across. If you peel back the mossy bark you may find charred wood beneath, evidence of fire. The story is that these trestles were blown up by Norwegian commandos training in Glenmore during World War Two.

Shortly before the plantation edge is reached and a view of distant brown hills opens up the line comes to a halt. Here is a wood pile, stacked up eighty years ago and abandoned to silent decay. The war ended, the horses were unhitched, the rails lifted, the men dismissed, and the last of the sawlogs were left to rot unheeded. I sit on the stack while birds sing in trees that have grown straight and tall in the intervening years. Among them are a few grotesques, Caledonian pines that were elderly when the Canadians inspected their rugged stems and huge twisting boughs and reckoned they were too misshapen to serve the war effort. So they survived the axe.

Another part of the forest. Two heavy-branching trees, gnarled giants in a shady dell spotted with shafts of sunshine, through which a small burn darkly dissipates in the moss. Here camped and laboured 110 Company. A forest road leads down the brae, makes a bend at the burn and banks steeply upwards, while fifty yards from the verge, in clear sight of passing walkers, bikers and cross-country skiers, a moss-garnished cube of old concrete sits embedded in the ground. Old bolts stick from it. Here was the Sluggan sawmill.

The Sluggan is still to come. A few hundred yards further on I leave the forest road to follow the Milton Burn through an open meadow of marsh grass bordered by spruce trees. Where will it lead? Conifers close in, the burn chatters in stony shallows, sliding through dark pools and over gravel beds. This is a secret glen, silent and peaceful, birdsong and the clatter of water apart. The only tracks belong to the

Here in Glenmore the Canadians built a sawmill. All's quiet now. Young trees crowd around an old-stager too gnarled even then to serve the war effort.

deer. Three grey wasted timbers poke from the stony bed like bony fingers – a relic of the wartime railway trestles? Or not. Possibly the remains of a sluice from the dam system of other days? Hopping back and forth across the narrow burn and peering into its waters I find no certain clues.

The hills close in and the pass narrows to a gorge heaped with rocks. Down these precipitous slopes the logs came swinging on cables. There's no trace of that activity now. A few bare tree bulks jam the river bed but they could have fallen at any time in the past. The going gets rough; I have to clamber over outcrops and cliffy knolls. Dense stands of conifers rise on either side until the burn emerges into the open where the slope has been recently felled. I climb to the forest road through lopped branches and sawn stumps. There's a fine old stump of Douglas fir. I count the rings – sixty years old or so, which makes the date of its planting some time in the early 1930s. A reparation for the trees the Canadians cut.

At the north end of the Sluggan the burn runs into the valley of the Spey. The far slope of Creag Mheadhonach is thick with ranks of conifers where the Canadians cut down the old pines, but on my side of the glen the heathery ground is only sprinkled with trees – big pines with a few tall Norway spruce among them and young trees growing up among groves of shaggy juniper. Was this what the old forest was like before the loggers stripped it?

Canadians, Newfies, 'Finns', captured Germans and Austrians all worked in the woods. But there was another potential source of labour. It was reported from one large estate that 'difficulties in employment on large scale of prisoners of war, Belgians, or even our own discharged soldiers, latterly turned the search for labour to a source tapped only in desultory manner previously'. This untapped source was female.

Women were enrolled in the factories, why not in the woods? (Better the brown-berry outdoors look than the yellow faces of the munitions girls.) Women and girls had long been employed as casual forest labour. Their heyday came in the great years of the tanbark industry, but long afterwards it was still the custom on many estates to hire women in spring to help in the labour-intensive, back-aching work of planting out young trees. Usually they were local women used to farm work. Best of all (in one forester's opinion) were the wives and daughters of estate employees who had been accustomed to helping out from an early age.

Some forest operations had always been thought suitable tasks for women, though not all. Mary Sutherland, a forestry graduate (surely one of the earliest of her sex) reported in 1917 on the activities of women gangs working on forest sites – including the Stirling Maxwell estate at Loch Ossian. This was an innovation at the time. Her study showed that heavy work such as trenching was 'not profitable', since 'obviously much work of the forest labourer can only be done by men, and though women are undertaking light felling and much work in connection with big timber felling, this is probably not sound forestry'.

George Leven might have demurred. Leven, with a quarter of a century's experience of supervising forestry squads, witnessed a wartime experiment on the Hendersyde estate in the Borders where a number of women were recruited to the forestry staff. They performed most of the work, felling, snedding, and cross-cutting several hundred heavy hardwood trees – oak, ash, beech and elm – and even 'sawing off of the roots of trees with cubic contents up to 230ft!' (his exclamation mark). Leven concluded that it was cheaper to have women clear and burn brushwood after felling than men, especially skilled woodmen, no doubt because they could be paid less. Other jobs women could do well were planting and nursery work (their traditional roles), digging pits for planting, putting up fences, and thinning and light pruning in the woodlands. Cleaning out surface drains on lighter soils was 'not beyond their strength', and clearing rank herbage from around young plants and cutting bracken and rushes all required 'a quick eye more than great strength'.

There are photographs showing Hendersyde women at work. In one shot a woman and a man clutching a crosscut saw between them

The women forest workers at Hendersyde who impressed a professional forester with their skill.

scamper clear as a big beech tree tilts and begins to fall. In another, a man and a woman kneel on the ground (the woman in ample skirts) with the saw they hold biting into the base of a tree. One shows three women standing beside the large tree they have just felled. Their clothing, compared to what their daughters wore in the next war, looks impractical: loose smocks down to mid calf and long sleeves buttoned at the wrist. Two are bare-headed but others wear floppy berets or in one case a wide-brimmed, Spanish-looking hat. Footwear isn't clearly visible; probably they wear boots. Men at that time tended to wear flat caps, waistcoats and collar and tie, but at least they got to roll up their sleeves.

Women were also employed by contractors brought in to fell for pit props. In some cases the heavier trees were 'laid in' and snedded by men, but elsewhere women took over most jobs. In Perthshire John Waddell, forester at Foswell, Auchterarder, oversaw the work of two girls during the four months from December 1917 to the end of March. The girls (age unknown) were keen to learn, worked out of doors in all weathers except in heavy rain or when it snowed, and after three weeks they could be left to themselves apart from marking which trees to cut (which required an experienced eye) or when the heavier felled trees had to be carried out. They were 'fairly good with the spade' when planting. When it came to cutting down large larch trees and sawing them into logs the two girls took one end of the crosscut saw, one at the handle, the other pulling on a rope attached to it, while the forester – presumably Waddell – took the other. On the second day of felling the three cut down eight larches, snedded them, cut them into lengths for fence posts, and burned the branches. All in a day's work.

Tall Lord Lovat inclines to share a joke with George V (the third man doesn't get it).
Lovat returned from his wartime work in the French forests to command the new Forestry Commission.

15

LET CONIFERS COVER THE LAND

As the guns roared and thousands stumbled to their death on the Somme, a group of influential men gathered in London to plan for peace, and specifically for the restitution of the forests. Lord Lovat turned up in his brigadier's uniform, commuting across the Channel from his headquarters in Le Touquet, where he presided over the cutting down of the French forests for the British troops in Flanders. Mark the man – we have met him before. His influence will change the countryside.

Tall, stiff-necked, won't suffer fools gladly. A hereditary peer and proud of it, landowner on a massive scale, Conservative by politics, old Catholic by religion, an officer and a gentleman – such was Simon Fraser, fourteenth Lord Lovat. In youth a gambler often seen at the tables in Monte Carlo, and a hunter. From shooting elephants in Abyssinia he sailed home to raise a squadron of irregulars to fight the Boers, persuading stalkers and gillies from his own and neighbouring estates to volunteer, in the belief that men accustomed to riding their own ponies and using a rifle and telescope would be well suited to skirmishing on the veldt.

His Lovat Scouts returned to the ranks in the Great War and were sent to Gallipoli, where Lovat caught dysentery before a shot was fired and had to be invalided home. His subsequent military career was spent usefully behind the lines as director of forests in France, where he oversaw the supply of timber needed by the British army in Flanders.

This 'able, domineering, arrogant man' is about to assist at the birth of a national forest owned by the state.

The forestry sub-committee, part of a think tank set up in the last days of Asquith's Liberal government to plan for postwar reconstruction, had heavyweight talent at its disposal. Alongside Lovat at the table sat his old friend Sir John Stirling Maxwell, and the venerable Sir William Schlich, German-born but long since naturalised, added the gravitas of his seventy-six years and his prestige as theoretician and former professor of forestry at Oxford University.

It became known as the Acland committee after its chairman, Francis Acland, a man apparently destined for a brilliant political career until Lloyd George sidelined him.[*] But it was not he who shaped the policies enunciated in the so-called Acland report. That, said Stirling Maxwell, was chiefly the creation of Lovat and the young committee secretary and wunderkind Roy Robinson. (He might have added his own name, but he was a modest man.) Robinson – an Australian, former Rhodes scholar, athlete and intellectual – was in his thirties and already showing formidable promise. Energetic and ambitious, he would end his days as Lord Robinson of Kielder Forest and Adelaide. Four of the Acland committee – Lovat, Lord Clinton, Stirling Maxwell and Robinson – were destined in their turn to head the Forestry Commission which emerged from their deliberations.

There was a sense of crisis as the committee met. Woods were being devastated to sustain the war effort and the damage had to be repaired. It was clear that many more trees must be grown as a reserve for the defence of the nation. Never again must Britain run short of timber in a world conflict, should the unthinkable happen again. (It happened.) The task of the Forestry Commission was to secure Britain's future by planting production woodlands over hill and dale – half of the new forests, as it turned out, to be planted in Scotland.

The commission was vested on 1 September 1919 and the ruling eight forestry commissioners were appointed within the month. Lovat (no surprise) was chairman. Four of the commissioners were landed gentry with great estates. This body was now to undertake a massive programme of afforestation on land to be acquired by the state. It would do so unfettered by departmental or ministerial interference,

---

[*] After the war, as a landed gentleman, he grew trees, walked, shot game and took up charitable work. In spare moments he wove ties for friends and sketched flowers. His handwriting was a joy to read, according to Stirling Maxwell.

Lovat saw to that. In today's terms it was a quango working at arm's length from the government. That privilege would eventually be withdrawn, but for twenty years men like Lovat and Robinson were to stamp their own vision on it.

There was no tradition of state forestry, no state forests and no state foresters. One of the first tasks was to hire senior staff. Apart from estate workers the only source of trained men was in the forests of empire. Britain's career foresters had traditionally found work in India and Ceylon, Canada, Australia and Africa. Thus the early leadership was given by men whose practical experience had been acquired in conditions very different from the Scottish Highlands. Mark Anderson (who, admittedly, had a chip on his shoulder) commented that the commission began life 'staffed almost entirely, at least in the higher posts, by amateur foresters and inexperienced professional foresters, mostly lacking in practical afforestation experience in Scotland'. As seen from below the new organisation often seemed disproportionately weighted at senior level with Oxbridge men who were inclined to ride roughshod over feelings north of the border.

There was a distinctly military, almost dictatorial flavour about the early service, down to the khaki uniform and the puttees worn by its working men. John McEwen recalled a field conference at Fort Augustus in the 1920s when rank and protocol were rigorously observed. The three commissioners present – the senior executives of the service – stayed in the best hotel. Officers and ordinary foresters were quartered less luxuriously with accommodation graded strictly according to rank. Officers had rooms of their own while McEwen and his fellow foresters had to share bedrooms. Segregation was complete. 'Officers and foresters were kept away from each other at meals and had no contact whatever in the hotel. That was Lovat's army procedure.' McEwen, a thorough-going socialist (and blunt critic of the land-owning aristocracy in his book *Who Owns Scotland?*), told of a dressing down he received when interviewed in London for promotion. Lovat snapped at him not to be so 'damned independent' if he wished to stay with the commission.

Who'll plant the first tree, and where? This was a hot topic at the first meeting of the forestry commissioners in London in December 1919, and it was resolved with a sporting challenge. Was it Lovat the betting man who threw down the gauntlet? The bargain was this: Lovat would take the night train north with the forest of Monaughty as his destination while his deputy Lord Clinton, another landed aristocrat, would head for Devon. Clinton romped home. He arrived at the small town of Eggesford in the early hours and set off in the dark with a small group of foresters for neighbouring woodland where they heeled in a few beech and larch seedlings. When Lovat emerged stiffly from his sleeper at wintry Elgin he was handed a telegram telling him he'd lost the bet.

Late in a September afternoon after heavy rain the forest is stately and mature, a sombre place. If it once had a proper name it hasn't now, only a number – Acquisition No. 1. These trees were some of the first planted by the Forestry Commission. Lovat and Co.'s new forest starts here, above the road on the north side of Loch Ness.

Down on the forest road it's like a lumber yard. Great fir logs are piled high for a mile or so on either side of the road. Naked, stripped of bark, the flesh is creamy and the heartwood cores show red at the butt ends. They perfume the air. Judicious harvesting has been taking place. Fellers have worked through the stand taking out a selection of the finest trees (the order is for power transmission poles in Ireland). But enough is enough – who'd dare to clear-fell such a place? According to Malcolm Wield at the forestry headquarters in Fort Augustus the cash value of Douglas logs of such quality is high, but in terms of aesthetics, amenity and historic interest the woodland is priceless.

Aiming to get to higher ground, I start to scramble over a pile of timber but hardly have my boots touched the wet bare logs when kerpow! I'm up in the air and backside down thump on raw Douglas fir. The pain! Wincing, I seek an easier way on to the hill.

The remains of a dry-stane dyke snakes upwards, left over from when this was open ground on a hill farm. In the deep shade at the base of the trees, among rocky debris thickly carpeted with moss, grow wood sorrel, hard fern and other things I don't know. I reach a steep embankment under cliffy outcrops where the trees – mainly Douglas fir, though there are large Sitka spruce among them – grow tall, with hazel here and there. The conifers, bark deeply etched, make columns a hundred feet tall, a tribute to the forester's skill. And on higher ground yet I see a later generation of trees springing up.

When I get back to the car and drive along the lochside through forest archways, observing massed conifers ascending hill slopes on the far shore, I reflect on Lovat and his plan for Glen Mor in

Spruce plantations as rural idyll. A romantic view of the new forests as promoted in an early Forestry Commission guide – a paradise not often achieved on the ground.

the years when state forestry existed only in the mind. He and his colleagues imagined the Great Glen forested much as I see it now (albeit with a different mix of trees), and it has come to be.

The commission made a good start. Within a year 1600 acres had been planted and the omens were good. Then suddenly everything changed and the commission teetered on the brink of disaster. The brief postwar boom collapsed, panic set in and Sir Eric Geddes was appointed to curb public spending. Geddes was the man for the job. It was he who shortly after the war had promised that Germany would be squeezed over payment of reparations 'till the pips squeak', and his programme of cuts, soon to be known as the 'Geddes axe', bit deep.[*] The Forestry Commission was high on the hit list; Geddes, according to one observer, making 'a dead set' against it. The purchase of land was to stop and no more planting would be done. The axe was poised. No land, no trees, no new forests; the death of state forestry in infancy. But Lovat called on friends in high places and state forestry survived, though not without tears. Newly hired staff were sacked. Hopes that financial support would be sustained were dashed and the annual grant cut in 1922 under Geddes, increased in 1924, cut in 1927, increased again in 1929, and finally cut savagely in the financial crisis of 1931.

[*] According to AJP Taylor Geddes was 'Lloyd George's best find in the business world'. Plucked from a senior post on the North Eastern Railway he joined the government to run military railways in wartime France and later to become first lord of the Admiralty. Thus he gained both red tabs and gold rings, first as a major-general and then an admiral. As postwar Minister of Transport he carried through the great railway amalgamation which reduced more than a hundred companies to four.

In the heady early postwar years the faith had been expressed that private landowners would match the Forestry Commission in planting zeal, and that 'the area to be planted by the State in subsequent years may be reduced in the same degree as private individuals come forward to undertake the work'. It proved a forlorn hope. Embattled woodland owners saw little profit in timber.

Even before the war they had felt the chill, and between the wars taxation became increasingly onerous. Great estates were sold entire or piecemeal. Lovat himself, encumbered by Beaufort Castle, his father's heavily mortgaged folly, snatched an opportunity during the brief postwar property boom to sell off 100,000 acres of deer forest and grouse moor amounting to almost a third of his estates.

Costs rose, timber prices plummeted and, with little capital to spare, investing in slow-growing trees looked like madness. Woodland was neglected. The practice of thinning young plantations was often abandoned because the resulting small timber sold at a loss. Planting trees seemed all too risky a business, and by and large it was left to the state.

While the depression slowed the pace of afforestation it did not halt it, and slowly the face of upland Scotland was changed. In the early 1920s, far up in Liddesdale, the first seedling conifers were pressed hopefully into boggy braes near Newcastleton, harbingers of a great forest that would eventually invade both sides of the Border. At the same time lines of young trees sprouted above the shores of Loch Ken near New Galloway. Later in the decade came the first inroads into moorland on the southern verge of the Lowther Hills in Dumfriesshire, the small beginning of what would become the Forest of Ae. By 1930 planters were busy in Strathyre encroaching on the bare lower slopes of Ben Vorlich on one side of Loch Lubnaig and Ben Ledi on the other. Close by in the Trossachs the hills around Loch Ard near Aberfoyle were being planted up on either side of the Duke's Pass.

In youth John McEwen had know the hills and shores of the Cowal Peninsula well. Much had changed by the time he joined a forestry excursion in May 1961. This outing celebrated a milestone – the planting of one thousand acres of naked hill land in Argyll with trees. After lunch the motorcade drove past Glenbranter near Loch Fyne, down the length of Loch Eck and over the hill to Ardentinny on the east shore of Loch Long, then followed the coastline round by

The hilly shores of Loch Eck 'miraculously' transformed –
in the eyes of John McEwen – by plantation trees.

Strone before turning north again to Benmore. For mile after mile it
passed through forests of trees grown tall and dense. To forester
McEwen the transformation seemed 'almost miraculous'.

Binning Wood in glory before it fell to the axe in 1940.

16

DEATH AND RESURRECTION

ONE DECEMBER DAY a head forester walked through the three hundred acres of Binning Wood admiring the forest giants around him. Binning was a historic wood. It had been planted, as we have seen, by the energetic sixth Earl of Haddington and his lady on sandy coastal dunes near Dunbar in the early 1700s, and since then had been carefully husbanded by successive generations of the family. Some of the glorious oak and beech trees were two hundred years old and of a great size. The head forester, who was employed by a number of landowners concerned by the wartime loss of their woodland, was particularly struck by a stand of three hundred Scots pine trees aged from fifty to a hundred years old which he considered particularly fine. 'Really lovely stuff,' as he wrote approvingly in his report.

But the year was 1940, the darkest hour, and all such trees were under sentence, destined to be claimed for the war effort. 'There are numerous timber resources in the country that could be tapped before this fine timber is sacrificed,' the woodman pleaded to the wartime authorities, but in vain.

Binning Wood was taken over under emergency powers and the loggers moved in. Down crashed, day after day, week after week, 4500 oak trees, 2300 beech trees, 690 sycamores, the same number of ash trees, 640 birches, alder, gean and other hardwoods, almost a hundred lime and horse chestnut trees, 82 hornbeams, 39 sweet chestnuts, and around a thousand conifers including the esteemed Scots pines. In the end nothing was left of the Earl of Haddington's fine wood but ten thousand stumps. It was heartrending – though he may have taken consolation on hearing that some of the best beech went to make Mosquito fighter-bombers in the war against Hitler.

Binning Wood was not an isolated case. Once again Armageddon decimated some of the best woodlands on the home front, and this time the casualties were even heavier than in World War One. On the densely wooded Seafield estates in the northeast three times as much timber was cut in the second war as in the first, when the toll had been bad enough. On Deeside the great Glen Tanar estate suffered serious loss. Rothiemurchus on Speyside, savaged before, was hit again. The Black Wood of Rannoch, spared at the eleventh hour in 1918, fell victim in the 1940s when most of the best trees were taken out. Shortly after the war the naturalist Frank Fraser Darling was moved to declare that 'our land is so devastated that we might as well have been the battlefield'.

What the axe and saw had spared wildfire might destroy. With so much waste matter lying on the ground, a tangle of small branches and withered foliage, there was tinder in plenty and outbreaks were not uncommon. Commandos on a training exercise north of the Great Glen were blamed for starting the fire that raged through a thousand acres of old pinewood around Loch Arkaig. At the close of the war brushwood left from heavy fellings in native pinewoods at Dulnain in Strathspey was set alight – probably by sparks from a railway locomotive – and the fire, blown this way and that by shifting winds, burned through the forest for a week.

One mistake made in the Great War was not repeated in the next. Then woodsmen volunteered and were eagerly accepted for the front. This time foresters and sawyers were exempted from military service. It wasn't enough. From early in the war women were recruited (far more than in the Great War), first by the Forestry Commission and then by a new formation, the Women's Timber Corps, kitted out in uniform of green jerseys, breeches and open-necked shirts. Most of the girls who joined up had never handled and perhaps never seen an axe. There were shop girls, clerkesses, maidservants, housewives and school leavers among them.

Memories must have been short, for although thousands of women had proved their skill in the previous conflict, the idea of women wielding axes and crosscut saws could still, in the 1940s, be treated as a joke. But men who mocked would learn.

'When passing through Kilmarnock and having an hour or two at my disposal,' forester James Tait informed readers of the journal *Scottish Forestry* in 1942, 'I chanced to walk along a country lane. There I espied thinning operations in progress entirely carried out by a squad of women without even the supervision of a man.' Intrigued by this bizarre scene, he went closer and was impressed by their skill. 'The woman in charge could lay-in a tree with the best of men and it is some considerable time since I have seen anyone so knacky in the handling of an axe.' No doubt many foresters would feel 'rather doubtful as to the employment in forestry of the weaker sex'; as for himself, Tait had no qualms. Indeed, 'a mere man will have to take care if he is to be recognised as a forester in the future'.

Once again aid was sought from a still loyal (but soon to be dismantled) Empire. The first to arrive were Newfoundlanders, followed by a batch from British Honduras (now Belize), equipped not with axes but with machetes as used in their own tropical forests. They were sent to Golspie on the northeast coast, where they shivered. The first shipment of fifty-eight Canadians arrived at Blair Atholl in October 1940, the advance guard of a force that would ultimately number two thousand men.

'The Canadians were here and cut down all our trees,' a Canadian historian heard repeated during a postwar sabbatical in the Highlands. Later he pieced their story together from records and folk memory, identifying thirty camps set up by the Canadian Forestry Corps in the Scottish forests in World War Two, and amassing considerable information about 'the sawdust fusiliers' (as he titled his book).

This time, unlike their predecessors who wore khaki but weren't expected to fight, the Forestry Corps of World War Two were classed as combat troops. They mounted guard at roadblocks and bridges, took part in exercises and were expected to play a part in repelling Hitler's threatened invasion. Invaders would have had a clear run at Cawdor early in 1941, where a newly landed contingent from Ottawa spent the whole of March unarmed except for their axes. The Québecois at Ballogie waited a month for rifles and bayonets and another four for the bullets. But a pattern of military preparedness was established. For five nine-hour days of the week the foresters laboured in the woods and on the Saturday they shifted into battle dress for infantry training.

No shot was fired in anger in the Highlands. Casualties suffered were usually accidental: unwary fingers sliced off by the saw, flesh gouged by the wilder axe swipes, bones crushed by awkwardly falling trees. Road accidents often befell timber-laden trucks on narrow icy roads. One Canadian was knifed by a Pole in a brawl between allies at Montrose, and a Canadian murdered his camp-mate at Southesk. It was all much as might be expected.

A lot of equipment was shipped over with the Canadians, including tractors, trucks, donkey engines and even their portable sawmills, these considered much superior to the smaller 'Scotch' mills provided by the Forestry Commission. Canadians heartily disliked these Scotch mills, at least at first, and with good reason, for they had to push logs towards the spinning saw by hand. Fingers were at risk and sometimes lost.

One of their most spectacular techniques imported from the New World involved preparing a spar tree for bringing timber down steep slopes in the operation known as high-lead logging. A tall straight tree was selected for use as a natural pylon, and once it had been fitted with pulleys and cable it could be used to swing sawn timber from the hillsides to the stack – one end of each log clamped and running high and the other swinging free or bumping off the ground in its descent. Once a suitable tree had been chosen the spar man, or high rigger, wearing spikes on his boots, shinned up into the crown in order to sever the treetop above him. The spar man was the aristocrat of the trade, a happy-go-lucky specialist with the most dangerous job in the woods: 'a slip of the axe could mean instant death if the tether rope was cut'. A Canadian documentary shows the spar man held fast to the stem as it swings wildly after the cut. When the tree settles he nonchalantly lights a cigarette.

In spite of mechanisation it was muscle power that laid the trees low, with axes and crosscut saws. The *Scotsman* war correspondent reporting from a frontline forest watched logging in Strathspey in September 1942. He described how 'two stocky men, wearing breeches, lumber jackets, and soft felt hats, selected a tall fir. They made a few cuts on one side with their axes, then passed to the other side and began sawing. In less than a minute and a half the fir tree swayed, hesitated a moment, then crashed with a crackle of splitting wood to the ground.

Heroic Forestry Commission tree
planters on a steep slope above
St Fillans, Perthshire. No date,
but possibly in the 1950s.

The two men passed on a few yards, repeated the performance, and brought another of the forest's thousands down.' He reported that a few weeks previously twelve men working in pairs had felled six trees in one minute and ten seconds.

By the middle of 1943, with Canada short of timber for its own needs, ten companies were sent back home to work the Canadian forests. Surprisingly few cheered the news. More left after the Normandy landings to cut in the forests of France and Germany. By the summer of 1945 with Germany defeated, the last units were disbanded and the Forestry Corps ceased to exist, leaving the scarred woods in peace.

For centuries woodmanship had followed a traditional pattern. I have on my desk Herbert ('Bill') Edlin's book *Trees, Woods and Man*, open at a black and white photo of a tree-planting squad. In the foreground above sun-shot fields, braced against a dark wedge of hillside, four men are outlined against the sky. One strikes a dramatic pose with his spade levelled above his head (like a Homeric hero with spear poised) ready to plunge it into the heathery turf. In the instant beyond the shutter click he will slice it into roots and soil.

The caption reads: 'Planting Scots pine on the steep slopes above Dalchonzie, St Fillans Forest, Perthshire; spring', so we know where the photo was taken, but when? Theoretically it could have been any time between the 1920s and the mid fifties, when Edlin's book was published. Trees had been planted much like this since planting began.

Such an image, in a variety of settings, might be multiplied a thousandfold. All across the wilder, steeper, rougher places of Scotland such gangs of men planted the nation's trees.

All aspects of forestry work was heavily dependent on working men. Men like Lord Lovat had assumed that it would remain so, and that tree growing would bring life back to the deserted countryside. It was not to be.

Alastair McLean, one of the old-stagers, a man who spent the best part of half a century working among the trees of Argyll, told me about life as a forester when I met him at his home in the village of Ardentinny on the Cowal coast. Alastair was fourteen when he left school to work for the Forestry Commission in Glenfinnart Forest in the 1930s. He had little choice; forest villages, like mining villages, were closed communities and Alastair followed his father into forestry as a matter of course. Alastair and the other boys, always called 'nippers', gathered bundles of plants from where they'd been 'scheuched in' – roughly dug into the ground first thing in the morning – to take uphill to the planters when they were shouted for. Squads of a dozen or so men were strung along the slopes at five- or six-feet intervals, each with a bundle of plants in his sack. In due course McLean graduated to a planting gang. In the days before mechanisation, draining ditches had to be excavated with a large two-handled spade called a rutter, then the turfs dug out in this way were formed into mounds where trees could be planted in the spring. The men worked in all weathers except snow. (Summer had its drawbacks too, mainly insects. They mixed a repellent called Citronella with olive oil and rubbed it on hands and faces, and when the midges were bad a crackling of dead insects could be felt when they touched their skin.)

Basic tools were axe, crosscut saw, spade and 'heuk' (sickle). Horses brought the plants to the hillsides in saddlebags and dragged felled timber from the forests. Eventually McLean and a mate bought horses of their own and were then paid for every log extracted plus a fiver a week (always a big white Bank of England note) to feed the beasts and keep them shod. McLean's horse Billy – half Clydesdale, with a garron's black streak down his back, a peaceable beast ('you could lie down and sleep with Billy,' said Alastair) – wrenched a leg when his hoof stuck in the roots of a tree and had to be put down. Alastair was heartbroken.

Brawn and muscle felled even the largest trees until well into the postwar years.

Horses were phased out in the sixties and McLean spent the rest of his time with a winch team bringing bundles of logs chained together off the hill. In his forty years with the Forestry Commission, until arthritis and a bad hip ended his career, he tackled all the customary tasks: weeding seedling trees in the nursery, cutting bracken on the hills, clearing away unwanted species like birch, willow and oak, planting conifers, brashing, thinning, felling and snedding. It was a healthy outdoor life and he relished it. Like many a forester, he remembers the good times fondly, for in retrospect it seems like a golden age.

Since then just about everything has changed. The horses have gone, replaced by tractors and even heavier vehicles. The forest is a lonelier place. The clunk of the axe and the rasp of the crosscut saw is hardly ever heard, and even the buzz of the chainsaw is a rare sound. Today's forests are felled by huge harvesters which in seconds can fell a tree, sned it, slice it up and stack the cut logs for collection, swiftly munching their way through great swathes of timber. One man in the cabin controlling his computer-equipped behemoth has superseded the labouring squads.

Alastair McLean's little stone cottage was one of fifteen built at Ardentinny in 1927 by the Forestry Commisson. Ardentinny was virtually a company village. Such settlements were a social experiment harking back to the days of Lord Lovat and his vision of repopulating the desolate lands with crofter-foresters.

As the Great War came to a close the idea of land settlement had been aired. Politicians who promised a land fit for heroes to live in envisaged soldiers returning from the trenches to labour healthfully on the soil. (Also, it might divert their minds from the lure of Bolshevism.) The idea of taking war veterans off the labour market and giving them crofts and land to work was seductive. In the grand design for a national forest service, forestry was seen as a useful supplement to part-time farming, whereby each smallholder would be guaranteed regular work in the growing forest. The first holdings were created in 1924 and by the outbreak of World War Two there were 1500 of them.

Alastair McLean's father, a ploughman turned forestry worker, had a typical smallholding. He had five acres of grazing land and kept a cow. Every year Alastair and his father walked eleven miles to Strachur to sell the latest calf – a time for celebration, for then there was money. They also kept a pig and Alastair, being the youngest, fed it. Each pig was their guest for a year until the local shepherd came over and slaughtered it in a barn – struck it dead with one blow of the axe, then cut its throat. Alastair's father rolled and salted bacon, long before there were fridges. In the kitchen garden they grew potatoes, and turnips for the cow. There was a lavatory but baths had to be taken in a tin tub before the fire, in water led straight from the hill. There was no electricity. Lighting was by oil and later Tilly lamps and the cooking was done on a black range with a high-barred open fire. Such was life on a forestry croft.

With the end of World War Two and a vast expansion of forestry, smallholdings could not meet the demand for forest homes. Forest villages were to be the answer. Clusters of two-storey, semi-detached timber homes made to Scandinavian design sprouted by the burgeoning forests, so simply constructed that a couple of men could put them up. They are still to be seen around the countryside, modified, gentrified, improved, but now seldom occupied by forest folk. Slushy official prose (probably not composed by a countryman) extolled the delights to be experienced by residents in these idealised settlements.

The first forestry village in Scotland was created above the Water of Ae which comes down from the high moorland between Moffat and Dumfries. The first fourteen of a projected hundred houses at Ae were built on bare land in 1947. The *Glasgow Herald* reported in April of that year that it would house workers 'who in return for honest labour will

Happily home from school in a new forest village. The dream proved difficult to realise.

be guaranteed a lifetime's employment in the forestry service' – too optimistic a claim, as it turned out. It offered, according to the *Herald*, 'a real solution of the economic problems of crofting'.

Ae village was more successful than most. Some were disasters. The most viable were built beside or close to existing populated places. But since the new forests were likely to be planted in remote areas the forest villages could offer little in the way of amenities. Incoming families had a roof over their heads, a prospect of windswept moorland and infant forest from their windows, a neighbour or two next door and not much else. The isolated life soon lost its appeal for many couples lured by the publicity and the need for accommodation after the war. Alastair McLean had come from a farming background and was accustomed to the country life, but many of the new forestry recruits were not. Wives were even worse off, tied to the home, cut off from relatives and friends and lacking the convenience of a corner shop. Few people had cars.

Loneliness was a place called Polloch. Twelve prefab timber houses put up on the southern shore of Loch Shiel in barren Sunart were occupied, gratefully at first, by families desperate for a home of their own. Most of them swiftly regretted it. For several years no road reached Polloch. No grocer's or baker's vans called with provisions. A trip to Fort William (only fifteen miles away as the crow flies, but the crow covers very broken ground) involved a boat trip on the choppy waters of long Loch Shiel in order to catch the train at Glenfinnan, with what might be a chilly wait there and the prospect of an overnight stop-off. Furthermore, Polloch gloomed in the shade of a hill which blotted out any hope of sunshine in winter. What joy could be found in such a spot? By 1970 all homes except the post office house lay empty. When fellers were needed to harvest the timber the men were lodged in bothies, and at weekends most of them made a beeline for Fort William.

Dalavich was another disappointment. This settlement was built half way along the north shore of Loch Awe to house workers in Inverliever. It was considerably bigger than Polloch and soon consisted of nearly forty homes with a school, a forester's house, a post office and shop, and it lay handily on the back road between Taynuilt and Lochgilphead. For a time it justified its existence, at least statistically. Only fifty-five people had lived in the neighbourhood before the Great War. By 1959 the population of the new village had risen to 318, including 125 school children. But it failed in the end. 'Dalavich should never have been built,' says John Davies, formerly the Forestry Commission's conservator for the west of Scotland. 'People came from Glasgow desperate for a house and with no idea of what it was like to live in the country. Food was expensive. They starved. They couldn't make a living in harsh conditions.' The turnover of tenants was constant and draining. 'In my time there were ten empty houses in this tiny village and little heart in it.' Tourism, not forestry saved it. Unoccupied houses were offered as holiday lets and snapped up. A few years later timber cabins were built among the woods on the edge of the village, a bar and lounge and a village hall were added, and in summertime now it's a lively place. It's a familiar pattern. The forest worker, a threatened species, moves out of his woodland home. The holiday tenant or white settler moves in.

The heroic age of state forestry ended with World War Two. And not just in the matter of the old ways, but in a spiritual sense too. Romantics had had their day and Churchill's caretaker government brought the Forestry Commission into the Whitehall fold, making its staff civil servants. Some years later the commissioners of the day humbly defined their role: 'The commission. . . is no more and no less than an instrument of government policy, like any other department of the crown.' (Birl in your grave, Lord Lovat!)

Roy Robinson – Lord Robinson of Adelaide and Kielder Forest – burly czar of the woods as chairman of the Forestry Commission in its heyday.

There is no doubt who dominated the commission's middle years – Roy Lister Robinson. Born in Australia, he came to Oxford as a Rhodes scholar, gained a degree in geology and a diploma in forestry and excelled at sport. He was a founding member of the Forestry Commission and went smoothly to the top. Knighted in 1931, chairman the year after, ennobled in 1947, he was to the Forestry Commission what John Reith had been to the BBC. Preceded at its head by two landed lords (Lovat and Clinton) and a baronet (Stirling Maxwell), Robinson was the first commoner to take the reins. This 'tough, single-minded man, deeply respected and feared by his staff', shaped the commission in his formidable image.

Experiments (pioneered by Sir John Stirling Maxwell at Corrour) showed that trees might grow on the most unpromising peaty morass. But digging, draining, planting and feeding by hand was slow, heavy and frustrating. When ploughing was attempted the horses wallowed in the mire. Tractors sank to the axles and beyond – some were even swallowed whole. It was not until crawler tractors fitted with wide caterpillar tracks appeared after the war that there was any hope of success.[*] By then only the barest, stoniest, steepest slopes and the most intractable bogland was beyond bounds.

Ploughing by tractor broke the waste land and tamed the wilderness. Mountain slopes and moorland tracts were scored with deep trenches, channelled and black-ribbed where the peat was exposed.

[*] Robinson once dashed off a sketch for a new type of tractor-drawn plough, which was built and christened with his initials – the RLR. Was there no end to his talent?

Man against nature in the drive to plant 'waste land' where no trees grew and no tree should. Some tractors sank without trace in the bog – hence the widened wheels on this one.

Inevitably it played havoc with precious ecologies, but in those days the voice of the greens was faint and barely heard. Time passed and the conifers grew, more or less healthily, some species better than others, and chiefly *Picea sitchensis*, the Sitka spruce.

What a tree it is in its native state! On home ground in northwestern America it flourishes along the indented Pacific coastline, from the Bering Sea to northern California. Happiest by the sea, it thrives on that moist, fog-bound littoral, often in the company of western hemlock and western red cedar. In the summer of 1931 the Forestry Commission sent a mission to the (at that time) remote Queen Charlotte Islands off the coast of British Columbia to asssess the suitability of Sitka for forest planting in this country. Making his approach by sea towards the misty, rocky coastline of Graham Island, bound as it was by mountain ridges, fretted by sea lochs and dotted with islands large and small, the commission's man (his name was Hopkinson) was struck by its similarity to the West Highlands: 'But for the ever present forest, one might easily imagine one was sailing up Loch Sunart.'

> *Sixty years after Hopkinson prospected in the Queen Charlotte Islands I stand on Bonanza Bay, a broad sweep of shingle and washed sand. Waves break on a spit of rock and beyond the breakers and a misty headland is the open Pacific – next landfall Japan. Shaggy mountains are in view. Tiny flowers cling to crevices in the rock and ropes of bull kelp seaweed straggle on the sand. Behind me, a crescent of dark forest fringes the shore. These trees are mainly sitka, known*

also in these parts as tidewater spruce, tall, heavy-branched, shaggy, clotted with grey lichens.

In Hopkinson's day the Queen Charlottes were virtually roadless and travel was a challenge, but that has changed. A forestry pick-up takes me inland to Yakoun Lake, where a narrow footpath leads by ups and downs and pools of dark standing water into the dank and dripping rainforest. On this drizzly day little light reaches the ground, carpeted with dead needles and tangled with underbrush. Swags of moss and lichen hang from the boughs and the many fallen trunks are felted with moss. This is old forest, never cut. Decaying stumps show where trees fell in the course of nature. Some of the living are mighty, all of them Sitka. Their crowns fan out high above, their stems straight and barely tapering, wine-dark where not encrusted with moss, grand columns in a roofless temple. I stand chesting a giant, arms outspread, palms on rough bark, and still the trunk swells out beyond my fingertips. Some cuddle! There are even greater trees four hundred miles or so to the south, on Vancouver Island, but those have become visitor attractions reached by boardwalks and ringed with viewing platforms and handrails; too much like museum pieces for my taste. You can't beat wilderness, I say – until the sight of a fresh bear dropping pulls me up short. Bears, they say, are shy creatures, but I'm no brave heart.

We drive into the interior of Vancouver Island, Charlie Cartwright of the forest service at the wheel. He fiddles with the radio, seeking the truckers' waveband. There's more than a hint of life and death in this, since the logging trucks come roaring down the mountain like juggernauts and give way to no one. The drivers sing out at regular intervals and it behoves you to harken. Charlie says he met a descending truck at a narrow bridge where there was no escape but to plunge off road into a ditch. These truckers, he says, are kings with nerves of steel; but alcoholism often lurks at the latter end. We pull aside – there's one on the way. The snarl of the engine is audible above the trees. It thunders past with a blast on the klaxon, piled high and bulging wide with logs bigger than any I've ever seen before. Then it's gone in a cloud of dust.

Roy Robinson chose Sitka as one of the prime trees to be planted by the Forestry Commission. Corsican pine might be fine for the south of England, but Sitka was best suited to the Scottish environment, particularly in the wetter west. And since the Queen Charlotte Islands lay roughly in the same latitudes as Scotland and had a similar climate – mild, with salt-laden winds driving in from the west – it seemed a good bet that the Queen Charlotte trees would provide suitable progenitors for a new generation raised in the Scottish uplands. And so it proved. Today Sitka spruce is the commonest forest tree in Scotland, though not the best loved. There are more Sitka than any other species. If you fell from the sky into a Scottish plantation the chances are high that you'd land on a Sitka. (Not a soft touch-down – its needles are sharp.)

In the cold war years the case for blanket afforestation was seen as a strategic priority – the Battle of the Atlantic had been a painful reminder of Britain's vulnerability to submarine blockade. World War Three might be just around the corner. Then as East-West tensions relaxed the argument came to be framed in economic terms; since Britain still depended heavily on imported timber, home-grown forests would – in the long term – help to cut the trade deficit. Tree planting took place on an unprecedented scale in the 1960s and 70s. The state led the way but by now landowners large and small, spurred on by grants and subsidies, were turning to woodland again, and a new force appeared in the shape of management firms offering aid to harassed or inexpert (or just would-be) woodland owners. For a fee they would do everything from filling up the paperwork to planning, planting the trees, thinning, felling and marketing the timber. The landowner, if he or she cared, need only sit back and pay the bills.

Tides of conifer forest surged up the glens and crept across the hillsides, stamping their imprint on the land more often than not in brutal rectangles. And since clear-felling was the order of the day, harvesting left bleeding hunks in the landscape, scarred wastes of raw stumps and exposed debris. These were not forests in the old-fashioned sense, but tree crops so dense and thinly rooted that in time, if the gale penetrated, they would fall in great gashes before it.

In 1945, after two bouts of wartime felling and twenty years of state planting, still only five per cent of the Scottish landscape was wooded. Fifty years later the area had trebled and the visible effect on the countryside was profound – either an inspiration or a calamity depending on whether you saw it with the approving eyes of a John McEwen or as a lover of the wide treeless landscapes that had been.

17

THE END OF GEOMETRY

CONIFER PLANTATIONS are dull, dark, lifeless and ugly: true or false? We say so, almost without thinking – everyone knows it's so. Truly there was little joy in the new forests from the start. 'Throughout the 1930s there was growing public concern over the planting of large swathes of the countryside with exotic conifers,' writes the official historian of the Forestry Commission. But the more enlightened state foresters saw that they must make their forests more people-friendly. 'The view from the charabanc was now acknowledged.'

Better still, the public was invited into the woods. National parks were in the air and the Forestry Commission, in the spirit of the day, created its first national forest park in Argyll in 1935, giving judicious access to the new woodlands of the Cowal Peninsula. Others followed. At the Duke's Pass, on the woody slopes above Aberfoyle, the David Marshall Lodge, a large log cabin, was built to welcome visitors to the new forest in the Trossachs. The official tone was optimistic: 'By taking a little thought and possibly incurring a little additional expenditure it may be possible to provide areas as highly prized by the public as the New Forest is today.'

Fine words. But as planting continued at redoubled pace and familiar landscapes were blanketed by battalions of dark, spiky young trees the chorus of discontent grew shrill. In time the Forestry Commission and the new commercial planting businesses on one hand found themselves locked in hostilities with an increasingly influential conservation lobby on the other.

Meanwhile a strange development took place in one of the remotest corners of the British Isles, a brutal incursion of alien trees into a precious landscape that had nothing to do with husbandry, care for the countryside, ecology or even sensible forestry, but everything to do with money.

In the far north a landscape of desolate beauty spreads almost to the Pentland Firth. As far as the eye can see a russet plain stretches under the wide sky. This moorland is by no means solid ground. Countless little pools and lochans glint among spongy beds of peat and moss – a rare and precious environment now widely known (though not by the locals) as the Flow Country, which extends over a thousand square miles. 'Probably in all Britain there are no scenes more impressive in their barren desolation,' wrote the naturalist Derek Ratcliffe just a few years before the invasion of the barbarians.

In such environments an age of cool, wet weather encourages the slow build-up of deep and yet deeper layers of peat in which the sphagnum mosses are the principal element, constantly drawing moisture to the surface and retaining it there like a sponge. There are, it's asserted, only a handful of similar sites in the world – for example on the Kamchatka peninsula and the neighbouring Aleutian Islands, and on Tierra del Fuego, at the tip of South America.

Derek Ratcliffe wrote – as one who had been there – that 'there is no better vantage point for viewing the flowe [*sic*] country than the centrally placed Ben Griam More or Ben Griam Beag near Forsinard. From these twin hills, blanket bog stretches away mile upon mile in every direction.'

I follow his lead and go. Ben Griam Beag rises to an elegant little peak above the moorland. A farm track leads into the wilderness, with here and there dark pools of peaty water of uncertain depth. The track ends at an isolated cottage; three ash trees grow at one corner. It's inhabited but no one's at home and no dog barks as I pass. Steadily rising ground leads over rough bogland and heather, and it's a struggle to mount the last steep cone in the teeth of a strong northwesterly. Near the top bunches of alpine bearberry, now in mid September turning bright crimson, wedge themselves around a litter of flat-topped boulders.

The morning has been bright but now grey clouds sweep in with curtains of rain and the long views I'd hoped for have vanished. Somewhere to the north is the sea coast and Orkney beyond it, but it's blotted out now. But the trees below are visible through the smirr.

Sphagnum aureum, the golden moss, flourishing in a Caithness flow. Trees would kill it.

A patchwork forest stretches for miles over the plain; angular, extensive blocks of green radiating from my viewpoint and swamping the browns and golds of the native moor. A rainbow arches over the eastern plantations and the squall buffets me with driving rain. I hasten down.

Trees don't grow naturally in the Flow Country, though they once did, long ago. Soon after the ice vanished seedlings took root in the post-glacial soil. Trees came and went as the climate changed, appearing briefly for the last time about four thousand years ago. Since then the land has been bare and open to the sky, naturally treeless, a place of secret delights such as I discovered on my first sight, close up, of a Caithness flow, in the company of the botanist Norrie Russell, warden at the RSPB's Forsinard reserve.

> Sphagnum pulchrum, *which means the beautiful sphagnum, glows in an orangey-yellowy mat over a dark mirror pool. Norrie Russell is pleased to find it. Bog ecologists, he remarks as he hunkers down for a closer look, can get quite excited about it here at the eastern limit of its range in Scotland.*
>
> *Close by we see beds of other mosses including* Sphagnum aureum *and the deep red* Sphagnum magellicum, *named after the Magellan Straits, south of Tierra del Fuego, where it's the dominant species. In a small pool two black darter dragonflies perform a delicate dance, the female clutching the male for support as she deposits invisible eggs on the surface of the water, dip, dip, dip with her tail.*

Today's forest, such as it is, infiltrated the Flow Country on the back of a tax dodge. When a smart accountant discovered that book losses on

Sylvia Crowe and disciple in the field, surveying the forest.

planting and growing trees could could be turned to profit by exploiting the current tax system, there was a rush to plant. Flow land, being hopeless for farming, came cheap. The quality of timber grown and the price it might fetch became secondary to the tax concessions that could be grabbed merely by 'investing' in woodland from a distance. This meant that rich people eager to trim their tax bills could pay commercial forestry companies to buy land and plant, manage and market woodland on their behalf. They need never see a tree. Eminent personalities were revealed to have made investments in Flow Country forestry, most famously the broadcaster Terry Wogan.

Opposition was vocal. The destruction of the Flow habitat enraged conservationists, with the RSPB – which had a reserve in the area – taking the lead. Royalty prepared to intervene. It was reported that Prince Charles was about to break his silence in the Lords to draw attention to the ecological disaster taking place in Caithness. Indeed he presented himself and took the oath but then shied away, having been advised that the subject was too controversial. The knot was finally cut when the Chancellor of the Exchequer Nigel Lawson withdrew the tax concessions, 'effectively sounding the death knell', as the *Times* commented, 'for private commercial forestry as it is practised for the purposes of tax avoidance'.

The Flow incursion was an aberration. No one could properly defend it. Meanwhile on more familiar territory the debate between heedless forestry planting and conservation grew fiercer. The Forestry Commission, newly sensitive to the mood and aware of past misdemeanours, turned in a moment of enlightenment to Sylvia Crowe.

Crowe was a woman of character.[*] Daughter of a Sussex fruit farmer, student of horticulture, she began by making gardens and moved on to designing landscapes for new towns, motorways, reservoirs and nuclear power stations. She was sixty when invited to advise the Forestry Commission in 1963 and when she retired thirteen years later foresters had learned to look at their plantations in a new way.

Her visits are still spoken of with awe. New planting was spreading over the uplands like an epidemic, swallowing two hundred acres a day on average. She would arrive at a site with her escort of forest staff – some very senior – in a convoy of trucks. There would be a quick explanation, she'd ask a few searching questions, scan the scene with binoculars, take notes and make rapid sketches. If time were short she'd offer instant solutions. Sometimes when it rained discussions were continued in the back of a truck.

This small white-haired woman in sensible footwear charmed even the most diehard traditionalists. She was fun to work with. She was soft-spoken and courteous and would listen to reason. But she could be stubborn, especially in the early days when her landscaping ideas were novel to foresters – invariably male. A participant recalls her 'fearless eye contact'.

Among forests she left her mark on were Glen Trool in Galloway, Archray and Ardgartan in the Loch Lomond and Trossachs area, Affric in the north, and Kielder in the Borders. The forester John Davies worked with her on the extensive Forestry Commission plantations bordering an eighteen-mile stretch of road linking New Galloway with Newton Stewart – the 'Queen's Way'. When driving along it recently he was dismayed to see what changes had been made since her day, in particular the destruction of a carefully designed visual *coup de théâtre*. Crowe had chosen to retain a dark tunnel of tall trees until, at a bend in the road, the forest pulled back to reveal a sudden view of bare mountain and crag. Later landscapers opened up the tunnel and destroyed the drama.

---

[*] During the war she drove an ambulance in France and brought some of the last wounded out of Bordeaux.

Before and after – bare hillside and Sylvia Crowe's suggested afforestation, from her Forestry Commission booklet *The Landscape of Forests and Woods*.

Crowe sought to make the commission's plantations look as natural as possible by moulding them to the landscape forms and highlighting its features. Rectangular planting and clear-fell squares were anathema to her. The key to it all was understanding the character of a landscape. Scale was important. The rolling Border hills could accommodate wide-spreading forests providing some ground was kept open and there was variation in the kind of trees. But the intimate mix of hill and dale in the Lake District had to be matched by sensitive planting. Contrast was important – as in Kirkcudbrightshire, where planted hill slopes rise above open valleys, or in Peeblesshire, where some hills were planted over and others left open.

Sylvia Crowe was asked what artists, if any, had influenced her work. She said Paul Nash and Henry Moore. Nash by his lyrical landscapes and delicate surrealism, Moore by his sculpture with its solids and cavities reminiscent of the organic world.

A stone by the roadside marks the border, Scotland on one side, England on the other. Trees sweep across the invisible dermarcation line and over the hills in long, unbroken waves. Wauchope Forest (a good Scots name) to the north, Kielder Forest to the south, along with their satellites Newcastleton, Kershope, Spadeadam, Wark and Redesdale forests – arbitrary distinctions for administrative convenience but all of a piece to the eye. Together they cover the middle Borders, a great forest where once the Cheviot hills were open to the sky.

Kielder, the heart of it, was Roy Robinson's baby. He witnessed

Spruce
Larch

the planting of the first spruce seedlings there, and after the war (by then Lord Robinson of Kielder Forest and Adelaide) he returned, cast aside his jacket, rolled up his sleeves (but didn't loosen his tie) and swung an axe at a young tree, the first thinning to be taken from the maturing forest. Reports don't say if he felled it by the strength of his arm or merely made the first cut, but in the photograph he looks the part, burly in waistcoat and plus fours, axe in hand, a noble woodcutter. (His last appearance at Kielder, in altered state, occurred in 1952 when his ashes were scattered among his trees.)

Since then the forest has doubled in size and the two hundred square miles of Kielder form the largest forest in Britain and one of the largest man-made forest in western Europe. Finally it acquired its own loch, more prosaically a reservoir – a feature unforeseen by the planters – created by the damming of the North Tyne in the late 1970s. This sheet of water is almost as large as Loch Katrine and is now the centrepiece of Kielder's tourist attractions (since the promotion of pleasure has become part of the Forestry Commission's born-again philosophy; walkers, bikers and horse riders being welcome).

Like every big plantation forest, Kielder has its computerised design plan. On-screen virtuality shows that forty years from now felling patches will be smaller and easier on the eye, geometrical patterns will have been replaced by flowing lines, and the rule of spruce relaxed by the introduction of broadleaf trees at salient places, mainly where people are likely to appreciate them. Blank walls of massed conifers will be breached to reveal the course of rivers and streams, a patchwork of trees young and old will replace dull uniformity of age, glades will be opened up to give breathing space, and above all the forest will conform to the features of the land – all in accordance with the Crowe doctrine. And not so much different, for that matter, from the principles Sir Walter Scott enunciated as he penned his views 'on planting waste lands' at his desk at Abbotsford two centuries ago.

The hills around Loch Lomond – the bonnie banks of the song – are justly famed for their beauty. Nothing wrong with the landscape there, you might say – who'd want to tamper with it? Well, Frank Bracewell for one. More of him later.

On a calm day Loch Lomond is a mirror reflecting mountain top and wooded slopes. As the seasons change the woodlands on the eastern shore below the Ben make a kaleidoscope of colour, fresh shades of green in the springtime, variegated with russets, fire and gold in the fall. The shoreline forest, once a working wood where the trees were coppiced, stripped of bark for tannin and cut for charcoal, is a pleasure ground now. There are car parks, picnic places, boating and bathing beaches. Soon it will become Scotland's first national park.

Conifers have been planted among the original oakwoods and further up the hill are large spreads of larch and spruce, partly Forestry Commission plantations, partly privately owned. Many are maturing now – fine timber woods, but already sentenced to early extinction. In another half century all trace of conifer plantation will be gone.

It's a tortuous story. Being hard up, the landowner of the time, the Duke of Montrose, had a notion to bequeath Ben Lomond and the bonnie banks (eastern side) to the nation and thus avoid death duties. But the Chancellor of the day (in 1931), Philip Snowden, turned him down and the duke sold it instead to his shooting tenants. After the war they too felt the pinch and offered it to the National Trust for Scotland. No luck – the trust could not afford it.

Hugh Dalton, Chancellor in Attlee's postwar Labour government, took a hand. Dalton, an idealist and country walker, set up a National Land Fund financed by the sale of surplus war material to acquire beautiful landscapes for the people. Thus in 1950 the whole eastern flank of Loch Lomondside including the Ben was bought with proceeds from the sale of warplanes, trucks and tanks, to be held in perpetuity as a memorial to those who had died in the war.

Perpetuity came abruptly to an end when Attlee fell and the incoming Tories renegued on the deal, thinking it smacked of land nationalisation. Ignoring its status as a memorial, the new government sold the lot to the Forestry Commission, with inevitable results. Where only oak and birch had flecked the slopes, swathes of conifers were now to flourish. The trees grew, and then in a new twist the Forestry Commission had its wings clipped by a new breed of Tories under Mrs Thatcher. In consequence the commission's unplanted land at Loch Lomond, including the Ben itself, was put up for sale. Conservationists horrified by the prospect of the nation's favourite mountain going to the highest bidder rallied to its defence, to such effect that the National Trust was at last enabled to buy the Ben and its surroundings.

Meanwhile the commission had seen the light and emerged as born-again environmentalists. In keeping with the mood of the time a plan was devised to soften the aggressive outlines of the state conifer plantations and make them friendlier to wildlife. The proportion of spruce was to be reduced in favour of more birch and oak. The solid mass of conifer trees was to be broken up. Such was the grand design for the new millennium.

For some, even this was not enough. Frank Bracewell scanned the wooded slopes from his home near the loch and dreamed of them transformed. Bracewell had been chief planning officer for the region, and in his view even the Forestry Commission's change of heart was insufficiently radical. He wanted rid of all the alien conifers.

Delving into the records, he unearthed the forgotten facts of Dalton's land fund and the purchase of Ben Lomond as a war memorial, and he used this knowledge as a lever in his campaign to transform the whole of the eastern side of the loch, from shoreline to the summit of the Ben, into a landscape that was wholly natural, where only native trees would grow, and where the public would be free to wander. At first he and his supporters met resistance; the Forestry Commission had its plan and would not budge. It took a *deus ex machina* in the form of Michael Forsyth, who doubled as Scottish Secretary and Forestry Minister, to resolve the impasse. Forsyth, on the brink of a general election that his party seemed certain to lose, and conscious that it was exactly fifty years since the end of the war, declared in December 1995

Larch in autumn glory reaching for the sky on the banks of Loch Lomond.

that the land owned by the Forestry Commission and the National Trust should become a memorial park to be managed jointly by both parties on strict conservation lines, with open access.

The details provoked a robust debate. The Forestry Commission had been set up to grow trees for timber. That was still its business and to do otherwise went against the grain. Some dedicated foresters felt that it marked yet another stage in the retreat from the principles of state forestry. In a rearguard action the commission refined its strategy further, proposing to cut back Sitka spruce severely to satisfy the environmentalists and to increase the number of larch trees – trees of great seasonal appeal.

It was a forlorn hope. Bracewell and his allies won the battle, the commission caved in and now embraces the greener vision with a whole heart. Year by year all the so-called alien species will be felled. The favoured native hardwood trees will be encouraged to spread, either naturally or by planting. By the year 2050, or so goes the plan, the bonnie banks will have been cleansed of all alien settlers and only native species will remain – a famous victory for the green crusaders.

One evening in late autumn I drive by the lochside, heading southwards on a narrow road dusted and brown with spent larch needles. Tall larch trees mass above me on either side, golden spires against blue sky. Nothing I have seen all day on Loch Lomondside makes a better show. Yet all are doomed to go, and I can't help feeling sad – yes, even though I know that from the start their destiny was to be cut down for cash. Only the blind could argue that this tree does not deserve its place.

Drumlanrig Castle in its silvan setting, much as the Victorians viewed it. Beyond the policy woods, twentieth-century commercial plantations give way to distant hills.

Oak and birch and the rest are lovely in season when the leaves are on, less so when bare. Fifty years from now when the evergreens are mostly gone, will the slopes below the Ben be bonnier without them? Will the tourists and day trippers at the lochside rejoice in the transformation – assuming they are aware of it? Will the wildlife care? Come mid century, we shall have the answers.

Eco-friendly forestry is dear to the Duke of Buccleuch, though cash is his bottom line. The duke's quartet of properties collectively form Britain's biggest private estate and at Drumlanrig he sits on the country's biggest single stretch of privately owned land. Trees are his bread and butter. They keep a roof over his head – it cost a million pounds recently to make Drumlanrig Castle rainproof.

Buccleuch is considered a people-friendly landlord, headlined in *The Field* as a 'one-man National Trust', which seems fair. The public are free to wander round his policies, or tread his corridors when he isn't at home. Even on outlying timber plantations there are waymarked footpaths. This is not a sudden change of heart. More than a century ago it was noted that on Buccleuch grounds 'notices of Trespassers will be Prosecuted and Keep to the Road and others of a like nature, by which a selfish and exclusive landlordism would seek to deprive the general public of enjoyments which are the heritage of humanity, are nowhere to be seen.'

Around the Duke's seat at Drumlanrig, a bluff pile of Jacobean aspect in the local pink sandstone, with domed turrets and a tower at each corner, are policy woods where the forester's touch is light – indeed the forester's judgment counts for less than private pleasure and the trees are sacrosanct. Some are mighty specimens, like the Douglas fir that started life as a seed sent back to Scotland by David Douglas himself to his brother, who was master of works at Drumlanrig, and planted it there in 1832. Further from the castle precincts, where conifers and broadleaf trees mingle in apparent happenstance, man may intervene, but lightly.

'This summer house is a work of art,' it says on the wall. 'Over 100 years old.' We stand in a rustic kiosk made of woven heather panels and birch bark, with the heather twisted into knot designs on the ceiling. From this vantage point we look down to Drumlanrig Castle, over a rhododendron in flower and an avenue cut through large mature trees. 'We've tried to re-create the view that they had in Victorian times,' says Graham Booth, the bearded head forester at Drumlanrig.

Driving through the estate, Booth explains that everything near the castle is done by the forester's eye. He seeks to promote the best tree in a setting, to find the key that will unlock the secret virtue of a place. Off the beaten track, still within home ground but less upfront, the treatment can be bolder. 'Our objectives change almost by the yard,' he says; yard by yard he selects here and there a tree which may be sacrificed to improve a view while others are allowed to flourish for the term of their lives or until harvest. He likes these woods to be relatively open – better woods to walk in, richer in wildlife.

We stop where a spruce tree and a red oak – an American native whose dying leaves take fire in the autumn – stand side by side at the edge of a lane. They will be too close for comfort as they grow larger. Booth will spare the red oak for the sake of forest colour and in due course will fell the conifer. Further on he has a similar dilemma, this time a spruce and a monkey puzzle, both fine trees. Fell the spruce to make the most of the Chile pine's exotic outline? Or leave them be? Booth hesitates; their fate can be postponed.

At a little stone bridge over the Marr Burn, his gentle thinning has created a glade prized by visitors. A young beech, a small rowan, two sycamores and a sad ash overhang the mossy parapet. In a few years' time they will overcrowd. Sycamores are ten a penny here and therefore expendable and will probably be sacrificed along with the unpromising ash. The beech tree is the key, says Booth. He imagines it in forty years' time – a lordly tree (its lower branches judiciously pruned) spreading a wide mantle over its attendant rowan.

Hard-hat choices – Drumlanrig's head forester Graham Booth on site, balancing economics and aesthetics.

Still within the sound of running water, a spot where the air is scented by the freshly cut timber stacked by the track-side – citrus, the distinctive smell of the grand fir tree. The timber of grand fir, fine though it is, is not easily sold in a market geared for assembly-line spruce; nevertheless the estate persists in its pursuit of a balanced forest.

Last stop in these near woods, very close again to the castle grounds, a fine stand of tall grey-barked conifers – these are the noble fir, so handsome in their maturity they have been selected as an officially approved seed source. Thus their descendants are scattered far and wide. A gift from Drumlanrig.

Booth takes to the hills, high above the valley of the Nith, where we look across river, road and rail to a wooded ridge seen against the distant Lowther Hills. This is Morton Hill, three hundred acres of conifers, mostly sitka spruce – a powerhouse of the Buccleuch economy, Booth calls it. Here trees are taken out wholesale and the operation begins to bring in cash. The open woods the duke and his public walk in show a loss on the balance sheet which has to be made up from commercial plantations. Otherwise, as Booth puts it: 'Lots of biodiversity and no money.' There's a naked wound on the hillside, a scar of clear-felling where loggers worked recently, leaving in their wake a brown devastation clearly visible even at a distance. For a year or two, as Booth admits, it will look like a bomb site until softened by new planting. He says a previous generation of foresters would have felled the whole hillside without scruple. Times change.

Last call is to another working forest which reaches nearly a thousand feet on the windy slopes of Cleuchhead Hill. Spruce does well on this hill and a good crop is promised; the trees grow fast and tight together, clean stems for the mill, trees for profit. 'We don't plant pure spruce any more, we plant a balanced forest.' Even in this high commercial plantation there's talk of cutting lanes so that people can walk there and enjoy the wide views – Everyman a duke for the day, without the headache of running an estate. On reflection, says Booth, 'I'd rather be the duke's forester than the duke.'

Deep in the dark wood something stirs. Can you hear it? See it? It's unlikely. Yet in the crepuscular depth of any large conifer plantation, a dank and mossy world barricaded by whippy branches and carpeted by dead needles, there is teeming life. In the night-in-day of close-grown stems you are in the presence of a multitude of living organisms. 'Microwildernesses exist in a handful of soil,' wrote the American naturalist Edward O Wilson, adding that a lifetime might be spent by the Magellan-entomologist circumnavigating a single tree trunk. At the extreme end of the scale are bacteria invisible to the naked eye. Spruce attracts a multitude of insects including some unusual aphids. There are bugs, mites, maggots, worms, caterpillars, aphids, spiders, springtails, booklice; all kinds of tiny life forms; all contributing in their millions to the diversity of woodland life.

On a patch of ground hardly bigger than a paving stone you may unearth many thousands of organisms. In a forest of Norway spruce near Oxford two scientists counted twelve species of spiders per square metre. When they broadened the area of search thirty-four different spider species came to light. Within each square-metre patch they would find on average more than 10,000 invertebrates. And surprisingly, when they turned their attention to a mature oakwood not far away they detected fewer than six hundred invertebrates in a similar area. Yet this was oak, the touchstone for forest biodiversity. Wildlife galore in a commercial plantation of thirty-five-year-old spruce. The known world turned upside down!

There is an unspoken hierarchy in our appreciation of wildlife. Feathered and furry creatures appeal more than the grubby earth-dwellers beneath our feet. But in the grand democracy of biodiversity this teeming underclass claims its place.

Spiders and aphids were not Bill Oddie's concern when he went to Kielder forest to make a programme for Radio 4. Oddie went to Kielder in search of birds. Where are they? he asked, standing among trees sixty feet tall in the gloom of what he called an arboreal cathedral. The birds were high in the treetops out of sight and earshot; crossbills, bullfinches, redpoles, tree pipits, wood warblers, owls and even goshawks.

The first casualty of moorland afforestation is the golden plover. No sooner are the seedling plants in the ground than they flee. The wheatear and ring ouzel remain a little longer before they too take flight. But for every loss there is a gain. In the case of Kielder the windchat, the occasional stonechat and more recently nightjars have been seen. New young growth provides good hunting for short-eared owls and hen harriers.

As the trees grow taller and thicker there are other population movements. At his next observation point Oddie stood among trees overtopping him by three or four feet, with plenty of vegetation underfoot. Self-sown birch trees had infiltrated, a godsend among conifers – fine for bullfinches on a mixed diet of birch seeds and spruce shoots. Bullfinches and redpolls had replaced the owls and hen harriers. Tree pipits filled the gap left by the meadow pipits.

By the time the trees reach thirty feet high the evironment has changed dramatically. All is dense and dark, ground vegetation has withered away, and crows and jays inhabit the trees. Abandoned crows' nests make cheap second-hand homes for merlins and owls. Goshawks, newcomers in Kielder, dodge through the trees like stealth raiders. At ground level silence reigns and the forest floor belongs to the hidden throng of nameless things.

Even in the thickest conifer plantation other woody things infiltrate and survive – on the forest edge, in gullies or alongside burns, or where the cover is patchy. Birch, for example, grows like a weed, and until twenty years ago most self-respecting foresters treated it as such. They tried but never quite managed to kill it off.

Birch is a star player in the biodiversity game. Not as highly regarded as the oak tree, it's true, especially the oaks of southern England, but in the harsher climate of the north and on the poor thin soils of the hills where oak is unhappy the birch tree is its nearest substitute as a wildlife centre. In the depths of a spruce forest there may be groves of old birch infested with a variety of lichens – delicate species that avoid the dry, acid bark of the surrounding conifers. Because it's an asylum for plants and creatures within conifer forests, birch is now encouraged to expand within them. This is the way the ecological wind is blowing.

Timber operations – with horse, axe and plenty of manpower – according to a cheerfully bucolic 1950s forest guide. Ill-planned plantations and ugly felling scars were often the norm.

Old growth is the thing. Old growth is ancient forest, virgin forest, forest in its natural state. In North America old-growth forest still exists in spite of the loggers' worst efforts. The nearest we have to old growth in Scotland – a long way from the original state – are the Atlantic oakwoods of the west and the pinewoods of the north, the old cores of Caledonian pine, birch and kindred species in the forests of Affric, Abernethy, Glenmore and Rothiemurchus, and around Loch Maree. Even these shreds of ancient glory are impoverished. Lacking the complex web of life that only the slow uninterrupted reign of nature allows to develop.

Life is richest in old-growth forest. There in light and shade, in the tangle of undergrowth and in open glades, among trees that range in age from saplings to centuries-old veterans, on living and decaying timber, in standing pools or running streams, in the slowly accumulating mould on the ground, is the perfect million-species universe. Lichens and fungi invade the woody debris, mosses and twining plants shroud the trees, creatures trample and poke among the roots and snip young shoots, bats and birds inhabit hollows in the trunks, woodpeckers drill, insects buzz, beetles tunnel and chomp according to their kind.

Whatever we do we can only approximate to this state of nature, given a sufficient lapse of time. The longer a plantation survives the richer is the sum of all living things within it, as simple observation suggests and numerous studies prove. In Galloway the number and variety of songbirds grows with the age of the plantation trees. More than twice as many birds, and more species, nest in century-old conifer plantations than in those of fifty years' growth. Old stands of Caledonian pine, rather than the new, are the preferred habitat for the Scottish crossbill and crested tit and for specialist groups of invertebrates and lichens. Red squirrels are most at home where trees are old and widely spread. Bats prefer their trees dead.

A prediction has been made that once the great Border plantation forests reach their most productive age, say in fifteen years' time when the estimated output is expected to be double what it is today, the timber juggernauts will pass on their window-rattling way through the village of Newcastleton at an average rate of one every five minutes. By that time most of the conifer forests planted so prodigiously throughout the country in postwar years will be ready for harvest, and all over rural Scotland the logging trucks will be on the move.

Ironically, all those trees planted so optimistically may prove an embarrassing excess when that time comes. As I write, market prices are severely depressed and the slump is exacerbated by imports of cheap timber from the vast forests of eastern Europe shipped from the Baltic ports. No one can forecast what the situation will be in five years' time, let alone fifteen.

We could, of course, make a decision to turn commercial glut to ecological advantage. Can we hope that some large parts of the man-made forests may be left in peace to mature instead of being hastened to market for a quick return? That reprieved plantation woodlands will be left to grow old, decay (if that's the word), to form the beginnings of a whole living, regenerating organism, a perpetual forest?

Within a great man-made forest of spruce or pine, say in Galloway or on Deeside, a sizeable area might be preserved, untouchable, in perpetuity. In a buffer zone around it only selected trees would be prudently harvested, taken out in small numbers or even singly, in a gentle progression towards the outer wood where commercial (but sensitive) forestry would rule. In the sacrosanct heart of the forest trees will die in their time, leaving dead wood as home and sustenance for a myriad creatures and plants. In fifty years' time the interior will be strangely different from an orthodox plantation forest, wilder and untidier; and in a hundred years and more, a place of dark mystery and delight. A new Wood of Caledon.

Jock Carlisle sets out in quest of ancient pinewood.
The shotgun is for bringing down cones – he found shooting at them less painful
than climbing into the branches and falling out again.

18

ON THE TRAIL OF THE ANCIENT PINES

I HEARD about the fabled Old Caledonian forest at school. We learned, I seem to remember, that you could see some of the last Caledonian pines just north of Loch Lomond, in Glen Falloch, on the way to Crianlarich.

Beyond the marshy headwaters of the loch the road north emerges into a landscape of bare hill and moorland. A single pine comes into view against the sky, a skewed stem topped by a dome of dark green foliage. I think of lines by the poet Kenneth White

> Behold the mad pine
> Stark on the sky-line. . .

This April morning after the snows have melted I boulder-hop big rocks that split the Falloch river, one, two, three, and clamber up the hillside. Below me lies the railway and the road, a cottage or two, a herd of cattle, with snow-veined hills beyond. Above me bare slopes. And, some way uphill, a single stunted but sturdy tree. I slap its rough flank.

Hail! old pine. The old Wood of Caledon starts here.

Some of the trees scattered beyond it are strong and healthy. A couple standing side by side are laden with cones, brown specks in dark foliage. Others are long since dead. Most show signs of age and injury. One, laid low by a recent gale, leans over water, its top still bushy and green though its roots have been dragged half out of the ground. A stalwart stands on a knoll among the torn wreckage of its massy branches.

Where the pines peter out a fallen trunk by the river sticks an arm in the air. And then no more. Larch trees in the big plantation ahead show fresh growth and the snowy cone of Ben More sparkles in the sun. Terminus.

'Many fyrre woods here alongs.' Timothy Pont's sixteenth-century map of Glencoe and Mamore implies considerable though possibly scattered pinewoods in an area where few trees remain.

John Evelyn the diarist had heard tell of them. 'In Scotland there is a most beautiful sort of fir growing upon the mountains', he wrote in *Sylva*, his great work on trees and woodlands, published in 1664.

The traveller Thomas Kirk had been there and seen with his own eyes: 'Some fir woods there are in the Highlands, but so inaccessible that they serve no other use than dens for those ravenous wolves with two legs.'

Daniel Defoe, too. He reported in his *Tour Through the Whole Island of Great Britain* that 'on the most inland parts of this country... they have vast woods of fir trees, not planted or set by men's hands, but growing wild and undirected, otherwise than as nature planted and nourished them up, by the additional help of time, nay, of ages'.

A narrow road winds into the hills north of the Great Glen, now pot-holed though it once was the road to the isles. * *Moorland. Rain and desolation. We peer into the hill fog at a distant patch, scrappy woodland dotted over the lower slopes. To reach it involves a hike of a mile across stubborn heather and bog, with a river to cross on the way. We splash through, noting the desiccated tree roots embedded under the banks – trees that lived before the peat began to form thousands of years ago.*

The wood, such as it is, now protected by a high deer fence, consists of old pine trees scattered over a mile or so of hillside. Some are dead, shorn of bark and decaying; others are on their last legs. The

---

* This road is padlocked to all but the landowner and friends, shooters, fishers and estate servants. The Sassenach laird wishes to protect the solitude of his glens. Nor does he want the location revealed.

The oldest known Scots pine tree, defying the elements in a 'secret' location beyond the Great Glen. This veteran and a handful of its scattered companions have survived for more than five hundred years.

survivors have been counted. The total was less than ninety when the count was made some years ago and at least one has gone since then. The foliage on several is ominously thin and sparse.

Among the living and the dead are many old stumps rotting away, weather-worn into spikes and hollows and sometimes capped with little gardens of vegetation. On one stump grows a medley of blaeberry and crowberry, several mosses and lichens, fern, butterwort, heather and heath.

At the eastern end of the wood several pine trees cluster among crags at the mouth of a small glen below a mountain hidden in the mist. Tim Clifford, a pony-tailed ecologist recently in charge of the Nature Conservancy's Beinn Eighe reserve, tells us he once abseiled down these crags to gather cones for seed. Closer to hand a giant pine grows straight as an arrow from a huge boulder on a knoll. Its tracery of roots clutching the rock has been undercut and exposed by running water, forming a moss-encrusted cavern. Less impressive to the eye are two neighbouring pines. They're old-stagers, for sure, tough and characterful but not otherwise remarkable − except that they are the oldest Scots pine trees known in this country. Cores taken from them a few years ago show that both have survived for well over 500 years. One may be as old as 550, though rot at the heart makes it impossible to age it precisely. These trees were young when Columbus set sail. They were already fine specimens when Bonnie Prince Charlie fled this way after Culloden.

Five hundred years is far from a record in tree longevity. Some species live for thousands of years, and even Pinus sylvestris, *our Scots pine, is thought to have reached 800 years on the continent of Europe. Until recently the normal lifespan of Scots pine in this country was assumed to be less than three centuries, and none was known to have*

reached four. But who knows what veterans lurk unrecognised in, say,
the depths of Glenfeshie or Glen Affric?

    Tim puts his arms round our venerable tree and touches his
forehead against its rugged bark. It's a spiritual moment. And then, as
we look back at the crags, a great dark bird launches itself into the air,
soars high and then sweeps down the wind, wings outspread, to alight
on top of a pine. A golden eagle.

The old pinewoods of the Highlands have been the subject of wistful fascination for at least three hundred years. These, after all, are the legendary Caledonian pines. But their inevitable fate seemed to be slow decay and eventual death.

    This was the general opinion when, in the early summer of 1933, before the midges were out, members of the Royal Scottish Forestry Society motored into the northwest Highlands. At Loch Maree they enjoyed a view of the bare mountain Slioch across the water, before their attention was captured by the trees. As 'the road gradually became fringed with pine forest we finally found ourselves in one of the best examples of natural forest in the country' – a patch of woodland known as Coille na Glas Leitir 'wood of the grey slope'.

    Stepping down from their vehicles for a closer look, they wandered about the hillside below the mountain Beinn Eighe before gathering round a particularly fine old pine tree. A Mr Ehrenborg, a guest from Sweden, suggested digging drains on the soggy terrain to encourage the woodland to spread – at that time and for years to come an acceptable doctrine for the 'improvement' of old woodland. But horror! anathema to conservationists now.

    The consensus was that the pinewood's only chance of long-term survival was acquisition, management and conversion into a timber forest by the new Forestry Commission. Timber, after all, was their concern, not the wildwood, not its wildlife. Thus agreed, the party boarded their vehicles and drove off, leaving the age-old forest to time and neglect. War came. Deer ate the seedlings as of old and a few more veterans succumbed. Little changed.

Not to despair.

    In 1935 the Royal Scottish Forestry Society approached the newly-formed National Trust for Scotland, lamenting the endangered state of the few remaining relics of Caledonian pinewood and suggesting a joint effort to acquire and protect at least one of them for posterity. The foresters, not having sufficient funds of their own, needed the backing of the trust's wealthy grandees. And the trust approved, perhaps swayed by Sir John Stirling Maxwell – he who had caused a forest to grow in the desert at Corrour, who had chaired the Forestry Commission, and who had been a principal founder of the trust four years earlier.

The foresters then cast their eyes about for 'a remnant of the old natural forest which could be acquired by the National Trust with a view to its preservation'. Word went round in aristocratic circles. Likely Highland landowners with old pinewood on their ground were approached. Who they were, which pinewoods were identified (and whether the Loch Maree pines were among them) and what price was offered is not known. It was all very discreet.

But it came to nothing. The secretary of the Forestry Society was forced to report that 'proprietors have been approached but none have been found willing to dispose of any of their natural woods'.

Then a seeming white knight cantered on to the scene in the form of the Forestry Commission (had Stirling Maxwell a hand in this too?) and this time the trust could be given better news: 'The Forestry Commission have intimated that they are entirely sympathetic to the society's proposals that some remnants of the natural forests of Scotland should be retained in their original state.' Indeed the commission, which had acquired core Caledonian pinewoods in the course of its business, could boast that it had already, unbidden, set aside some sites for preservation.

Thus far and no further. 'The Forestry Commission cannot hand over any part of its property, voluntarily, but the National Trust may be sure that the areas selected will remain in the possession of the Crown and that the stock of trees upon them will receive all proper attention henceforward.'

They didn't. War came and many of the old trees were chopped down. The commission continued to neglect or compromise the old woodland sites in its care, and half a century would pass before it saw the light.

*

Pathway into the Glen Derry
pinewoods in the 1930s – much
as Jock Carlisle tramped it twenty
years later.

After an uncomfortable night in 'the most dismal hotel in the world' a young Englishman with a public-school background, recent wartime service in the RAF, and degrees in biology and forestry made his way to the university forestry department at Old Aberdeen. The visit was to have a momentous consequence, beginning with the publication in 1959, nine years later, of a book called *The Native Pinewoods of Scotland*, now better known simply as Steven & Carlisle from the surnames of its joint authors.

Henry (known to a few intimates as Harry) Marshall Steven, professor of forestry at Aberdeen, had been involved in the practice and theory of forestry for many years. He had been the Forestry Commission's first research officer in Scotland, then a forest manager and, during the war, controller of the home timber supply. Back in academia at Old Aberdeen he conceived the idea of locating, surveying and appraising all the old pinewoods.

Some were already well known. A cursory reconnaissance had been made by Arthur George Tansley, at the time professor of botany at Oxford,[*] for his landmark book *The Vegetation of the British Islands*, published on the eve of Hitler's war. Tansley's view of the old pinewoods was necessarily selective. In Perthshire he saw the Black

---

[*] At this stage in his life 'his silvering hair, tallish, spare figure and somewhat unathletic movements suited his unassuming distinction' (*Dictionary of National Biography*). He was a man of probing mind: botanist, biologist, proto-ecologist (he coined the term ecosystem); an interest in philosophy and psychology led to his giving up lecturing for a year to study with Sigmund Freud in Vienna.

Wood of Rannoch, and he noted (possibly through the eyes of a colleague who took off northwards on his own) where old remnant pinewoods grew in many of the glens beyond the Caledonian Canal. Not surprisingly he concluded that the two greatest spreads of ancient pinewood were to be found east and west of the Cairngorm Mountains – it would be hard to miss them. He tramped through the king's forest at Ballochbuie, next door to Balmoral, and looked up from the glacial sands and gravels through which the River Feshie winds to trees clinging to the crags, reaching 'about the highest altitude of any woodland in the British Isles'.

The fate of the pinewoods seemed inevitable. They would die, and were being helped on their way. The evidence of heavy felling in the Great War was all too clear. Another threat came from state forestry. Tansley reported that what remained of the pinewoods north of the Great Glen was being rapidly destroyed by the Forestry Commission and that the old forest in Glenmore, once entirely a native pinewood, was being diluted by exotic species. A neutral and objective witness, he expressed no regret.

Tansley's list was far from comprehensive and as for the rest – how authentic were the stands of seemingly ancient pinewood scattered through the Highlands? Or those isolated clumps of gnarled pine on crags and in gorges? Were they truly natural or had they or their ancestors been planted in past centuries? This was what Steven and Carlisle set out to establish.

Jock Carlisle (properly Alan, though he seldom uses the name) turned up at the right moment and became Steven's leg man, researcher and co-author. The task took him all over the Highlands, lodging in shepherds' or stalkers' cottages, or occasionally in some unspeakable hotel with only a poor peat glowing in the grate or no heating at all – this being the 1950s, before tourists demanded better – or, if he was lucky, as a guest in the 'big house'. Many times he slept under the stars. There were mishaps and adventures, one of which nearly ended his life.

Steven and he, I guess, were not soul mates. Steven was reserved and austere. Former students, now into their sixties and seventies, remember him with respect. Carlisle was outgoing and ebullient in spite of a debilitating stammer, fond of sporty cars, and apt to be pugnacious.[*]

For six years Steven and Carlisle were yoked awkwardly together on the pinewood project. At first the brief was was nebulous – Carlisle remembers simply being told to 'go and study the native pinewoods'. He spent a fortnight living in a bothy over the stables in Glen Tanar, where, day by day, he would tramp over the ground with his taciturn mentor, the head forester Duncan Ross, a legendary man in his time, whose observation and canny instinct made him in Carlisle's eyes the equal of any scientist.

After this initiation Carlisle set off to identify those pinewoods which, in the words of the book still to be written, had 'descended from one generation to another by natural means' – the lineal descendants of the ancient forest on its home ground. It was easier said than done. Some were already familiar, especially the larger and more accessible sites in Strathspey and Glen Affric. Many were not. Carlisle diligently followed up even vaguely remembered hints of old pinewoods in distant glens and more often than not drew a blank. He scanned hazy aerial photographs for signs of unrecorded woodlands, with limited success. Above all he tramped the hills, compass and map in hand, making for the high ridges from where he could spy down the length of a glen, out in all weathers, all seasons, walking distances of twenty miles or more through heather and bog, over rocky outcrops and plunging through burns in spate. Snow on the ground made it easier to spot distant trees.

Before the days of lightweight, quick-drying clothes he wore jumpers under a tweed jacket, cord riding breeches, gaiters and heavy nailed climbing boots. Sometimes he slept out for nights in a row, huddled under a rock. His iron rations were dates, raisins and biscuits. He carried a camera, a shotgun for shooting down cones (after a few bone-shaking falls he gave up tree-climbing), and a telescope for identifying distant woodlands. Into his rucksack went stones, soil, cones and twigs for analysis in the lab. The filled pack could easily reach fifty pounds in weight.

---

[*] Hence a fist-fight on his first night as an airman. Room-mates – he says they were Glaswegians – mocked his stammer and posh accent, and he retaliated.

Those six years were an epic. Once, heading for Diebidale in Easter Ross, he nearly died. On cresting a ridge with a fierce wind driving snow in his face, he slipped, fell over a cliff edge and concussed himself. When he came to he couldn't move at first and thought he was paralysed – he remembers dreading a hungry fox or a bird attacking him. Once he got moving he crawled and staggered for miles, sometimes hallucinating. He forded an icy river, holding his clothes above his head to keep them dry, and managed to light a fire in the shelter of a ruined cottage.

In all, he thinks he covered about eleven miles before he lay down by the roadside in Strath Carron and was picked up by an old gent in an ageing jalopy who drove him to a small hotel at Ardgay run by two maiden ladies who bathed, fed and nursed him back to fitness.

There's no record of this episode, or any other of his adventures, in the book that emerged. *Native Pinewoods* is not that sort. Of Jock Carlisle's near-fatal excursion it says not a word.

Steven & Carlisle begins with a flourish: 'Scots pine is the most widely distributed conifer in the world.' Then, having delineated its spread across the Northern Hemisphere from the Atlantic almost to the Bering Sea, it makes a large claim for the few vestiges of ancient pinewood left in Scotland, where

> Even to walk through the larger of them gives one a better idea of what a primeval forest was like than can be got from any other woodland scene in Britain. The trees range in age up to 300 years and there are thus not very many generations between their earliest predecessors about 9000 years ago and those growing today; to stand in them is to feel the past.

That last phrase has become a mantra routinely intoned by today's conservationists. It reflects Jock Carlisle's belief that he could sense, after a time, whether a pinewood was truly ancient or not. This eerie consciousness was shaped by the character of individual trees, the patterns in which they grew, the subtle way they blended with the land and the landscape, and what other trees, shrubs and plants grew among them.

True veteran pinewood or just an old plantation in decay? How do you tell? Records prove that these trees at Braco, near Crieff, were planted. In such a case, when there was nothing else to go on, Jock Carlisle trusted his intuition.

The book ranged over many topics but the heart of it was a series of chapters describing thirty-five separate pinewoods. Since then more have been identified, but by and large the canon remains as Steven & Carlisle defined it. (It's salutary to note that a quarter of a century later the area of woodland described in the book had shrunk by a fifth – such has been the accelerating pace of their decline.) The task that Steven & Carlisle began has now been completed under the auspices of the Forestry Commission, whose Caledonian pinewood inventory seeks to establish the whereabouts of every last group of pine trees that can be considered a true relic. Most of the late additions are small in scale, like the canyon-clinging pine trees sprinkled among birch above Little Loch Broom in Wester Ross, or the barely accessible cluster of wiry survivors niched on the far side of the big mountain An Teallach.

The conclusion Steven & Carlisle came to was clear and unambiguous: 'From every point of view these woodlands should be preserved and perpetuated.' In time it would come triumphantly into its own. The argument which carries most weight today was that the old pinewoods formed a unique ecosystem, such as 'all civilised countries' agreed should be preserved, and that 'it would be a national loss if [they] were allowed to disappear.'

Finally the authors called on landowners, foresters and 'biologists specially interested in the native pinewoods' (conservationists were still to emerge as a separate species) – to work together to achieve this aim.

Optimistically, they suggested that the Forestry Commission and the Nature Conservancy might jointly take the lead, and in a curious way, it came to pass. Between them the Forestry Commission, now having adopted a green philosophy, and the Conservancy in its new guise as Scottish Natural Heritage, are partners in the drive to restore ancient native woodland – and not just the pinewoods, but leaf-tree woods as well.

Shortly after the publication of the book, members of the Society of Foresters came from all over Britain to Inverness for their annual meeting. On an outing to Glen Affric, Steven – a founder and past president of the society – addressed the members. Look on this beauty, he said. If you do nothing these ancient pinewoods will die. They listened, nodded, and his words blew on the wind. Ideas, too, may be slow to grow.

Sixteen years later there came a response. A landmark conference on native pinewoods, held in Aviemore, discussed the topics raised by Steven & Carlisle and essentially laid down the principles for the future native woodlands movement. Now conservation has become the orthodoxy of the day, promoted by government and environmental bodies and buttressed by grants.

If you take the road in Glen Affric to the end of Loch Beinn a'Mheadhoin and then follow a footpath to the top of a heathery knoll, you will come to a memorial which recognises the contribution of Harry Steven and others unnamed towards the rescue of the native pinewoods. Standing by the bronze plaque, set in a stone table facing west, you will see what Steven saw when he spoke to his fellow foresters. The blue hills of Kintail are visible on the skyline and below you the River Affric winds into the small shimmer of Loch Affric, round which cluster the dark trees of the old pinewood. Caledonia for ever.

Seventy years ago a group of foresters gathered round an ancient pine tree at
Coille na Glas Leitir on the shores of Loch Maree and bemoaned the terminal state of the native forest.
They were too pessimistic. It became Britain's first nature reserve.

19

CHAOS THEORIES

'THESE WOODS should be preserved and perpetuated,' wrote Steven & Carlisle, and though it took time for their words to sink in, it came to pass. The Forestry Commission bought Glen Affric in 1951 and in accordance with its brief proceeded to lay siege to the old pinewoods with blocks of spruce and lodgepole pine. In neighbouring Cannich it set about felling the natives wholesale. Very little was left. But the mood was changing and things took a turn for the better when their man Findlay Macrae appeared on the scene a decade later.

Macrae, a big, bearded, kilted, bagpipe-playing, Gaelic-speaking west-coaster, had not been pleased to be posted to Dingwall as district officer for the north of Scotland. First sight of the Affric forest converted him – he stayed on, happily, for twenty-three years. Affric, he says, is at its best twice in the year – in May with a little snow on the tops and fresh growth on the birch showing against the deep green of the pine, and in autumn when the birch is ablaze with reds and yellows. It was spring when he first saw it and it was an epiphany – not merely because there was 'no semblance of a plantation about it', as he says, but because its beauty overwhelmed him; it was 'an awe-inspiring place, a wonderland'. Deep in its recesses, when going about his business, he felt at peace.

The state had not been wholly insensitive to Affric, and some attempt had already been made to rejuvenate the old pinewood. Two thousand acres of ancient forest along the southern side of Loch Beinn a'Mheadhoin had been enclosed by a fence in the forlorn hope of keeping the deer out and allowing the pines trees to regenerate.

'Native wood-notes wild'. Findlay Macrae, aka Mr Pinewood, plays to the forest in Glen Affric.

Deer seeking shelter from hard winters on the hill broke through the fence and, once inside, roamed freely over the whole forest. Natural regeneration failed. Macrae appeared to be presiding over a woodland in terminal decline.

Unwilling to sit back and watch it decay, he took action, including a blitzkrieg on browsers. Two of his keepers were instructed to shoot on sight – red deer, roe deer, stags, hinds, bucks and does, in and out of season – until numbers fell. They fired away. Simultaneously, as a fail-safe, some planting went ahead using young pine trees grown from seed collected in Affric. In the end the forest began to seed itself and first the birch and then the pine spread marvellously.

'Mr Pinewood', as colleagues christened him, met some resistance from his peers, and his decision to opt for conservation roused the ire of forestry traditionalists. But in time there came a change of heart, culminating with a decision by the commission to clear the glen of all foreign tree species and to give it over entirely to wild nature (barring a little gentle tourism). As a mark of their intent they dubbed it their first 'Caledonian forest reserve'.

A modish title. Nature conservation was in the air as World War Two came to a close and the planners looked ahead to a better Britain; which meant, among other things, that care for the countryside and the protection of wild nature gained a place on the postwar agenda. Thus the Nature Conservancy was formed in 1949 to create national reserves where habitats rich in plant and bird life could be saved for posterity. The guiding spirit and first chairman of the conservancy was Arthur Tansley; as the core of its first reserve it acquired Coille na Glas Leitir, the woodland above Loch Maree described by Tansley on his pre-war reconnaissance as the best natural pinewood in the northwest Highlands, and by the travelling party of foresters before him as 'one of the best examples of natural forest in the country'. The woodland covered only 750 acres but with it the conservancy acquired a huge tract of moorland rising from the shores of the loch to the craggy skyline of the Beinn Eighe massif (which gave the reserve its name) – more than ten thousand acres 'thrown in cheap', as the conservancy's Earl of Wemyss declared, at a bargain price of £4000.

A job lot, no doubt, but size was found to matter. The woodland formed part of a much wider ecological system, and deemed just as important as the trees was the 'transitional' moorland which typically replaced woodland in a wet climate. (Wet? Eighty inches – 2000mm – of rain in the year.) The forest was an essential part of the whole biological unit, as Professor William Harold Pearsall – opinionated, a bit deaf, a great mountain walker, author of a notable book on mountains and moorland and the conservancy's chairman of scientific policy – pointed out in his draft recommendations for the management of the reserve.

Members of the conservancy were soon wrangling over the proper way to run Beinn Eighe, and when members and staff visited the site in the summer of 1952 a hot debate broke out under the trees. The conservancy's Scottish director Dr John Berry later confessed to being shaken by the rift between eminent ecologists and the vehemence with which their antagonisms were expressed.

A key issue was to what extent, if at all, forestry methods should be introduced into the wildwood. A statement made after the field visit sounded an ominous note. It was agreed that the woodland must be fenced against sheep and deer. More contentiously, it was suggested that small groups and patches of native trees might be planted out among the existing pines and an 'experimental re-creation of woodland' should be attempted on open ground in the southern slopes of the reserve by planting Scots pine seedlings, possibly sheltered by non-native types of faster-growing conifers. All this could be undertaken 'under the guidance' of the Forestry Commission who were the experts in such things.

This sounds like inviting the wolf into the fold, and the wolf was already sniffing at the fank in the guise of Sir Henry Beresford-Peirse, the Forestry Commission's director in Scotland. Beresford-Peirse declared magisterially that the Forestry Commission also had 'an interest' in Beinn Eighe since it had a 'duty to achieve the maximum productivity of the woodlands of this country'. He added that the aims of both parties would be best served by handing over the core woodland to the Forestry Commission who would then get on with 'the actual regeneration'. Everyone would benefit. A forestry project would be carried out, fittingly, by the country's forest authority and the conservancy would be spared the heavy expense of work 'which is really in the sphere of another organisation'. At this point, in the words of a recent manager of the reserve, the fledgling Nature Conservancy project at Beinn Eighe was perilously close to being swallowed whole.

But the jaws did not close. True, the small band of recruits to the new Conservancy were more familiar with the microscope than the spade and the mating habits of butterflies and birds than the nurture of forest trees, and they were ignorant of forestry techniques. Nor had they any trained woodmen on the payroll. But they resisted the blandishments of Beresford-Peirse. As the zoologist Maurice Yonge put it, 'there is a gulf between the outlook of the botanical ecologist and that of the forester'. And the 'disingenuous' report of the unharmonious meeting at Loch Maree drew a stinging rebuke from Conservancy's first director general Cyril Diver: 'The discussion appears to have been based on the tacit assumption that the Conservancy's function should be so to modify the pinewood at Coille na Glas Leitir so as to make it, as nearly as possible, by silvicultural standards a good wood. [A good wood, in forestry terms, being plenty of tall, straight trees ripe for the sawmill, a plantation by another name.] That this provides a valid basis for considering the regime of biological management which should be applied to one of the Conservancy's few first class national reserves, I must categorically deny.' To Diver a programme of wholesale planting, a landscape churned up by the tractor and plough, was too horrid to contemplate.

Dick Balharry in Creag Meagaidh.
'A tree in a fence is a tree in a cage'.

And so, for a while, the soft touch was favoured. People were relaxed about how the wood might develop. They understood that a scrub of birch, rowan and pine mixed together would probably appear. Meanwhile a series of careful experiments was conducted by the scientist Donald McVean, and by and large the forest was encouraged to grow as it willed, with just a little help from its friends.

As time went by nature failed (or so it seemed) to rise to the challenge. There supervened a nervy sense that something radical must be tried. Perhaps the soil, starved of goodness by long years of heavy grazing, needed a fertilising booster. Perhaps infant trees should be planted more thoroughly among and around the old-stagers to speed things up. Perhaps (but whisper it!) the Forestry Commission might know a thing or two. According to the revisionist view which now prevailed it was hopeless to expect the restoration of Coille na Glas Leitir by natural regeneration alone. So the attempt was abandoned in favour of ploughing, draining and feeding, and seedling pine trees from various sources were planted in considerable numbers.

But there are swings and roundabouts, and after twenty years or so yet another new chapter opened in the story of Beinn Eighe. After much digging and delving, and 300,000 new pine trees and 100,000 broadleaves later, the whistle was blown and caution restored. Intruder conifers were ripped up again and nature was given a second chance. And so it stands today.

*

Thirty years after the Nature Conservancy acquired Beinn Eighe it bought another mountain, where only a smattering of native trees grew, and no pine. In this case the motive was not to safeguard woodland but to stave off the threat of commercial afforestation.

The great tableland of Creag Meagaidh spreads over many square miles of grass, moss, lichen and rock between Badenoch and Lochaber. This high moorland, long sacred to sheep and red deer, is encircled by sporting estates where deerstalking is a paying business. Yet in spite of continuous grazing, a fascinating range of plants grows in succession from lochside to the stony plateau. Bird life includes the eagle, hen harrier, dotterel, dunlin, golden plover and short-eared owl. And trees? Mostly scattered scrub – though this is changing – alongside the Ardair Burn which curves down from a silent, cliff-bound lochan past the former farm of Aberarder towards Loch Laggan.

Creag Meagaidh was acquired in 1979 by a forestry company which proposed to smother more than a thousand acres of the species-rich hillside in conifers. Plants and nesting grounds would be lost, access to the mountain might be impeded, and a stark beauty impaired. Environmentalists, mountaineers and lovers of wild place joined forces to protest; both the Nature Conservancy and the Royal Society for the Protection of Birds became involved, and the extrovert naturalist David Bellamy offered his body for the cause, threatening to lie in the path of the first bulldozer to approach.

It didn't come to that. The forestry application was referred to the Scottish Secretary Michael Forsyth, whose judgment of Solomon[*] pleased no one. Fountain Forestry, piqued, put the property back on the market and in a happy turn of events the Nature Conservancy bought it, though at a price. Fountain Forestry, not having planted a single tree, made a handsome profit. But the speculators were seen off the ground and Creag Meagaidh became a nature reserve.

Neighbouring landowners whose properties marched with the reserve feared the worst, not so much from the entry of environmentalists as the rumoured grand slaughter of red deer by the Conservancy. It was muttered that every single beast on the reserve, stag, hind or calf, would be massacred so that Meagaidh's precious vegetation could recover undisturbed. The presence of deer is a

[*] He gave permission to plant – but only on half of the ground proposed.

necessity for a sporting estate and Meagaidh's neighbours had the nightmare vision of herds deserting their hills for the lusher (and safer) pastures of the new nature reserve.

It wasn't the Somme, though in early years the toll was heavy – during the spring of 1987 more than two hundred animals were killed on the open hill – and over ten years the resident population in Creag Meagaidh's two herds of red deer, estimated originally at a thousand, declined to less than a hundred, a number considered to be environmentally acceptable. The procession of asylum-seeking stags across the hill into Creag Meagaidh did not happen; the 'vacuum' did not fill. As Richard Sidgwick, agent for one of the sporting estates – a 'well-whiskered, well-spoken, tweed-clad gent' in the words of the environmental writer Auslan Cramb – admitted, 'our misgivings were unfounded'. And suddenly the long-repressed, bitten-back latent woodland is springing back lustily from the undergrowth.

Creag Meagaidh, October. Storms threaten. Three of us walk into the glen, the naturalist Dick Balharry in the lead. Balharry, big man, thickly bearded, once had charge of this ground for the Nature Conservancy and is still a frequent visitor.

The lower part of the glen is dotted with small trees, old and gnarled and feathered with lichens – but that's not what draws the eye. All around, covering acres of ground, a new forest is rising, and so we walk through groves of delicate young birch, some bushes already taller than we are. Their leaf tracery has been thinned by autumn winds but still they make a fine show, gilded by stray beams of sunlight. In a few years' time there will be thickets too dense to break through.

Close by stands a great boulder dropped on the hillside by a retreating glacier thousands of years ago, covered with a crazy pattern of many-coloured lichens. Balharry says that time might be measured by these lichens – you could gauge how long the boulder had lain there if you could read the signs.

A lesser stone at the side of the path marks the end of a transect, a narrow strip of ground stretching across the burn and on to the opposite hillside, where changes in vegetation can be observed. Since the deer were culled the number and variety of plants has increased dramatically. At first botanists checking the plants could cover the ground in a couple of hours. Now a day is too short.

Towards the head of the glen the flush of seedling birch thins out. There are few old parent trees and the few successors that push out

Nesting ospreys at Loch Garten lured the RSPB into forest ownership at Abernethy.

of the heather have their shoots bitten off. Balharry speculates that there may be still too many deer on the hill. The trees end, the slopes are bare. The lochan in the corrie lies just out of sight, and so does the solitary bird cherry tree Balharry says grows beyond it. He thinks it may be the oldest tree in the glen. In time, will this oldie take part in the general advance? Will its cherries fall, seeds germinate, plants grow tall and a new generation spring round the feet of Methuselah?

We retrace our steps, seeking to cross the burn in spate and investigate the trees on the far side. We have to wade. There, such trees as survive are small and crippled, often wind-damaged, senescent. Or dead. Broken timber lies on the ground, some covered with moss, some recently fallen, showing fresh wounds. A picturesque but melancholy sight. Ring counts from fallen stems indicate a mean age of about a hundred years, which is generally taken to be the limit of a birch tree's natural life. Early in the twentieth century most of these trees sprang up and no more followed. Why this should be is a puzzle.

We poke around in the vegetation but find little sign of seedlings getting away. They exist, but most are chewed off at heather height. Balharry frowns. He says it's a matter of fine adjustment; a slight decrease in grazing, a slight increase in the number of seedlings coming through, and the balance could be tilted enough to allow the woodland to renew itself.

Patience is Balharry's watchword. Let nature take its course. Let deer amble among the trees, but not in the number encouraged by a century of protection for sport. Let them nibble the new crop of seedlings, checking its tendency to rampant growth but without obliterating it.

To Balharry, fences are an abomination: 'A tree in a fence is a tree in a cage.' And planting a curse: let the trees sow their seed by

scattering. The evidence is before our eyes. Here on the higher reaches
trees are always likely to be sparse, but on lower ground where the soil
is rich and exposure less, a pattern of dense thickets, scattered clumps
and patches of open glade will spread across the landscape.

Nesting ospreys brought the RSPB to Abernethy, and both stayed on. There was great excitement in the bird world in the 1950s when a pair of ospreys – fish-eating hawks – were observed nesting in a tree near Loch Garten, where they raised two chicks. In the next few years migrant ospreys returned to breed successfully in Scotland for the first time in nearly half a century. Slowly the visiting population increased and by 1986 more than forty pairs were nesting over a wide territory stretching from high glens to coastal plains. Ospreys plunging feet first into the waters of loch or river and rising with a fish in their claws became a sight much appreciated by birders. Unfortunately their presence also attracted bird-nesters and egg robbers.

The RSPB set out simply to protect the osprey nesting sites and ended up as a major landowner sitting on thirty thousand acres in Inverness-shire. Its involvement began in a small way when it bought Loch Garten and the land around, and once started it couldn't stop. Loch Garten was the first in a series of acquisitions which gave the RSPB a huge landholding running almost from the banks of the Spey at Nethy Bridge to the summits of Cairngorm and Ben Macdui. Within it are 4500 acres of ancient pinewood – the most extensive in the Highlands – and a vast swathe of high open moorland. The largest piece in this jigsaw, bought with considerable public money and a whip-round of members, included much of the Abernethy pinewood, the great forest once owned by the Seafields.

Not everyone is happy. The RSPB has often been accused of arrogance and intolerance, with a knack of offending local opinion. (Such criticism has been levelled at other conservation bodies, too.) Some people felt that the charity should stick to protecting birds and not get entangled in major Highland landownership. But like it or not, the RSPB acquired mountain, glen and forest and set about transforming the landscape. The forest it inherited was a patchwork of old and new, native and alien. Even the oldest and seemingly most natural parts had been worked for timber in the past, and extensive planting took place in recent times. Probably the most damaging for the ecology happened

A stag in a woodland setting is a fine sight, but too many deer mean too few trees.

within the last twenty-five years. Ground within the old woodland area which could have regenerated on its own, given the chance, was ploughed, drained and planted with young trees from the nursery.

Debate raged inside the RSPB and in public over whether to intervene, and if so, how thoroughly. The radical interventionists won and ranks of young trees were felled and laid to rot in the drainage troughs where vegetation would eventually creep over them. Old drains were blocked to make the peaty areas wet again. Larch, spruce and lodgepole pines – even fine, mature trees between fifty and a hundred years old – were felled wholesale, leaving the ubiquitous native Scots pine as the only conifer.

Dense woodland was thinned in a random pattern to allow light to penetrate and a carpet of blaeberry and cowberry to spread over the newly opened glades – good feeding for caterpillars which in turn are devoured by breeding birds. Young capercaillie chicks – an endangered species – need a diet of caterpillars, and later they feed on the berries. Some parts of the forest were kept open while elsewhere thinning stopped and the trees were encouraged to grow thickly. There's a reason for this. Crossbills like space among older trees, crested tits prefer to be crowded in. So, in a way, birds rule in Abernethy.

Ecologically, Abernethy is a precious place and nesting ospreys are only a part of it. The unique Scottish crossbill, the crested tit, the capercaillie – all species peculiarly adapted to life in the ancient pinewood – add variety. On ground level, among the heather and blaeberry and the vegetation of the wetland edges, are special plants

Stalker Peter Ross and pony Duchess bring another stag down from the hill in Creag Meagaidh reserve.

like creeping lady's tresses (an orchid), twayblade ('twa blades' in Scots, referring to the two leaves at the base of the stem) and the twinflower. There are rarities among the insects.

But all's not light in conservation. There may be a darker side, and in Abernethy as elsewhere the shadow is cast by the presence of too many deer and how to deal with them. When the RSPB took over, Abernethy sheltered an average of twelve red deer per square kilometre, which doesn't sound catastrophic but was enough to prevent woodland regenerating. The deer could have been fenced out, but fences kill or maim low-flying birds, and the RSPB decided to shoot its way out of the problem. Stalkers took a heavy toll in the first year, aiming particularly at the hinds in order to bring down the birth rate.[*] The number of deer grazing in the woodland almost halved in the first years of culling and the survival rate of seedling trees and other threatened vegetation measurably improved. Young Scots pine, rowan (which increased dramatically) and juniper raised sturdy sprigs at last above the heather.

Eventually, it's hoped, the forest of pine and its allies will double in size, spreading across the moorland to link with the northern edge of Glenmore forest, probing deep into Strath Nethy, and rising on all sides to a height of more than two thousand feet (650 metres), which is judged to be the natural tree line in present conditions. Stunted pine and a mix of dwarf birch and willow may find a foothold even higher.

---

[*] Perversely, it seems that fecundity increases when numbers fall, no doubt to compensate.

237

It could be a hundred years before the forest reaches out significantly. As for the montane scrub above it, slow to establish – who knows? The 'full restoration' of Abernethy forest, according to Stewart Taylor, the RSPB manager at Abernethy, will probably not be realised until well into the twenty-second century.

> *Strath Nethy, as I reach it from Abernethy, is wide and heather-clad, with bare hills on either hand whose lower slopes I try to imagine clothed in woodland. I cross the Water of Nethy by a wooden bridge beside the tin shack called Bynack Stable, in a green hollow where willow and alder might grow. The Nethy, often hidden in the heather but always audible, winds over a bed of pink-white granite. Not a tree, bush or shrub to be seen, though old pine roots jut across the track almost to the summit of the pass at 2500 feet.*
>
> *Funereal slabs of rock hem me in as I enter the gorge and clamber among a mass of boulders. Successive twists and lurches bring me to the high point from which I look down at Loch Avon, or Loch A'an (which is the way it's pronounced), a sombre stretch of water on this dull, humid day. Loch A'an, deep in its cliff-edged bowl at something over 2000 feet in altitude, is notionally just within the natural range of the envisaged forest, but will trees ever get to it?*
>
> *It's hard to believe. Even if the forest stretches to its utmost imagined point there's still a stretch of several bare miles to the loch. A congregation of trees around its shores? I stand on my rocky plinth and can't foresee it.*

Sixty years after the National Trust for Scotland had unsuccessfully scouted around for 'a remnant of the old natural forest which could be acquired with a view to its preservation' – an ambition long forgotten by the 1990s – it acquired almost by default the vast Mar Lodge estate; 117 square miles of mountain, moorland, bog and some spectacular remnants of the Caledonian forest in Deeside's deepest recesses. The estate, once a fiefdom of the the earls of Fife, featured a grand shooting lodge, if lodge is the word for a great house with a hundred rooms in pink granite and vaguely Tudor in design, built for Princess Louise, grand-daughter of Queen Victoria.

Lodge and all had passed, as is the way of Highland estates, into the hands of foreigners, ending with John Kluge, a rich American. It was a case of the millionaire and the showgirl. Rumours abounded in the little town of Braemar that Mrs Kluge, a former dancer, had been captivated by the idea of living next door to the Queen at Balmoral. She brought horses over from the States and occasionally drove into Braemar in a carriage.

But things turned sour and the reign of the Kluges did not last. Even before Mar Lodge was put on the market a swiftly formed consortium of conservation interests attempted to buy. Vested interests looked on the prospect of this huge tract of wild country falling into conservation hands with alarm. The Duke of Atholl, whose huge estates bordered on Mar Lodge, wrote to the *Scotsman* newspaper that it would be 'an absolute disaster' if conservationists were to succeed. 'I very much hope it will be bought by a private person who will continue to run it as a deer forest. I think all my neighbours have the same view.' No public money was made available by the Tory government and in the end the greens pulled out in frustration.

Then a shadowy body called the Easter Charitable Trust materialised. (A rumour that its presumed wealthy backers had the ear of Prince Charles was quashed by the Palace.) Behind the scenes, the National Trust for Scotland was persuaded to enter the fray, with a guarantee that deerstalking for sport would continue, and thus Mar Lodge came to be secured for the nation for £5.5 million.

The trust contemplates a long-term natural expansion of native woodland, spreading from the basin of the River Dee to the edge of the Cairngorm plateau. Deer will gather on the green flats by the Lui, as they do now. On the high slopes above the presumed tree line dwarf birch, dwarf willow, dwarf juniper and even small stunted pine will find a niche up to the 850-metre contour. The vision will take at least two hundred years to realise, by which time nature will have taken its course. The result may be, in the words of a cheerful forestry consultant, 'completely chaotic – and delightfully so'.

Capercaillie in home territory. Once again the survival of the great bird of the pinewoods is under threat.

20

A FOREST TAPESTRY

THE FORESTER Richard St Barbe Baker (apt name for an eccentric), ruminating on the wealth of natural life within the forest, declared seventy years ago that no forest could be thought of merely as the sum of all its trees. Rather, it was a single organism, an 'organic whole in which all other organisms of the forest also belong'. St Barbe Baker's ideas may have seemed idiosyncratic, not to say plain daft, to many of his hard-bitten professional contemporaries.* They appear less so now.

In our time the American environmentalist Chris Maser has said that the term 'forest' comprehends a multitude of interacting forces – seeds, soil, water, air, sunlight, climate and time – and all the infinite biological interactions taking place within it. 'All things in Nature's forest are neutral,' he wrote. 'Nature assigns no values. Each piece of the forest, whether a bacterium or an 800-year-old Douglas fir [he was speaking of North America; there are none such in Scotland] is allowed to offer its prescribed structure, carry out its prescribed function and interact with the other components. . . None is more valuable than another; each is only different from another.'

What have I glimpsed of this web of life on my way through the Scottish forest? Just a little of it, perhaps.

---

* Richard St Barbe Baker was assistant conservator of forests in Kenya and Nigeria between the wars. In the 1920s he founded an international conservation group which he called Men of the Trees – which still exists under a less gender-specific (but duller) name. His enthusiasms were too much for some; Jock Carlisle remembers sitting beside him on a flight – 'I thought he was mad,' he says. Baker was badly wounded in World War One, and decorated for bravery.

The pass of Ryvoan and the Green
Loch on the edge of Glenmore forest.

*A cold wind blowing as I wait, and mist on the hilltops. Gus Jones
drives up in his elderly car, a bit battered, painted sky blue over the
rust. Gus is the Scottish Wildlife Trust's part-time warden at Ryvoan,
where the last trees of the great Glenmore pinewoods thin out over the
foothills of the Cairngorm mountains.*

*First we walk through plantation trees, immigrants from
North America, namely lodgepole pine, which is much like our own
Scots pine but without its warm orange tints on the upper boughs. Gus
picks a cone from the ground and hands it to me. The bristles prick my
fingers – a defence, he says, against North American red squirrels,
smaller cousins of our own but equally greedy for pine seeds. Another
lover of pine trees makes itself heard: the call of the crossbill, a finch-
like bird, also adept at prising seeds from the cone. This Scottish
crossbill (in botanical terminology* Loxia scotica*), slightly bigger
than its southern namesake, was categorised only recently as a
separate species. It's unique to the Caledonian pinewoods.*

*Gus points with approval to a devastated hillside on our right.
Once covered in flourishing trees, it's now a tangle of grey stumps,
broken limbs and withered foliage, among which a few spared pine
trees stand in skimpy isolation. Why so? The wildlife trust persuaded
an initially reluctant Forestry Commission to weed out all the planted
non-native trees in order to give the surviving Scots pines a chance to
multiply. Gus stoops from time to time to pluck out bright green
seedlings of spruce, an 'exotic' species reluctant to cede the territory.*

*We penetrate the dark interior of a still-flourishing spruce
plantation, where we find an old discoloured concrete water tank sunk
in the ground. A shadowy stone bottom is visible through the greeny
water, home to newts and other pond-loving creatures. Such tanks
were built as reservoirs in case of forest fire. Close by, enveloped in*

Tom Prescott searching vainly for hazel nuts on the island of Hoy.

misty gloom, is a trio of rugged old pine trees, crowded round by ranks of spruce and slowly dying for lack of space and light.

In the heart of Ryvoan lies the little Green Loch, An Lochan Uaine, at the bottom of whose foggy waters the shape of long-drowned trees can be discerned. A few pine trees still cling to the steep scree slopes directly above and every so often another takes a tumble and slides down into the watery graveyard.

We climb through thick heather and patches of tall juniper bush. Woodlands are more than trees. Primroses are everywhere. At a boggy patch, a sundew spreads sticky, penny-shaped leaves ready to trap insects. We see wood sorrel, dog's mercury, and wood anemone, whose purplish bell flowers appear just in time to catch the sun before the deciduous trees come into leaf and cast them into shade.

Surreal fungal forms, mushrooms, toadstools and weird fruitbodies sprout everywhere from the damp forest floor and the bulks of decaying trees. They are the visible manifestation of a vast subterranean network. The whole forest, from treetop canopy to underground roots, is a teeming life force.

It's a far cry from the spreading green forest canopies of Strathspey to the northern isles, which are so often dismissed as treeless. This is not true. Forests and woods come in many guises and each has its own fascination, no matter how small. Look closer.

Green hills, grey houses at the head of the glen, a slice of blue Atlantic beyond – we're on the island of Hoy in the Orkneys, a windswept landscape shorn of forest cover. Rough grass, heather, bare rock, sandy shores and bog is more like it.

A track through the heather leads towards a rocky outcrop called Grut Fea – strange name, Norse I suppose – and a cleft in the hillside edged by twiggy little trees and bushes. This is Berriedale; and Berriedale, so it's said, is the most northerly native woodland in the British Isles. Woodland? This poor scrub? So where are the tall trees?

Tom Prescott leads the way. Tom is (or was at the time – he has since moved on) the birdman of Hoy, officially the RSPB's warden on the island, but also guardian of the trees of Berriedale.

We enter the thicket, pushing through bracken. It's August and midges are biting – I try to ignore them. 'Can you smell the birch?' Tom asks as we plunge into the tangle. I sniff hopefully; what does birch smell like? Pine I'd know, pine's easy, anyone can tell pine. But birch may be a more delicate thing.

Small willow trees are clustered together, hedge-like, and then the birches, with honeysuckle in flower winding through them. A single rowan tree is laden with russet berries still to redden. Its glory won't last long. Come October the birds will strip it in days.

Beyond a briar bush there's a clutch of aspen stems, straight, slender, smooth and pale, spreading up the steepening gorge – a dozen or more all springing from a single root system so old, says Tom, that it may have been established in that soil for thousands of years.

Tom – his flop of black hair and striped T-shirt caught in a ray of sunshine – moves on to find the particular tree he has been looking for, a great rarity. Only three hazel trees grow on Hoy and two of them are in Berriedale gorge. Tom takes a hazel twig in his hand, hoping to find nuts developing. But the three hazels of Hoy are reluctant to fruit in the chilly north. A single infertile nut was picked from this tree more than a decade ago and that was the last seen. The hazel is healthy but impotent.

I explore deeper in the gorge on my own until the burn, dropping over a sheer slab of rock, blocks my way and I clamber out above the trees, where I'm attacked by 'bonxies' (giant skuas), diving on me in defence of their moorland nests. I turn and run.

Run to Glasgow, where no bonxies nest and scavenging seagulls are the most aggressive birds you are likely to meet. But there too, at the outer edge of the urban sprawl – unlikely as it may seem – there are faint traces of a long-lost forest.

Above me the golfers are out on clipped fairways. Below, at the bottom of the hill, a last rank of barrack-like tenements marks the frontier between town and country. They were built in the sixties and now that people have drifted away some are to be demolished to make way for houses with gardens. Cries of children are in the air and there's a hum of electricity from pylons.

The place is Drumchapel, a large housing estate on the edge of Glasgow. The date a Sunday in September. On the falling ground between golf course and housing estate lies the wood of Garscadden. Even in its distressed state it bears hidden traces of antiquity. It's had a lot to put up with. There are black scars on the ground where fires have been lit. A larch tree, leaning at an angle, has been unsuccessfully attacked by an axe some time ago. The Vs bitten out of the trunk by the blade have callused over. Several of the larger trees have disappeared since the houses went up, presumably felled and sawn into logs for fuel by enterprising citizens.

Garscadden, says Simon Marshall, who works for a local conservation project, is at heart a conventional Scottish broadleaf forest, a mixture of the native ash, oak, rowan, birch and thorn, along with beech, sycamore and larch. I see one little holly tree growing bravely. There are nettles, bracken and feathery spires of faded willowherb whose wispy seeds drift in the still air. Tangled brambles are dotted with berries, black and red.

Most of the wood was clear-felled and replanted with oak trees – now sparse – towards the end of the nineteenth century. Written records go no further back, but there is evidence of much older growth – decayed oak coppice stools hidden in the undergrowth and now not easily found – whose age is estimated at four hundred years. Simon thinks that Garscadden may have been a managed woodland at least as far back as the Middle Ages. Now that there are no grazing animals about there's hope of renewal – we see clusters of saplings. Rabbits, a natural enemy of young trees, are no longer numerous, presumably – Simon speculates – having been shot for the Drumchapel pot, 'a piece of indirect but effective woodland management'.

No old trees, no plants typical of old woods – not even bluebells. 'This, it's got to be said,' – and it's Simon saying it – 'is the poorest ancient woodland you can imagine.' Poor but precious.

The conifer forests of Galloway are anything but ancient. The views from Raiders' Road (a name borrowed from a yarn by Samuel Rutherford Crockett) reveal a vast landscape of trees sweeping almost to – and sometimes over – the hilltops. Most of these millions of green spires were put into the ground as seedlings in a ten-year burst of postwar planting. SR Crockett's imagined cattle rustlers of long ago had a pretty straight run of it over these braes – broken ground in his time, granite crags and bog, mostly, with little more in the way of trees than scrub clinging to rock and river's edge.

See over there, says Bob Chester, the man from the Forestry Commission (he's addressing a party of landowners and foresters, with a few hangers-on like me). Bats roost in the old bridge built to carry the abandoned rail line to Stranraer – the 'Paddy' – over the river. It's a conservation area now. Pipistrelles and the less common Daubenton's bats inhabit the arches: 'We do an annual bat walk.' And here's a squirrel feeding box. Southwest Scotland is one of the few areas not yet penetrated by grey squirrels and so the home-bred reds are pampered with a feeding programme. And there are nightjars to be encouraged – summer visitors at the northern limit of their range. Nearly half the known population of nightjars in Scotland can be found in the neighbourhood of Raiders' Road.

We stand at the roadside and see vast swathes of conifer forest above, beyond, and on every side. But the age of brutalism has passed. There are design plans now, strategies to dull the pain of massive felling and to re-create the forest in a fashion more pleasing to the eye, friendlier to humans passing through and to the resident wildlife. The transformation will not be fully effected until half a century hence, for there's no short-termism in the woods. At present 'we've got to hit it pretty hard'; in later cycles the man-made gashes in the landscape can be smaller, less grievous to the eye.

Bob Chester and his colleagues show where the start has been made and what will happen in the future: hilltops cleared of trees (good for nesting eagles), views opened up to the crags and down to the dark pools of the Black Water of Dee. Tumbling tributary burns, long hidden, seen again. The low mossy walls of a forgotten village, visible again after recent felling, will be left open to the sky. Thickets of plastic tubes sprout where broadleaf trees like oak and birch have been planted to provide a contrast to sombre evergreens, and to supplement the few native trees surviving from the old days. We see a solitary, mossy old oak tree which some day may reign over a new generation. Drifts of tall larch trees near the roadway have been reprieved because of their spring and autumn colours. We admire a group of Douglas fir, one of the most handsome of the evergreens, now safe from the harvester (though maybe not from the worst of gales – judgment is reserved on that). Fine Norway spruce trees clustered round a patch of water under a handsome old railway viaduct are doubly secure – people picnic in their shade, and up in their foliage red squirrels scrabble for seed.

Bats, red squirrels, nightjars even – but what's missing?

Jimmy Oswald stands stock-still in the heathery undergrowth clucking and smacking his lips. We watch and listen. Jimmy wears a

Jimmy Oswald surveys young pine trees spreading over the heather moorland in Glen Tanar.

baggy old tweed jacket, breeches threadbare at the knees from constant use, and bright blue stockings. The tweed is the livery of Glen Tanar estate, on Deeside, where weatherbeaten Jimmy has worked outdoors for forty years. With this lip-smacking display he's hoping to decoy a capercaillie into the open. We're in luck. A cock bird, black and heavy but surprisingly deft despite its bulk, flies through the trees and alights on a bough where it spreads its mantilla-like tail. Then another.

'Capers love these old trees,' says Jimmy approvingly (and so does he). He lists the attractions for capercaillies among old pines. The trees provide shelter and strong boughs for a perch, and the soft green early shoots are good eating – as are the heather and blaeberries on the ground below.

Capercaillies are the great birds of the pinewoods, but their numbers have dwindled drastically and their survival is doubtful. Once, says Jimmy, keepers were instructed to kick over their nests in the heather and break the eggs, and they were shot as game. Jimmy blames the dark plantations of commercial forestry for their decline.

Then we bump and jolt over the forest track in his Landrover by the banks of the River Tanar. Jimmy points to a grassy patch on the far side where a sawmill operated in the early nineteenth century. The mill is long gone but a tree marks the site – oddly, in this situation, a lime tree, not one of the natives. We stop by a cairn erected by a former landowner in Victorian times to celebrate more homely trees:

> The pine is king of Scottish woods,
> And the queen, ah, who is she?
> The fairest form the forest kens,
> The bonny birken tree.

Our last stop is on the extreme southern edge of the forest where moorland undulates for miles, rising to the snowy pyramid of Mount Keen. Here the unbroken pinewood frays into a scattering of fresh young trees, mere spikelets dotted over the brown heather. All this new growth, says Jimmy, came away after he burned off stretches of heather in the 1960s. Fire, usually thought of as an enemy of the forest, can be a great gardener, a cleanser of the ground and maker of fertile seedbeds.

Later in the day we ascend rough tracks towards a hillside where old domed trees, real Caledonian pines of the ancient forest, are scattered. Here pine trees have grown unmolested for centuries. But these rugged specimens have no successors, except in a patch fenced around to keep out hungry deer, where the old-stagers are now surrounded by drifts of young tufted pines and slender wands of birch and rowan. But for the most part it's a forest seemingly in terminal decline.

Such trees live long and death comes slowly, and usually singly; maybe having survived two hundred years or more one last gale blows down a survivor, or simply age takes its toll and finally the green foliage fails to renew itself and the branches are left bare. But for plantation trees the end comes swiftly and all fall together, mown down at a blow.

Last call. Forestry talk. Woodmen all, apart from me. We survey a forest that was, and is no more – acres of conifer stumps and a litter of lopped branches. The stumps go right to the edge of a small burn once gloomed over by the trees. Someone jokes that the planters of forty years ago would have stuck trees in the river bed too, if they could.

This spot in Appin, near Loch Creran, was a Forestry Commission plantation until privatised in the 1980s – it's now in corporate hands. On the brow of the hill a huge harvesting machine munches through the last of the standing trees.

This awful desolation will not be repeated. Appin peninsula is, in the jargon, a national scenic area. Next time around the timber trees will be planted more sparingly, leaving open spaces and a pleasanter mix of trees. A few spindly trees of the leafy kind already survive in the chaos – birch and oak saved from the cutter – and hopefully they'll scatter seed and multiply. 'I believe that where a tree wants to grow, let it grow,' says the owners' agent. I hear the voice of enlightenment.

Perhaps the last word should go to Mark Anderson, shrewd commentator on the woodland scene who has been a presence in the background throughout this book. Practical forester though he was, he knew that the forest had a richness ignored in the short-term philosophy of his more conventional professional peers. He wrote forty years ago that 'the forester deals not in years and decades but in centuries, and it is true to say that he is interested not only in what was done two centuries ago but also in what happened in the forest a thousand or more years ago'. And, he might have added, what may happen in long years to come.

Solitary rowan in a bare glen – what hope of future plenty?

21

A DREAM OF ROTTEN BOTTOM

ON THE FLOOD TIDE of green politics native woods and native trees are the thing. In the last quarter century public money has underpinned a dramatic surge in old woodland conservation and new planting, all based on the primacy of the grand confraternity of oak, birch, Scots pine and the like whose ancestry stretches back almost to the last melting of the ice. The new native woodlanders are a heterogeneous lot; they include great charities like the National Trust for Scotland and the RSPB, smaller but no less active organisations such as the John Muir Trust and the Woodland Trust, plus many other bodies and individuals – towns, villages, local community groups, landowners, farmers and all.

Most recently millennium money (which means lottery money), added to the pot in the mid nineties, has helped in the restoration of old oakwoods around Loch Sunart in the northwest, or the planting of pine and oak in Barisdale in remote Knoydart peninsula, or the restitution of willow scrub along the Ettrick flood plain in the Borders.

Carrifran is different. At Carrifran enthusiasts had to raise the money themselves for their impossible dream.

Late in 1992 Philip Ashmole took the road to Damascus, as he describes it – in fact it was the A9 and he was driving south after attending a conference on the restoration of Highland pinewoods when it came to him that something of the kind could be attempted in the Borders where he lived. It seemed a forlorn hope. But Ashmole, a zoologist recently retired from Edinburgh University, began to explore the scraps of old relic woodland straggling over scree slopes or

Happy dreamer: Philip Ashmole framed in gorge foliage.

clustered along gullies – 'cleuchs' is the local term – carved in the hillsides by rushing burns. There's not much to make a forest from. Old woodland covers a negligible part of the Border landscapes. Nothing like the core pinewoods of Glenmore, Rannoch or Affric exists in the Southern Uplands.

Ashmole and friends – now formed into a 'wildwood group' under the wing of the Borders Forest Trust – came to the conclusion that in order to realise their dream they needed nothing less than a whole watershed, a valley and the ring of hills around it. A chance came when they heard that Gameshope, a long winding valley that terminates in the hills north of Moffat, was about to be sold.

Ashmole shouldered his rucksack and reconnoitred the ground, making a promising start, for near Talla he came on some fragments of old woodland not recorded on any map. He walked on past little Gameshope Loch, the highest in the Borders, and climbed to the peaty watershed at a spot called Rotten Bottom. On the far side he looked into another valley, shorter but more dramatic than Gameshope, a great ice-scooped bowl drawing the eye down into Moffatdale. The wide sheet of the Solway Firth glinted in the middle distance, with the blue lump of Criffel to the side and Skiddaw and the Lakeland hills visible on the far shore. It was, strictly speaking, a magnificent irrelevance, being on the wrong side of the march with Dumfries-shire and so outside the Borders area. Anyway, the valley had only recently changed hands.

Actor and enthusiastic archer Robert Hardy draws his bow in
Carrifran – a replica of the ancient weapon found at Rotten Bottom.

The dream faded when Gameshope went to another party, sold
before the short-pocketed friends had a chance to appeal for money to
make a bid. The wildwood group set about looking for another suitable
valley, which meant a watershed of not less than a thousand acres
stretching from valley bottom to the surrounding hilltops. They fixed
on ten possible sites and got none of them.

Then Carrifran, the tantalising valley Ashmole had glimpsed
earlier, swam into view again. It was heard on the grapevine that
Carrifran's new owner, a Lancashire farmer and businessman, might be
willing to part with it – at a price. With land selling at a premium, he
asked a sum far beyond the wildwooders' means. They haggled. The
owner continued to drive a hard bargain – it was good grazing land and
he had no reason to sell. But at last the parties shook hands on a deal,
with the price fixed at £330,000 due two years ahead in November 1999.
When paid, Carrifran would be theirs. The snag was that since the price
was still well above market value it did not qualify for millennium
funding. The group had to rely on opportunistic and determined
fund raising, helped by the timely emergence of the Rotten Bottom
bowman.

In 1990 Dan Jones, a psychiatrist from Melrose, when hillwalking
along the watershed at Rotten Bottom, noticed a curious stick half
buried in the peat. When he took a closer look it seemed to him more
like an artefact than just a long, curved bit of branch (and where were
the trees?). He strapped the stick to his rucksack, took it home and then
to the Edinburgh museum, where it was identified as a yew hunting
bow dating from around six thousand years ago.

It was a godsend to the publicity-hungry wildwooders. Carrifran instantly became the Valley of the Bow and the film actor Robert Hardy, an archer and authority on the longbow, was invited to Carrifran to launch the appeal by drawing a replica bow in the presence of the press. The money was raised on time and the first token trees were planted on 1 January, 2000.

From the roadside Carrifran, one valley down from the famous Grey Mare's Tail, appears to be utterly bare, with not a tree in sight. Fifteen hundred acres of grass, boulder scree, rocky cliffs and peat hag. A patch of tree scrub is just visible where the Carrifran Burn dips into a cleuch before passing under the road to join the Moffat Water. Further upstream a single rowan tree hangs at an angle over the burn; higher up the valley the burn flows through another deep cleft, where clusters of plants, a burnet rose among them, vie for space on a few narrow ledges, and small trees root in the crevices; a rowan, a few birches and willows, one bird cherry. This oasis is the Carrifran woodland in embryo.

What trees grew in Carrifran long ago? Researchers from Stirling University who took a core from the peaty soil of Rotten Bottom down to the bedrock gained what is probably the most comprehensive pollen record of upland vegetation in the whole of Britain, in an unbroken line from the end of the Ice Age to the present. It revealed the presence at one time or another of all our native tree species, including traces of Scots pine, which seem to have grown there at a time when pine is generally believed to have died out in the south of Scotland. Other cores taken in the neighbourhood helped to fill out the picture of past tree cover. One shows that yew grew in the next valley between the Talla and Megget reservoirs 5800 years ago, which is roughly the age of the Rotten Bottom bow. So the bow may have been cut from a handy local tree.

What may Carrifran look like in the future? Ashmole hopes it will reflect the kind of woodland that might have survived had humans never interfered, say a thousand years ago or more.

Why bother? What's wrong with the landscape as it is? It has the mystic allure of a gaunt, sculptured glen. But to an ecologist such as Ashmole it is also profoundly depressing, starved of the myriad life forms – trees, plants, birds, beasts and insects – that would flourish there if nature had been left to take its course.

Ecologist Adrian Newton explains the practicalities of bringing biodiversity back to a bare glen.

It would take an incalculable time for the trees to return if Carrifran, merely emptied of sheep and protected against wandering goats and roe deer, were left to its own resources. There is no reservoir of old, bitten-back shrubby things in the undergrowth waiting to surge into growth, as at Creag Meagaidh, and as there often is under Highland heather. Constant heavy grazing saw to that. By general agreement the existing trees – the lone rowan and two nests of cleuch scrub – can never, in the imaginable future, repopulate the whole valley.

The solution arrived at by Ashmole and friends was to plant much of the suitable ground with saplings, nursery grown mainly from seed collected in Carrifran and nearby. Not too hastily (there is a ten-year planting programme) and not at random. The cleuchs will be given their chance – ash already seeds itself there – but nature will receive a hefty shove.

Ground is being left clear along the banks of the burns, on uncongenial scree slopes and on sites of archaeological interest. Moist patches rich in sedges, mosses and liverworts will not be disturbed. Hardly anything except a few montane plants such as dwarf willow will be planted above 1500 feet, or 450 metres, which is thought to be the natural tree line.

Once the ten-year programme is complete, interference with the course of nature will be minimal, on the principle that a wildwood should be left to grow wild. Nature's tendency to untidiness will take over. Some trees will find a niche in places unsuspected by the ecologists. Hawthorn and ash, which root naturally among rock rubble elsewhere in the Southern Uplands, may establish themselves on the screes, exploiting pockets of thin soil between the stones. In the end the wildwoodlanders hope to replace close-cropped minimalism with a rich and extensive woodland teeming with wildlife, a dream none of the authors of the design will live to see realised. As a preface to their fund-raising pamphlet the Carrifran enthusiasts imagined how their valley was in the distant past and what it might become in the future:

> Along the valley floor, otters patrolled the Carrifran Burn, which meandered through a dense woodland of alder, ash, elm, cherry and downy birch. Ivy and honeysuckle entwined the trees, and fallen logs sprouted many kinds of fungi. Songbirds, butterflies and deer foraged in clearings rich with wild flowers. On the slopes, the hunter scrambled through hazel, holly, oak and thorn, while far ahead the crags where the ravens nested emerged from a woodland of birch, rowan and juniper. On the plateau above, the woods were replaced by willow scrub, and finally by open heathland on the summits.

How long will it take? It's the old story – a hundred years and maybe much more.

Of course attitudes may change. The Ashmole fraternity with their wild imaginings may be succeeded by a more cautious set of people taking a pragmatic view of how the landscape should be managed. Private interest and public policies may alter; the environmental movement may shift ground. There's no long-term guarantee that Carrifran will flourish in the way that its godfathers intend. Only time and the trees will tell.

22

WOOD WITHOUT END

To THE NATURALIST Frank Fraser Darling, the lost Caledonian forest of ancient time was a place of enchantment. 'The imagination of a naturalist can conjure up a picture of what the great forest was like,' he wrote in his *Natural History in the Highlands and Islands*. And he confessed: 'The present writer is inclined to look upon it as his idea of heaven[*] and to feel a little rueful that he was born too late to "go native" in its recesses.'

At the threshold of the twenty-first century an extension and reinvigoration of our too-patchy contemporary forest is being mooted – somewhat short of Darling's paradise, it's true, but no doubt he would have approved. An idea now canvassed in heritage circles is that more of our scattered tree cover, everything from wide-spreading woodland like the Strathspey forests and great plantations such as grow in the Borders to pockets of native woods, riverside scrub and even the lines of trees that shelter farm fields should be linked together by cautious new planting to provide a relatively seamless garment of greenery, a woodland mosaic (in the phrase favoured by ecologists) where birds, beasts and all life down to the humblest insect and slow-moving lichens can roam, spread, creep, infiltrate, scatter their genes at large instead of being hemmed in as they are now. There are obstacles, of course, including the competing claims of land use and ownership. Given goodwill, they may be overcome. But even that ambition is not a grand enough vision for some.

---

[*] Though heaven, as Darling admitted, must have had its drawbacks – not so much boar or brown bear as malarial swamps and mosquitoes.

Frank Fraser Darling, naturalist and seer.
The Caledonian wildwood was his idea of
heaven (apart from the mosquitoes).

Seers exist in the woodland world, not all of them impractical dreamers, who envisage a great forest in all its glory with its 'sylvan environment and its rich wild life' (in Darling's phrase) once again established over a large tract of Scottish soil. Some believe that its slow return has already begun. The vision goes even beyond the ambition of the planters at Carrifran or the ideas of the conservationists in Abernethy, Creag Meaghaidh or Mar Lodge.

There is the question of the wildlife that has been lost over the ages. Should it return?

The elk and the bear are not in the frame. Nor, as yet, is the wolf. Boar is a possibility. And beaver? Beaver is on the way back. If all goes to plan, half a dozen beaver families from Scandinavia will be set free on a river bank in Knapdale peninsula of Argyll, there to chomp their way through the riparian woodland and rework their surroundings to suit their watery preferences.

Beaver, once a native Scot but long extinct, has a niche in the wildwood of our envisaged future. Since not everyone is enthusiastic about their return, Scottish Natural Heritage has been cautious in promoting the prepared reintroduction. It remains a trial – beaver is on parole.

The extent to which the beaver devastates riverside woodland is the sore point. Friends of the beaver contend that the dams they build are small and easily breached and that tree felling is restricted to a waterside margin. They point out that the beaver is vegetarian and doesn't poach fish. And they warn against confusing the European

Loch Garten, the start of a tour in potential beaver country. But the first experimental introduction of beavers is scheduled to take place in Knapdale on the west coast.

beaver *Castor fiber* with its larger and much more destructive North American cousin *Castor canadiensis*. It's the former which paddled in the ponds of Caledon and nibbled at the trees of the Great Wood, and it's Mr C Fiber who gets the offer of a return ticket.

> *Loch Garten, late May and chilly for the time of the year. Roy Dennis and I are standing by the water's edge. Swallows darting for insects skim over the smooth surface dimpled by rain. No beavers are here – but there could be.*
>
> *A dark curtain of conifer forest surrounds the loch, managed exclusively as pinewood until relatively recently. The typical ground cover of heather and blaeberry in such woodland is not to the beaver's taste. It was better when pine trees shared the ground with other native species and a richer mix of vegetation grew below them. Already there are clear signs that birch is coming back, mingling with the darker pines.*
>
> *A willow leans over the water. Willow is a favourite beaver food for autumn and winter, and they snip off manageable branches and stems. Dennis is unperturbed by this. Beavers leave debris in their tracks – a snagged branch here, a broken twig there – and since willow sprouts vigorously, any slip lodged in the soft mud of the waterside has a good chance of taking root. Dennis says that far from clearing the forest, the busy beaver may well cause willow to spread.*
>
> *Across the water are patches of bog where water lilies grow, and a small burn wanders for half a mile through the forest into another, smaller loch. Along the way are plenty of grasses, sedges and annual flowers, the beaver's favourite food. An outflow stream continues in a winding course till finally it debouches into the broad River Spey. All this is ideal beaver habitat. A family could establish*

themselves in such a network of lochs, pools and tiny burns – often barely a yard wide and only a foot or so deep, just enough to swim in and give cover if danger threatens. A congenial territory where they could forage at will through the secret heart of the woods to the great river itself.

A surprising number of half-hidden little watercourses cut sounding channels through these pinewoods of the valley floor, making endless traceries of streams, rivulets and lochans. Resident beavers would be active there, creating new patches of watery habitat, opening up corridors, keeping them in good order, weaving little dams and weirs of mud and twig to impound small ponds – not fixed impediments to the flow of water but structures easily breached by sudden spates.

We search deeper in the forest for promising habitat. A burn meanders through a marshy clearing in the pinewood among alder, willow, bird cherry, plenty of birch and even a few young sycamores. Here's mixed feeding – alder is only so-so but birch is tasty. Also, on the ground, wood avens, meadowsweets, raspberry and water docks. Another modest burn runs under a pole bridge where king nuts and kingcups, 'perfect for beavers', grow on the verges. We follow narrow tracks through the undergrowth and find grasses, rushes, lady's smock, marsh marigold, foxglove – not much willow because it has been stripped out in the past, but it's coming back – the very sort of stream a beaver would dam, flood for maybe twenty yards, then dam further down in a chain of pools through the forest. Beavers constantly change and diversify their watery surroundings, creating successions of deep and shallow pools, sluices, swift-running channels and slow eddies – good for voles, shrews, aquatic birds and also for insects. Dennis cites evidence from abroad showing a threefold increase in dragonflies where beavers have been introduced. He thinks that where we have four or five species present now, the number could increase to twelve or fifteen were beavers around.

Day in, day out, they work at their dams sloshing mud, hauling branches around, littering the water with torn-off leaves and bark chips, debris that carries a resident or transitory population of bugs, grubs and all manner of invertebrates which become food for the local fish and eels, themselves an item in the diet of otters.

It's for this that ecologists like Roy Dennis promote the case for beavers. Not for the tourist potential – though people will want to see them. Beavers are born environmentalists and given a chance will help to create their own habitat. 'My interest in getting beavers back has always been for nature conservation and the environment,' Roy Dennis says. 'It's the enhancement and enrichment of the ecosystem that's the real value.'

Beaver in its element.

Beaver is one thing, large mammals like the brown bear, the boar and the wolf – all former residents of Scotland – are something else. Yet wild boar are already at large and thriving in the south of England, having escaped captivity, and the return of the wolf to the Highlands is frequently canvassed – admittedly by the more radical nature lovers.

All over the world the wolf has been a pariah, hated, harried and at last exterminated. Fear and ignorance have played their part, but there is some reason in the war. Farmers and herdsmen have immemorially branded the wolf as a rapacious killer of sheep and cattle. Wolf hatred surfaced furiously with the proposal to reintroduce wolves in Yellowstone Park, the greatest stretch of wilderness in the United States, barren of wolves since they were hunted out seventy years ago. In the teeth of hostility from farming organisations, ranchers and the hunting lobby (jealous that wolves might compete for prey with gun-toting humans), several pairs were resettled in Yellowstone in 1995 and began to breed, while the legal battle raged on.[*]

No wonder the return of wolves to the Highlands of Scotland is a ticklish subject. Even enthusiasts know that it will take time to convince the opposition. Fifty years? That's the timescale that Aberdeen University zoologist Dr Martyn Gorman thinks feasible for their reintroduction in sufficient numbers for them to survive in the wild –

---

[*] Recalcitrants took the law into their own hands, as in the case of a rancher who shot a 122lb beast, almost as big as a man, for which he was fined. Since then caution has been the watchword. The motto 'Shoot, shovel and shut up' appeared on T-shirts.

in other words, not just a pair or two but several packs hunting and breeding. Given such numbers, he believes wolves could survive in some large area of the Highlands, but he suspects it will take at least half a century to convince the doubters. 'These animals are carnivores' he says. 'There is no doubt they would take sheep, and if numerous, would try killing small cows.'

It's argued in favour of the wolf that it would keep down the red deer population (bluntly, by killing them). Deer destroy the growing forest and wolves kill deer; therefore more wolves mean fewer deer, and fewer deer more trees. It's an elegantly simple proposition, provided you are willing to accept the sacrifice of an unknown number of deer for the cause. Just how much impact preying wolves would make on deer numbers compared to heavy culling by rangers is unknown.

Kenny Taylor of the RSPB is both a romantic and a realist. He may dream of the wolf's return to the Highlands but accepts that it won't happen in his lifetime: 'It's unfair for people living outside the Highlands to make bold assertions about creatures like the wolf when they don't have to live here and it's not their sheep that might be taken.' Martyn Gorman told a conference in 1995 that 'the reason why these animals became extinct was through human persecution and it would be both folly and extreme cruelty to consider reintroducing them without first dealing with that prejudice'.

If the prejudice can be overcome, if the forest extends sufficiently, if farmers can be brought to accept (and be compensated for) the occasional loss of lamb or calf, what then? What's the gain?

A tourist attraction? For sure. In Canada's Algonquin Park the 'wolf-howl' is an advertised event and people pay money to join the party. Since the return of wolves to Yellowstone 'wolf walks' have become hugely popular; over a summer forty thousand people were led into the park in the hope of sighting or hearing its latest residents.

> And then arose the long wolf howl. It came with a slurring rush upward, swelling to a great heart-breaking burst of sound, and dying away in sadly cadenced woe – then the next rush upward, octave upon octave; the bursting heart; and the infinite sorrow and misery, fainting, fading, falling, and dying slowly away.
>
> Jack London in full cry in *The Call of the Wild*.

Or this:

> When the moon rises over the Cairngorms, we will howl. Howl all
> bloody night if we want to. Howl a song that hasn't been heard in
> these hills for hundreds of years. This is the place to which I would
> return – were I a wolf.
>
> The nature writer Paul Evans of the *Guardian*.

And in soberer mood:

> I'd love to think that generations from now someone might be able
> to hear the growl of a brown bear. When they've made their camp
> at night, as they lay down to sleep, what better than to be listening
> to the howl of some real Highland wolves again, echoing through
> these glens and across these straths?
>
> Naturalist Kenny Taylor.

Sights and sounds on a tourist trail – there's more to the wolf than that.
Surely its native grace justifies its existence? Nature in all its wild glory,
as we have known it in the past – so the argument goes – demands the
presence of the wolf, since without him the pattern is incomplete.

Yellowstone spreads over 3350 square miles, an area equivalent to
a ninth of Scotland's landmass, and is partly surrounded by a buffer
zone of dense forests. If ever wolves return to the Highlands it should
be on a grand scale – who wants wildlife compounds and safari parks?
If it takes two hundred square miles to support one pack of ten animals
– which is Martyn Gorman's estimate – then even the great and future
forest in the north of Scotland envisaged by the conservation body
Trees for Life, all six hundred square miles of it, may be barely big
enough.

As yet it's a dream for the witching hour when shadows fall, the
light gleams in the bar and the talk takes a speculative turn. Who
knows?

Alan Watson Featherstone, founder and director of Trees for Life (one
of those who say yes to the wolf) is no idle dreamer. He runs a business,
employs people, handles large sums of money, negotiates with national
organisations. But he is an idealist, too, with a vision of reforesting the
treeless landscape.

Alan Watson Featherstone
(in hat) explains the Trees for Life
philosophy to visiting enthusiasts
in Glen Affric.

Since he worked for mining companies in remote parts of North America he has travelled worldwide and witnessed the destruction of the forest everywhere – industrial logging in North America, rainforest clearance in South America, New Guinea, Sarawak and Borneo, bush clearance for agriculture in Australia. Everywhere the trees topple. But it's not all devastation; many remnants of virgin forest are still inviolate. He visited south India where local people had planted two million trees on desert land that had once been woodland before it was stripped. He reckoned that what was done by that Indian community could be attempted in Scotland too.

'Wild nature speaks to me and inspires me,' he says. He answered the call by setting up Trees for Life, an inspirational group based at the Findhorn community in northeast Scotland. Its logo is a pair of cupped hands cradling the globe within the crown of a tree. Featherstone preaches the doctrine of ecological restoration, the healing of degraded ecosystems. Seeing the relic native pinewoods of Scotland as a prime case for treatment, he fixed on Affric and its neighbour glens as an ideal locus. For some years Trees for Life has been working there, in close association with the Forestry Commission, where one of its projects has been to locate and regenerate colonies of aspen, a relatively uncommon and vulnerable tree in the old pinewoods.

A major aim is to link up the isolated relic woodlands by creating wildlife corridors along the watercourses. A start has been made along the Allt na Muic, a picturesque burn which makes its way southwards through a gorge between glens Affric and Moriston,

Ancient of days. New growth springs up around the wreck of an aged tree, whose slow decay will enrich all life around it. But this is Slovakia, where primeval forest remains, not Scotland where it doesn't.

flowing over a bouldery bed, festooned with a ragged mixture of Scots pine, birch, rowan, aspen, alder and juniper. It is, as Featherstone wrote in a Trees for Life leaflet, 'a beautiful cascading stream, with fresh scents of the forest floor, the delicate sounds of life and the green light as the sun comes through the trees'.

In May 2000 Trees for Life announced an agreement with the landowner under which it will begin a scheme of woodland regeneration around the gorge by natural growth and judicious planting, the first stage in the creation of a corridor of native woods linking the relic pinewoods in Glen Affric and Glen Moriston, and a stepping stone, perhaps, on the way to a great forest of the north.

In his mind's eye Featherstone sees a vast forest of pine, birch and native broadleaf trees spreading out from Affric, joining up the pinewood remnants in the nearby glens of Cannich, Strathfarrar and Moriston, climbing over the watershed into Kintail and down to the western sea at Loch Duich, a corridor of native woodland stretching for thirty miles across country and covering an area of six hundred square miles.

'Our long-term aim is to return an area of approximately fifteen hundred square kilometres [580 square miles] to a condition of natural forest,' he says. 'This area in the north-central Highlands is largely roadless and almost completely uninhabited, and is therefore one of the very few large tracts of land in Scotland which have the potential to be restored to a wilderness state.' In Featherstone's vision a vast wild forest growing as nature decrees and untouched by commercial

265

logging (he excludes even enlightened forestry practised in sustainable ways) will cover the land, functioning as a rich natural ecosystem, with not only trees but all the plants and animals 'which have been absent for the last few hundred years but which rightfully belong there'. It might take hundreds of years; far beyond our lifetimes but hopefully within the span of some of the native trees already growing there.

There's fresh snow on the hilltops, though it's already mid May. But Affric's birch and pines are magical in any season. From the power station at Fasnakyle, near the village of Cannich, they fill the glen westwards in rich profusion, unbroken forest all along Loch Beinn a'Mheadhoin (at least on the southern slopes where no traffic penetrates) until, at Loch Affric, the trees begin to thin and finally give way to open moorland.

A sign tells me that I'm entering West Affric, owned by the National Trust. Near a bridge over floodwater rushing from the hills there's a pretty group of shrubby rowan trees, the last I'll see for miles on my way to the west, and I notice the gorge above them has been fenced to encourage new growth. There are other new enclosures where burns cut down through the hillsides and as I walk along I hear the clonk of a hammer – someone hired by the National Trust is up there driving in a fence post.

Beyond the isolated climbers' hostel of Alltbeithe, a bare glen opens out between high hills, treeless except for dots of scrub, in striking contrast to the eastern pinewoods of Affric. Deer herds gather here in winter. Under a spur of Ben Attow the lower ground crumbles into a waste of hags, with the dead roots and stumps of age-old pine showing through the black moss. Somewhere in this wilderness, I'm told, two small pine trees survive, stunted but alive. Where? All I can see is bare moorland.

All West Affric, and beyond it the mountainous Kintail Forest, so called (where few trees grow), was bought by the National Trust for Scotland in 1994 and subsequently surveyed to assess its potential for forest restoration.

I try to imagine the scene as it might be some day according to those projections: open woodland on the valley floor instead of rough grassland and bog as at present; stands of thicker woodland on the lower slopes; alder by the river; birch and pine trees scattered over the damp flat bottom; oak trees, birch and rowan clustered in the lower gullies and mingling on the rising ground; willow where it's damp; pine trees with companion birch on the higher slopes; only a few hardy, stunted trees and juniper bushes on the upper fringes – and above that? Hilltops bare as they are today.

I head for the watershed through a waste of bog and rocky knolls, fording fast-flowing burns. Ahead the mountains close in over a narrow pass. Clouds rolling in from the Atlantic pile up here to form the 'Kintail curtain', a climatic demarcation line between the wet west and the drier east. The curtain is down this day.

I climb through the pass and then follow a steep zigzag track westwards down into another green valley, the meeting place of deeply gouged glens, where a different river rises and flows noisily towards the salt waters of Loch Duich and the sea. Through the mist I spy a considerable wood in the distance – but not the sort to gladden a visionary. It's plantation forestry of the conifer kind, woodland by artifice that has transformed so many Scottish landscapes in the recent past. Like it or not, this is a typical Scottish forest of the day.

A word of caution. Are the tree stumps poking from the bog under Ben Attow sure evidence that the ancient Caledonian forest flourished there for thousands of years until cold, wet, peat and people finished it off? It seems not. Recent studies indicate that even at the best of times the woodland may have been relatively sparse, and what woodland there was may have been very different from the forest that luxuriates in eastern Glen Affric today.

The stumps embedded in the peat probably represent a short interval when pinewood flickered briefly, then died out. Clues point to vegetation constantly shifting in the low-lying meadows and marshlands, changing with periods of inundation and drying out as the floodwaters rose and fell. Some of the ground was already bare three thousand years ago and stayed that way. In other parts woodlands still flourished when the early Stewarts sat on the throne (albeit shakily in the Highlands) a mere six hundred years ago.

James Fenton, the National Trust ecologist, is cagey when it comes to talk of bringing back the forest. He warns that our love of trees should not blind us to the value of the landscape as it is. Blanket peat is an increasingly rare and ecologically precious phenomenon in Europe. These empty glens have never been more than thinly populated and so people can have made little impact in the five thousand years of their presence in the neighbourhood.

Hence an uncompromised landscape has evolved more or less naturally in the ten thousand years since the melting of the ice. Fenton believes we might regret a rush to plant trees in West Affric and

On a misty morning in Strathspey it's possible to imagine the forest extending further than the eye can see. It's an illusion. But might it come to be?

Kintail, just as we regret the heedless afforestation of so much Highland moorland by the Forestry Commission in the recent past.

A healthy forest, for Alan Featherstone, is rich in wildlife and thrives down the ages without benefit of human intervention. Scale is important. Separate pockets of woodland, even large tracts, won't do. He points out that if ever the large animals at the top of the food chain, the wolf and the bear, were to return, they would need freedom to roam and to spread their genes. Even his imagined forest around Affric would scarcely be large enough without woodland corridors linking it to other forests.

The naturalist Kenny Taylor, standing among the ancient trees of Rothiemurchus, one of the largest remaining Caledonian pinewoods, recorded his feelings in a radio programme. 'In my terms,' he said 'this is a big wood, not a forest.'

And what is a forest? It is a place, he answers, when you can start walking through the trees on a summer morning, passing through clearings and skirting bogs, where you can continue all day on your woodland trail and still, in the gathering dusk, be enclosed by trees: '*That* is a real forest. That's what a lot of us are aiming for. And it might come about.'

Aldhous, JR (ed.), *Our Pinewood Heritage*, proceedings of a conference at
Inverness, jointly published by Forestry Commission/RSPB/Scottish
Natural Heritage, 1995 (hereafter referred to as *Aldhous*).

Anderson, ML, *A History of Scottish Forestry*, Oliver & Boyd, 1967 (*Anderson*).

Edlin, HL, *Trees, Woods and Man*, Nelson, 1956 (*Edlin*).

Grant, Elizabeth, of Rothiemurchus, *Memoirs of a Highland Lady*, 1898,
republished Canongate, 1988 (*Grant*).

Leathart, Scott, *Whence Our Trees*, Foulsham, 1991 (*Leathart*).

Mitchell, Alan, *Alan Mitchell's Trees of Britain*, HarperCollins, 1996 (*Mitchell*).

Murray, David, *The York Buildings Company: a chapter in Scotch history*, 1883,
republished Bratton Publishing, Edinburgh, 1973 (*Murray*).

MacCulloch, John, *A Description of the Scenery of Dunkeld and of Blair in
Atholl*, 1823.

Hamilton, Thomas, 6th Earl of Haddington (ML Anderson, ed.) *Forest Trees*,
1953, first published as *A Treatise on the Manner of Raising Forest
Trees*, 1761 (*Haddington*).

Hunter, Thomas, *Woods, Forests and Estates of Perthshire*, 1883 (*Hunter*).

Pringle, Douglas, *The First 75 Years: a brief account of the history of the
Forestry Commission 1919–1994*, Forestry Commission, 1994 (*Pringle*).

Smout, TC (ed.), *Scottish Woodland History*, Scottish Cultural Press, 1997 (*Smout*).

Steven, HM & Carlisle, A, *The Native Pinewoods of Scotland*, 1959, facsimile
edition Castlepoint Press, Dalbeattie, 1996 (*Steven & Carlisle*).

Wills, Virginia (ed.), *Reports on the Annexed Estates 1755–1769* (*Wills*).

Journals

Principally the *Transactions* of the Scottish Arboricultural Society, which became the Royal Scottish Arboricultural Society in 1887 and the Royal Scottish Forestry Society in 1930 (by which time the *Transactions* had become the Society's journal)

(*Transactions* 1860 (vol. II)–1927; *Scottish Forestry* 1928–2002)

Manuscript

Murray, John, 4th Duke of Atholl, *Woods and Forests as they are – as they were – as in all probability they will be*, c.1825.

Scott, Sir Walter, *Sylva Abbotsfordiensis: Memoranda concerning the woods and plantations at Abottsford, commenced 1st January 1819*.

Short titles – as *Anderson* – refer to publications listed in the Bibliography.

Prologue

pxi   'To stand in them is to feel the past' – the friend of the pinewoods quoted here is Jock Carlisle in *Steven & Carlisle*.

1   In the beginning was the Wood

p3   Maps indicating the advance of tree species in Scotland are based on the work of HJB Birks of Bergen University; as, for example, in his 'Holocine isochrome maps and patterns of tree-spreading in the British Isles' in the *Journal of Biogeography* 16, 1989.

p4   I found relic tree stumps in the Black Mount by following up references in 'The history and palaeoclimatic significance of subfossil remains of *Pinus sylvestris* in blanket peats from Scotland' by MC Bridge, BA Haggart and JJ Lowe in the *Journal of Ecology* (1978).

p5   'We can picture that dim, long forgotten time' – envisaged in *The Scenery of Scotland*, by Sir Archibald Geikie (1865).

p7   The great stag and the auroch featured in *The Influence of Man on Animal Life in Scotland*, by James Ritchie (1920).

p9   Edlin described his Stone Age axemanship in *Edlin*; the woodcutting efforts of his Danish counterparts Iversen and Troels-Smith are recorded in *The Archives of the Peat Bogs*, by Sir Harry Godwin (1981).

p10   Occasional wisps of woodsmoke over northern Europe – a scene imagined by JGD Clark in *Prehistoric Europe: the economic basis* (1952), quoted in *Steven & Carlisle*; bush fire as land management is discussed in *Changing the Face of the Earth: Culture, Environment, History*, by IG Simmons (1996). The secrets of Over Rig are revealed in (for example) 'Medieval woodland history from the Scottish Southern Uplands' by Richard Tipping, in *Smout*, supplemented by WE Boyd's analysis of wood fragments from archaeological sites in the *Journal of Archaeological Sciences* (1988); conversation with Dr Tipping has also been illuminating.

2   The medieval greenwood

p13   Blind Harry quotations and note on the Torwood snuffbox (p15) are from *Wallace: the life and acts of Sir William Wallace of Ellerslie*, by Henry the Minstrel, ed. John Jamieson (1869) – a more accessible version is *Blind Harry's Wallace*, ed. Elspeth King (1998), in William Hamilton of Gilberfield's 18th century English.

p15   Balladry is quoted from my 1931 edition of *Minstrelsy of the Scottish Border* (1802–3), by Sir Walter Scott.

p18–19 What Caledonian forest? asks TC Smout in, for example, 'Highland land use before 1800: evidence and realities', in *Smout*. 'The sceptic might even doubt . . .' as does David J Breeze in 'The Great Myth of Caledon', in *Scottish Forestry* 46 (1992) – but see correspondence in *Scottish Forestry* 47 (January & April 1993). The Wood of Celyddon is recognised in *The Quest for Merlin*, by Nikolai Tolstoy (1985). Confident (if confusing) descriptions are quoted from earlier writers – Boece et al – in *Anderson*. Common sense prevails in 'The Scottish forests and woodlands in early historic times' by Hugh Boyd Watt (c.1898) – my copy of the paper does not specify its orgin.

p20   Wolf tales and gory encounters can be found in *The Influence of Man on Animal Life*, by James Ritchie (1920); also in *Anderson*, which quotes James I's decree (p21).

p22   Rackham's observations on browsing damage are in *Trees and Woodland in the British Landscape*, by Oliver Rackham (1976).

p23   *Smout* speculated on the spreading crowns of oak on Loch Tay and ash at Rassal in his 'Highland land-use before 1800'.

3   When the tree falls

p29   Bruce Walker, at the Scottish Ecological Design Association conference at Inveraray in 1995, emphasised the importance of timber in early Scottish domestic building. The Archibald Menzies reference to creel houses 'covered with fale' is in *Wills*.

p30   The footnote reference to 'Two thousand of the best and straightest trees' required to build one small house is quoted in *The Sunart Oakwoods: A report on their History and Archaeology*, Sunart Oakwoods Research Group (2001).

p34–5 Information on French shipbuilders and the *Great Michael* is from *Anderson*; the statement that her construction 'waistit' the woods of Fife is in the *Historie and Chronicles of Scotland* by Robert Lindsay of Pitscottie (1570); see also *In Search of the Great Michael*, by AC McKerracher in *The Scots Magazine* (January 1977).

4 Poor land, with prospects

p37 'Here again ye shall see . . .' Leslie's observation is quoted in
'Sir Walter Scott and forestry' by James F Ogilvie, in *Scottish Forestry*
39 (1985). John Slezer's life and works are recorded in *A Vision of
Scotland: the nation observed*, by Keith Cavers for the National
Library of Scotland (1993).

p39 Observations by Fynes Morison and others are in *Early Travellers in
Scotland*, ed. P Hume Brown (1891). *Anderson* quotes Cobbett's
put-down of Dr Johnson. Trevelyan's notional English traveller
viewing Scotland with distaste is from *English Social History*,
by GM Trevelyan (1944).

p41 The 'oriental rudeness' of agricultural implements is noted by
Murray, and the desolation of the countryside is described in
Scottish Farming in the Eighteenth Century, by James E Handley (1953).

p42 Information on Sir Duncan Campbell of Glenorchy (Black Duncan)
is in *The Black Book of Taymouth*, ed. C Innes (1855).

p43 *Haddington*, with Anderson's introduction, describes the tree
planting efforts of Thomas the sixth earl and his wife Helen;
additional material on his life and character in *'Scotland's Ruine':
Lockhart of Carnwath's memoirs of the Union* ed. Daniel Szechi with
foreword by Paul Scott (1995). Haddington's 'many millions of trees'
– in *Anderson*.

p46 The landscaping activities of three generations of Adams are
described in *Remarks on the Blair Adam Estate*, by William Adam
(1834).

p47 Handley (see above) quotes Sir Archibald Grant's recollection of the
distressed state of Monymusk in his youth.

p51–6 A wealth of information on the annexed estates is in *Wills*.
I took the Lord Kames punchline from *Anderson*.

5 How green was my bloomery

p57 Charcoal burners' huts on the road to Inveraray seen by the 18th-
century traveller B Faujas de Saint-Fond – from *A Journey throughout
England and Scotland to the Hebrides* ed. Sir Archibald Geikie (1907).

p60 Loch Lomondside smelting sites are described in 'History of the
Loch Lomond oakwoods' by Ruth M Tittensor, in *Scottish Forestry* 24
(1970). Historic Scotland's booklet *Bonawe Iron Furnace*, by Geoffrey
P Stell and Geoffrey D Hay (1984) is a mine of information for this
section, as is 'The iron industry in the Highlands', by JM Lindsay,
in the *Scottish Historical Review* 56 (1977); further details in
The Industrial Archaeology of Scotland: 2, Highlands & Islands, by
John R Hume (1987).

p61   The activities of Irish entrepreneurs were investigated by Fiona Watson (see *Notes* of the Scottish Woodland History Discussion Group meeting, April 1997).

p63   The French example of a fuel-hungry furnace is given in *The Medieval Machine: the Industrial Revolution of the Middle Ages*, by Jean Gimpel (1976).

p64   Like others, Ritchie (see Chapter 1 notes) blamed the iron industry as 'one of the most potent forces for the destruction of the natural forest'; Frank Fraser Darling condemned English 'agents of destruction' in his 'History of the Scottish Forests', a paper read to the British Association in 1947 and reprinted in the *Scottish Geographical Magazine* 65 (1949). For Rackham's alternative view see Chapter 3 notes.

p66   'Living evidence' of medieval management in venerable stumps at Dalkeith is observed in *The Wild Woods*, by Peter Marren (1992).

p68   'Old Nicol Luke' at Ardkinglas is referred to by John Noble in a letter to *Scottish Forestry* 24 (1970); Donald McKichen (p69), joiner at Ardtornish, in *Morvern Transformed: a Highland parish in the nineteenth century*, by Philip Gaskell (1968).

6   Tall firs shall fright the seas

p71   Woods in Morar 'altogether unprofitable' quoted in 'The Golden Groves of Abernethy: the cutting and extraction of timber before the Union', by Jean Munro, in *A Sense of Place: studies in Scottish local history*, ed. Graeme Cruikshank (1988), citing *The Chiefs of Grant*, by Sir William Fraser (1882). Naval interest in Abernethy in the early 1700s is documented in the *Grant of Grant Muniments* in the National Archives of Scotland, along with references to former seafarer John Mason and carpenter Martin Sanford.

p76   The pessimism of Frank Fraser Darling (see Chapter 1 note); is countered in, for example, 'Highland land use before 1800' by TC Smout, in *Smout.*

p77   The reference to the river 'which runneth of a great loch' is in *Highways and Byeways in Central Scotland*, by Seton Gordon (1935), quoting in turn from MacFarlane's *Geographical Collections* (1908). References to 'four hundred cuts of fir' in Loch Tulla and cuts 'on both sides of the water of Orchy' are in the *Breadalbane Muniments* in the National Archives of Scotland. Waterlogged trees in Strathconon were referred to in 'The Caledonian pine forest', by MJ Penistan, *Quarterly Journal of Forestry* 36 (1942).

p78   The 'pretty set of miniature lakes' is so described in *Grant*. 'Vast logs . . . amidst the foam' – *Anderson*. Scenes of logging in Rothiemurchus, and also the sad tale of Allan Grant (p84), are vividly recounted in *Grant*.

7   Planting dukes and the march of larch

p87   The 'Highland gentleman Mr Menzies' appears in *Hunter*, an essential source for this chaper.

p88   Boutcher enthused about larch in *A Treatise on Forest-Trees*, by Thomas Boutcher (1775).

p91   The salt water saga of the vessels *Athole* and *Larch* is chronicled *Hunter* (he also admired the transformation of 'the previously desert ranges' of Tay and Tummel).

p94   *Anderson* quotes Sir Bourchier Wrey.

8   MacCulloch's ride

This chapter is largely sourced from John MacCulloch's *A Description of the Scenery of Dunkeld and of Blair in Atholl* (1823).

9   Very Robin Hoodish

Blair Adam from 1733 to 1834, by William Adam (1834) and Scott's *Sylva Abbotsfordiensis* are the essential sources in this chapter. Also *Sir Walter Scott: the great unknown*, by Edgar Johnson (1970), and 'Sir Walter Scott and forestry' by James F Ogivlie, in *Scottish Forestry* 39 (1985).

10   A yearning for exotica

p109   'Honey sweet yearning' is from *Direadh III* by Hugh McDiarmid.

p112   I read of the monkey puzzle at Kleve in the *International Dendrology Yearbook* (1990). *David Douglas: explorer and botanist*, by Ann Lindsay Mitchell and Syd House (1999), quotes extensively from his journals.

p114   Information on the Oregon Association and passages from John Jeffrey's journal are from *John Jeffrey and the Oregon Association*, by James Todd Johnstone (HMSO monograph, 1939) – part of the rich source of information to be found in the library at the Royal Botanic Garden, Edinburgh (where I also found an unidentified newspaper cutting reporting George Patton's sorry end – see note to p128).

p116   Changing fashions in the naming of the new trees (e.g. 'Prince Albert's Spruce') is recorded in *A Handbook of Coniferae and Ginkoaeceae*, by W Dallimore and A Bruce Jackson (4th ed. 1966).

p117   'On the discoveries of Mr John Jeffrey and Mr Robert Brown', by James McNab, in the *Transactions of the Royal Botanical Society of Edinburgh XI* (1873) states that 'no one could have worked more conscientiously'.

p117–27 The race to bring back Wellingtonia by 'another of those indefatigable Scots' is recounted in *Mitchell*, along with much background on the new species; *Leathart* was also useful. I have quoted liberally ('32 varieties of the newer coniferae' etc) from *Hunter*, with its store of information on Scottish tree-loving landowners; I read Hunter's

obituary in the *Perthshire Constitutional and Journal* (Feb 24, 1904)
in Perth Museum archive; likewise two articles by Magnus Jackson
from *The British Journal of Photography* (Feb 1881).

p128   Patton's suicide is recorded in an unidentified newspaper cutting –
Scotsman? – of September 1869, in the McNab book at the
Edinburgh Botanic Garden.

11   Grandees, tall trees, great expectations

p131   The Seafield family history is recorded in the *The Chiefs of Grant*
by Sir William Grant (1883) and in the articles in the *Strathspey and
Badenoch Herald*, by GA Dixon (1991); George Dixon also provided
useful additional information; I found letters concerning Lewis-
Alexander in the *Seafield Papers* in the National Archives of
Scotland.

p132   Sir John Ramsden's activities at Ardverikie are referred to in
Revival of the Land: Creag Meagaidh national nature reserve by
Paul Ramsay (Scottish Natural Heritage monograph, 1996).

p134   'There is no more desolate region in Scotland' – Corrour so
described in *Scottish Gardens*, by Sir Herbert Maxwell (1908).
Old photographs of Corrour and Sir John Stirling Maxwell are
in the Pollok House archive, Glasgow.

p137   Munro-Ferguson's plaint about the depressed value of woodlands
is in *Transactions XVI* (1897).

p140   Forestry to better the lot of the crofter – 'enabling him to extend his
holding': *Lord Lovat: a biography*, by Sir Francis Lindley Darwin (1935).

p142   The Glen Mor vision was expounded in *Afforestation in Scotland:
forest survey of Glen Mor and the consideration of certain problems
arising therefrom*, by Lord Lovat and Captain Stirling of Keir
(published as *Transactions* XXV (1911). Lovat's '*Daily Mail* stuff' is
referred to in Darwin's *Lovat*.

12   The arborists' outing

The arborists' excursion is reported at length, anonymously, in
Transactions XIV (1895).

13   Eyes across the ocean

p151   Daniel Dewar's reading list is mentioned in Darwin's *Lovat*
(see Chapter 11 notes).

p152   Scott's affectionate comment on Tom Purdie is from the *Life of Scott*,
by John Gibson Lockhart (1837–8).

p152–5 Glowing reports of visits to Continental forests appeared in
Transactions of various dates. Boppé described his whistle-stop tour
in 'The Forests of Great Britain' by L Boppé and E Reuss (1886),
translated by ML Anderson in *Scottish Forestry* 14 (1960);

Schwappach's 'A Report on a visit to the forests of Scotland', by
Dr Adam Schwappach, appeared in *Transactions* XV (1898).
Schlich's criticism of British forestry is from *Manual of Forestry*,
vol 2, by W Schlich (1904).

p155 William M'Corquodale criticised the lack of forestry training and
praised his mentor the Duke of Montrose in *Transactions* IX (1881).

p158 I learned of the spat between Tullibardine, Lovat, Stirling Maxwell
and others in correspondence at Blair Castle archive.

14 The cruel years

p159 Robert Munro's wartime view from the train window is in
Transactions XXXII (1918).

p160 'Every shell that is fired' is from *Forests and Forestry in Great Britain*
by William Ling Taylor (1946), as is the reflection that 'our home-
based assets were the nucleus of a forest service, far too small. . ..'

p162 Gilbert Brown's statistics for denuded Abernethy are cited in
The Native Woodlands of Strathspey, a Scottish Natural Heritage
report by BMS Dunlop (1994). Scrymgeour Wedderburn's lament on
the sacrifice of his woodland appeared in the *Scottish Forestry* journal
53 (1939). Locheil's marker trees were mourned in *Highways and
Byeways in the West Highlands* by Seton Gordon (1949). Stirling
Maxwell's blunt warning on the dire prospects for woodland in the
war is reported in *Transactions* XXXII (1918). The recovery of
Abernethy pinewood was noted in *The Cairngorms* (Scottish
Mountaineering Club guide) by Sir Henry Alexander (2nd edition
1938).

p163 The Atholl factor's envious reference to cheap PoW labour is in the
Chronicles of the Atholl and Tullibardine Families, vol 6.

p165–9 Information on Canadian foresters at Glenmore and elsewhere is
from articles in
The Aberdeen Free Press by Henry Alexander (October 1918) and the
same author's 'Canadian Timber Corps in Speyside', in the *Cairngorm
Club Journal* (1920), and also from *The Canadian Forestry Corps: its
inception, development and achievements*, by C W Bird and Lieutenant
JB Davies (HMSO 1919).

p169 On the subject of wartime forest railways I received invaluable help
from David Rose, including sight of articles (author unidentified)
from the *Inverness Courier* (1919).

p172 George Leven's praise of women foresters and especially those at
Hendersyde appeared in *Transactions* XXXIII (1919); John Waddell's
similar view from Auchterarder (p173) is in *Transactions* XXXII
(1918).

15 Let conifers cover the land

p175   Facts on the founding and early years of the Forestry Commission are given in *Pringle*. 'Able, domineering, arrogant' – Lord Lovat described in *Who Owns Scotland: a study in land ownership*, by John McEwen (1977), where he also told of class distinction at the forestry conference.

p181   McEwen again, for the 'almost miraculous' transformation of Cowal, in *Scottish Forestry* 15 (1961).

16 Death and resurrection

p183   The destruction of Binning Wood is catalogued in 'Notes on Binning Wood, Tyninghame', by the Earl of Haddington, in *Scottish Forestry* 22 (1968).

p184   'We might as well have been the battlefield' – from 'History of the Scottish forests', a paper by Frank Fraser Darling read to the British Association in 1947 and reprinted in the *Scottish Geographical Journal*.

p185   James Tait tells of 'knacky' woodswomen in *Scottish Forestry* 56 (1942). The Canadian historian on sabbatical in the Highlands was William C Wonders; see his *The 'Sawdust Fusiliers': the Canadian Forestry Corps in the Scottish Highlands in World War Two*, Canadian Pulp and Paper Association (1991).

p190–2 Wonders is also my main authority on forest villages: 'Forestry villages in the Scottish Highlands', by William C Wonders in the *Scottish Geographical Magazine* (December 1990), abridged in *Scottish Forestry* 52 (1998); on forest villages I received personal information from John Davies. Subservient forestry commissioners are quoted in *Pringle*.

p193   'Tough, single-minded' Roy Robinson is so described in *The Scottish Forester* by John Davies (1979).

p194   In the 'Mission to Queen Charlotte Islands', by AD Hopkinson, *Journal of the Forestry Commission* 33 (1964), Hopkinson described his trip thirty years earlier to see Sitka spruce in its native setting.

17 The end of geometry

p197   The official Forestry Commission historian quoted is *Pringle*.

p198   'Probably in all Britain there are no scenes more impressive in their barren desolation': Derek Ratcliffe in his chapter 'Mires and Bogs' in *The Vegetation of Scotland*, ed. John H Burnett (1964).

p200   I learned of Sylvia Crowe from Duncan Campbell, and also from the obituary by him in *Forestry*, vol 71 (1998) and the interview by Sally Festing in *New Scientist*, 18 January 1979; further information supplied by John Davies; see also Crowe's Forestry Commission booklet No.44 *The Landscape of Forests and Woods* (1978).

p204 Frank Bracewell gave me chapter and verse on the Loch Lomondside saga.

p207 Graham Booth imparted much information on forestry at Drumlanrig; for extra information on Buccleuch estates I turned to 'The One-Man National Trust', by Caroline Bankes, in *The Field* (January 1993).

p210 'Microwildernesses exist in a handful of soil' is from *Naturalist*, by Edward O Wilson (1995); witness the multitude of spiders and invertebrates found in conifer plantation by Andrew Foggo and Claire Ozanne, as reported in the *Scottish Environmental News* (Sept 1994), and cited in *Scottish Forestry* 49 (1995). Bill Oddie's birdwatch in Kielder was broadcast as Radio 4's *Spruced Up!* (December 1997).

p212 On dreams of old growth I took heart from *Old-growth Conservation within British Upland Conifer Plantation Forests*, by GF Peterken and others; I was inspired by *Sustainable Forestry: philosophy, science and economics*, by Chris Maser (St Lucie Press, Florida 1994).

p213 The prediction on convoys of timber trucks was made by Christopher Cairns in 'Widespread felling set to cause rural chaos' in the *Scotsman*, 20 August 1999

18 On the trail of the ancient pines

p215 'Interpretations of a Twisted Pine' is from *The Bird Path: collected longer poems*, by Kenneth White (1989).

p216 The Evelyn, Kirk and Defoe quotations are in Anderson's *History*.

p218 The foresters' 1933 excursion to Loch Maree is described in *Scottish Forestry* 47 (1933).

p219 RA Lambert's 'Preserving a Remnant of the Old Natural Forest' in *Scottish Forestry* 51 (1997) led me to the archive of the National Trust for Scotland and correspondence on the abortive attempt to buy a relic pinewood.

p220 I learned of Jock Carlisle's adventures in search of old pinewoods from his own lips, supplemented by sight of his unpublished autobiography.

19 Chaos theories

p227 Findlay Macrae provided much information on Glen Affric.

p228 The battle for Beinn Eighe is detailed in 'Beinn Eighe National Nature Reserve 1944-1994', by Timothy Clifford and Andrew Forster, in *Smout*; also personal information from Tim Clifford. Further information on the naturalists involved was found in *The New Naturalists: half a century of British natural history*, by Peter Marren (1995).

p232 Paul Ramsay's *Revival of the Land* provided much information on Creag Meagaidh, while Dick Balharry guided me over the ground.

p233 The reference to the 'well-whiskered' Richard Sidgwick is from *Who Owns Scotland Now?* by Auslan Cramb (1996).

p235 'Pinewood restoration at the RSPB's Abernethy forest reserve', by S Taylor, in *Aldhous*, was informative; also personal information from Stewart Taylor.

p239 The cheerful forestry consultant at Mar Lodge was AH Nicol.

20   A forest tapestry

p241 Opening quotations from *I Planted Trees*, by Richard St Barbe Baker (1944) and *Sustainable Forestry: philosophy, science and economics*, by Chris Maser, St Lucie Press, Delray Beach, Florida (1994). Guides and informants as in the text. Closing quotation (p249) in *Anderson*.

21   A dream of Rotten Bottom

Personal information on and off site mainly from Philip Ashmole.

22   Wood without end

p257 A seamless garment of greenery... The linking of discrete woodlands is proposed in *A Forest Habitat Network for Scotland*, by GF Peterken, D Baldock & A Hampson, SHN research report 44 (1995).

p261–3 Wolves: personal information from Dr Martyn Gorman; Kenny Taylor imagined bear and wolf in the Highlands (and defined a 'real' forest) in a Radio 4 natural history programme *Footprints*; Paul Evans fantasised on being a wolf in the *Guardian*.

p267 James Fenton explained his cautionary approach to me, and then to a wider readership in *Scottish Foresty* 51 (1997).

APPENDIX I

JOHN FOWLER'S FAVOURITE WOODLANDS

After reading this book you may be inspired to see the woods yourselves.
There are plenty of them, but the following are among my particular
favourites.

The Black Wood of Rannoch

The first pinewood I explored when this book was beginning to germinate
in my mind. Gales, floods and landslips had closed the only roads in that
winter day, and I had to plough through floodwater to reach it. Surely you'll
have no such trouble. The heart of the Black Wood, bounded by two burns
that rampage down through rocky ravines, is a confusion of knolls and dells
on the south side of Loch Rannoch, mantled by rich vegetation. Underfoot
are dark peaty puddles, spongy hummocks of moss and heather, and networks
of bare roots from which rise the craggy stems of the old pine forest. Such
handsome trunks they are, heavily armoured at the base with rugged bark
that softens and turns an orangey-tan colour in the crown. See them afire
in the sunset! You reach the Black Wood via a narrow twisting road north of
Pitlochry. On the approach you may see – weather permitting – the graceful
mountain Schiehallion.

Glen Affric

North of the Great Glen, long glens and lochs form the Beauly catchment.
Remnants of old pinewood can be found in several glens, but the best of all
is Glen Affric – some miles of seamless birch and pine forest, mostly along
the southern shore of long Loch Beinn a'Meadhoin, a mouthful of a name
easier to pronounce if you try an old spelling Beneveian. Leave your vehicle
at the Forest Enterprise Dog Falls car park and walk along the forest road,
eventually reaching the smaller Loch Affric where the trees begin to
dissipate in a bleaker landscape. My fondest memories of Affric are from a
frosty week in October when there was snow on the peaks and the birch was
a blaze of autumn colour set off against the dark pine, all mirrored in the
glassy surface of the loch below.

Glenfeshie

On the north side of the Cairngorms the spreading forests of Strathspey, old and new, are easily accessible at Glenmore, Abernethy and Rothiemurchus, all areas criss-crossed by tracks for the walker. To the south of the Cairngorms, however, Glenfeshie has sequestered pleasures. Soon after reaching the isolated dwelling called Achlean, well known to hill walkers, you enter a green strath dotted with noble pines, almost like a park. Here I skinny-dipped in the river on a hot August day – out of sight, I hope, of the grand hunting lodge on the far side. There's a stone bothy hereabouts, occupied occasionally in Victorian times – so I'm told – by the artist Landseer on field trips. Beside the bothy stand two majestic old trees, one a craggy beech, the other – well, I wasn't sure, but I took home a twig or two and had it identified as grey poplar, a hybrid of the native aspen. A long hike will take you at last among stands of tall pines where the braided Feshie river works its way through broad shingle banks. Stunted trees of curious shape hang on desperately to rocky shelves and debris on the steep slopes above.

Knapdale and Sunart

Knapdale is a very different landscape. For a start, it's in west Argyll and close to the sea. From a point near the Crinan Canal you can look out across salt marsh and sandbanks and several islands to the Sound of Jura, while behind you stretches a rough-and-tumble of abrupt little hills (known here as 'knaps', hence the name) covered for the most part in woodland. Long rocky ridges run parallel towards the sea, enclosing the walker in green walled gardens, and when you clamber to higher ground you're sure to spy a lochan glistening below. Knapdale woods are classed 'Atlantic oakwood', but oak trees are by no means predominant. There's birch in plenty and, best of all, groves of hazel dripping with a multitude of lichens, some tiny specks and crusts, others big as cabbage leaves dangling from the branches. Broadleaf trees are only part of the scene. Large plantations were created here in past decades and now in maturity they bring Canada to mind, especially where they form a jagged skyline. Knapdale is a rich mix. Further north, in Sunart, there are jewels of deciduous woodland strung out along the shore of the sea loch of that name, among them the Ariundle woods, wet, misty and dank, a rich habitat for ferns, mosses and lichens. Ariundle is reached from the village of Strontian.

Carn a'Mhadaidh

My final choice may seem perverse – at least whimsical. It's a long way to go, it involves a long hike from the nearest road end, not many folk know it, there's not a lot of woodland to see – mere scrub, you might say – and, to cap it all, I've been there only once. Once seen, never forgotten. It's a scrap of ancient birch woodland in Caithness, just south of Tongue, a landscape of moorland and isolated, surreal mountains (namely, the bens Hope and

Loyal). I tramped along above the winding Kinloch River towards Carn a'Mhadaidh, a jagged little peak, bare and stony with one side sheered off in a tumble of great boulders among which contorted little trees, mainly birch with some rowan among them, find a precarious footing. So did I, but very cautiously, as I gingerly scrambled among rocks big as a house. Trunks and stumps and branches of old dead trees, rotten with age, added spice to the descent. These trees, I believe, are relics of an age-old forest. I love it: it's my secret place – but I share it gladly.

And some others:

Drumlanrig, near Thornhill, Dumfries-shire
There are many magnificent trees to be seen in the castle policies, with a number of woodland walks in the outlying plantations.

Younger Botanic Garden, Benmore, Argyll
A wide variety of introduced trees from east and west – see the Chilean forests re-created, as well as a spectacular avenue of giant redwoods. An out-station of the Royal Botanic Garden, Edinburgh. While there, see Puck's Glen nearby, with woodland walks and an impressive gorge – owned by the Forestry Commission.

Glen Nant woodlands, near Taynuilt, Argyll
Heavily exploited in the past for charcoal burning and tanbark – witness the multi-stemmed oaks, evidence of past coppicing. Now gently returning to nature. Old charcoal burners' platforms may be discovered by the sharp-eyed.

Beinn Eighe, near Kinlochewe
The first national nature reserve to be designated in Britain, at the south-west corner of Loch Maree. The heart of it is a fragment of ancient Caledonian pinewood called Coille na Glas Leitir. There's mountain and moorland besides.

Rassal Ashwood
A nature reserve in Wester Ross, this is the most northerly ashwood in Britain. Apart from the trees (hazel is abundant as well as ash), there are many special plants, including ferns, mosses and liverworts. Lichens love ash bark.

Culbin Forest, near Nairn, Moray
This was first planted as an experiment in stabilising the shifting Culbin Sands of the Moray Firth – hence you can admire the finest dune system in Britain. Surprisingly, for relatively young woodland, it is notable for its many species of lichens.

Dell Woods, near Nethy Bridge, Inverness-shire
Once heavily exploited for timber, now the undisturbed haunt of the Scottish crossbill, crested tit and capercaillie, wildcat and pine marten. Part of Abernethy forest, the most extensive remnant of Caledonian or Scots pine woodland. It's a national nature reserve owned by Scottish Natural Heritage.

Royal Botanic Garden, Edinburgh
Arboretum delight – nearly two thousand conifers and hardwoods, many in groups 'so that it is possible to wander among groves of oaks, limes, maples and rowans', it says in the guide. Plus attendant shrubs.

Dawyck Botanic Gardens, near Peebles
A collection of many fine specimen trees introduced in the nineteenth century, including Douglas firs raised from seed sent home by Douglas himself and other North American conifers, as well as trees from China. Another out-station of the Royal Botanic Garden, Edinburgh.

ORGANISATIONS LINKED
TO WOODLANDS AND FORESTRY

Borders Forest Trust
Monteviot Nurseries,
Ancrum, Jedburgh, TD8 6TU
01835 830750

Forest Enterprise
231 Corstorphine Road,
Edinburgh EH12 7AT
0131 334 0303

John Muir Trust
41 Commercial Street,
Edinburgh EH6 6JD
0131 554 0114 or 0131 554 1324

National Trust for Scotland
5 Charlotte Square,
Edinburgh EH2 4DU
0131 243 9300

Reforesting Scotland
62-66 Newhaven Road,
Edinburgh EH6 5QB
0131 554 4321

Royal Botanic Garden, Edinburgh
20a Inverleith Row,
Edinburgh EH3 5LR
0131 552 7171

Royal Scottish Forestry Society
Hagg-on-Esk, Canonbie,
Dumfries-shire DG14 OXE
01387 371518

RSPB Scotland
Dunedin House,
25 Ravelston Terrace,
Edinburgh EH4 3TP
0131 311 6500

Scottish Native Woods
1 Crieff Road, Aberfeldy,
Perthshire PH15 2BJ
01887 820392

Scottish Natural Heritage
12 Hope Terrace,
Edinburgh EH9 2AS
0131 447 4784

Scottish Wildlife Trust
Cramond House,
Kirk Cramond,
Cramond Glebe Road,
Edinburgh EH4 6NS
0131 312 7765

Trees for Life
The Park, Findhorn Bay,
Forres IV36 3TZ
01309 691292

The Woodland Trust Scotland
Glenruthven Mill,
Abbey Road,
Auchterarder,
Perthshire PH3 1DP
01764 662554

WWF Scotland
8 The Square,
Aberfeldy,
Perthshire PH15 2DD
01887 820449

ACKNOWLEDGEMENTS

Jim Dickson of Glasgow University was the first to instruct me in the matter of the Old Wood of Caledon and subsequently led me (along with his students) to the grave of an ancient forest on Rannoch Moor. He gave advice and encouragement on several occasions. Peter Quelch, native woodland adviser to the Forestry Commission, and Graham Tuley, formerly his colleague and now a forestry consultant, provided much information and insight, both in the field and on the phone. Jock Carlisle regaled me with his adventures in search of the ancient pinewoods when I visited him at his home in Canada. I have sat profitably if metaphorically at the feet of environmental historian Christopher Smout (he may be unaware of this) and have literally dogged his footsteps on outings and meetings with the Scottish Woodland History Discussion Group, which he founded.

Members of the Forestry Commission were prominent amongst those who devoted time to advising, instructing and in many cases walking through woodlands with me. Malcolm Wield drove me through Glen Affric, volunteered information on other occasions, and helped to make my walk from Dog Falls through Affric and Kintail to the west coast relatively painless. Charlie Taylor introduced me to the Black Wood of Rannoch. Graham Gill first talked of Kielder and then led me on a voyage of discovery in it. Mike Steward showed me the oak wood at Bailefuil Wood. At the commission's northern research station, Roslin, I was welcomed by former director David Rook while Alan Fletcher, also now retired, opened my eyes to the merits of sitka spruce and pointed me towards the forests of the Canadian west coast, where John King and Charlie Cartwright of the British Columbia Forest Service furthered my education and proved good companions. At Roslin Jonathan Humphrey expounded at length on the ecology of plantations.

I am grateful to Michael Osborne, former director of the Royal Scottish Forestry Society, for much practical help and advice. His successor Andrew Little aided my search for illustrations. Graham Booth devoted a long morning to showing me over the extensive woodlands at Drumlanrig, where he is the Duke of Buccleuch's head forester. Jimmy Oswald entertained me till past lunchtime at Glen Tanar, whereupon forestry consultant Irvine Ross took over for the remainder of the day. Chris Langton, when head forester at Atholl estates, explained forestry developments there. My host at Abbotsford was the late Mrs Patricia Maxwell Scott; forester Steve Kendall took me round the woods there.

Peter Matyjasek demonstrated the extraction of oak from Bailefuil with the help of his Clydesdales and at Stirling Castle, where the oak was translated into the Great Hall hammer-beam roof, Horace Peaseland of Historic Scotland instructed me in medieval building methods. Andrew Thomson, then with the John Muir Trust, hosted me in the Barisdale pinewoods. Christopher Dingwall of the Garden History Society provided useful information. Martin Gardner of the Royal Botanic Garden in Edinburgh aided my research there, and Peter Baxter and his assistant David Whyte showed me around the botanic out-station at Benmore. Basil Dunlop talked knowledgeably of the Strathspey pinewoods and the veteran ecologist Adam Watson spoke wisely of native woods. Several meetings with Tim Clifford – the first when he managed the Beinn Eighe nature reserve, whose history he expounded in detail – culminated in a visit to the oldest colony of pine trees known in Scotland. I viewed the threatened flows of Caithness with Norrie Russell of the RSPB and possible beaver territory in Abernethy with Roy Dennis. I learned to be a little wary of gung-ho utopianists from James Fenton, ecologist for the National Trust for Scotland. John Blyth of Edinburgh Unversity invited me to see the Glentress experimental woodland. Duncan Campbell provided information about the landscape consultant Sylvia Crowe, as did John Davies, formerly a power in the Forestry Commission, who advised and lunched me when I visited his home. John Hunt reviewed the achievement of the Millennium Forest for Scotland Trust as we sat in the sunshine of his garden in North Berwick. Toby Metcalfe of land surveyors Smiths Gore presented the acceptable face of landlordism while pheasants strutted past us at Mar Lodge. In Laggan the late Ian Sutherland demonstrated the possibilities of community-owned woodland. On Deeside Robin Callander envisioned a greater spreading native woodland. Abroad, I visited Merv Wilkinson in his inspirational wildwood at Yellowpoint on Vancouver Island.

Enthusiasts abound. John Boluski first encouraged me when he was a Forestry Commission researcher at Lairg and I continued to benefit from his knowedge and enthusiasm after he had privatised himself. Findlay

Macrae eulogised his Affric wonderland, Frank Bracewell gave me chapter and verse on Loch Lomond, David Rose led an expedition through Glenmore in search of the lost forest rail tracks of the Great War, Gus Jones took me on a nature trail through Ryvoan, Tom Prescott of the RSPB was my guide on Hoy. The optimistic Philip Ashmole clothed bleak Carrifran in future foliage while botanist Adrian Newton explained how it might be achieved. Dick Balharry triumphantly led the way through the renascent birch-flourish at Creag Meagaidh. At Trees for Life in Findhorn Alan Watson Featherstone proved a quiet and persuasive visionary.

Archivist Jane Anderson gave me unstinted help (along with the occasional cup of coffee) at Blair Castle. Rosemary Watt at the Burrell Collection in Glasgow enabled me to research Sir John Stirling Maxwell's contribution to forestry. George Dixon gave me pointers to the Grant dynasty and Seafield estates. Sue and Bob Mowatt were informative in the matter of the *Great Michael*. I must also thank Alan Hampson, Ewen Cameron and Duncan Stone of Scottish Natural Heritage, Gavin Sprott of the Museum of Scottish Country Life, forestry consultant Felix Karthaus, Jill Aitken of the Woodland Trust, and Eric Easton for interest and assistance. I fear there are others who have helped in the course of my researches whose names are omitted; my apologies. Douglas Green advised on appropriate photographs from the Forestry Commission's picture library in Edinburgh, and George Gate, his counterpart at Alice Holt Lodge, Surrey, gave further help.

It was a delight to interview many people with an interest in woodland. The redoubtable Bonnie MacAdam at Lundin Links regaled me with many tales of women foresters in World War Two, eighty-six-year-old William McGregor recalled seeing Canadian foresters at work in World War One when he was a boy. Alastair McLean recalled early forestry days at Ardentinny. Frank Sutherland told me about past days in Glen Affric; Bill Gibson of Inverness also reminisced.

Several knowledgeable people kindly read and commented on sections of the draft text. They include Richard Tipping of Stirling University (who also gave invaluable help on interpreting the woodlands of the remote past), Jan Oosthoek, and Virginia Wills – who, as well as being a historian and authority on the records of the annexed estates, runs an excellent second-hand bookshop in Bridge of Allan, where I have browsed profitably. Agnes Watson gave valuable advice and encouragement. Paul Ramsay nobly read through the (almost) finished version. Above all I am grateful to my friend Jean Reid, whose shrewd observations on different drafts have much improved this work. And, lastly, let me thank Donald Reid, my diligent and resourceful editor at Canongate.

INDEX